S0-AJV-079

Current Topics in
Developmental Biology

Volume 24

Growth Factors and Development

Contributors to This Volume

Eileen D. Adamson
I. B. Black
Igor B. Dawid
E. DiCicco-Bloom
C. F. Dreyfus
Martin Farber
Denis Gospodarowicz
Richard T. Hamilton
Susan Heyner
F. Michael Hoffmann
Brigid L. M. Hogan
Lynn M. Matrisian
Albert J. T. Millis
Marc A. T. Muskavitch
Marit Nilsen-Hamilton
Anna-Maija Partanen
Frédéric Rosa
I. Y. Rosenblum
Thomas D. Sargent

Founding Editors

A. A. Moscona
Alberto Monroy

Current Topics in Developmental Biology

Volume 24

Growth Factors and Development

Edited by

Marit Nilsen-Hamilton
Molecular, Cellular and Developmental Biology Program
Department of Biochemistry and Biophysics
Iowa State University
Ames, Iowa

Academic Press, Inc.
Harcourt Brace Jovanovich, Publishers
San Diego New York Boston London Sydney Tokyo Toronto

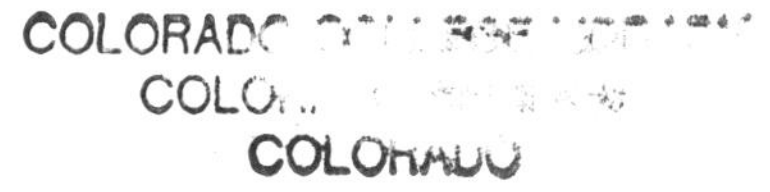

Front cover photograph: Expression of TGF-ß2 and tissue inhibitor of metalloproteinase transcripts in developing bone. (For details see Chapter 8, Figure 1.)
Courtesy of Lynn M. Matrisian and Brigid L.M. Hogan.

This book is printed on acid-free paper. ♾

ACADEMIC PRESS, INC.
San Diego, California 92101

United Kingdom Edition published by
ACADEMIC PRESS LIMITED
24-28 Oval Road, London NW1 7DX

LIBRARY OF CONGRESS CATALOG CARD NUMBER: 66-28604

ISBN 0-12-153124-4 (alk. paper)

PRINTED IN THE UNITED STATES OF AMERICA
90 91 92 93 9 8 7 6 5 4 3 2 1

Contents

3

Fibroblast Growth Factor and Its Involvement in Developmental Processes

Denis Gospodarowicz

4

Transforming Growth Factor-β and Its Actions on Cellular Growth and Differentiation

Marit Nilsen-Hamilton

5

The Insulin Family of Peptides in Early Mammalian Development

Susan Heyner, Martin Farber, and I. Y. Rosenblum

6

Nerve Growth Factor and the Issue of Mitosis in the Nervous System

I. B. Black, E. DiCicco-Bloom, and C. F. Dreyfus

7

Developmental Roles for Growth Factor-Regulated Secreted Proteins

Richard T. Hamilton and Albert J. T. Millis

8

Growth Factor-Regulated Proteases and Extracellular Matrix Remodeling during Mammalian Development

Lynn M. Matrisian and Brigid L. M. Hogan

9

The Role of Growth Factors in Embryonic Induction in Amphibians

Igor B. Dawid, Thomas D. Sargent, and Frédéric Rosa

10

Homologs of Vertebrate Growth Factors in *Drosophila melanogaster* and Other Invertebrates

Marc A. T. Muskavitch and F. Michael Hoffmann

Contributors

Numbers in parentheses indicate the pages on which the authors' contributions begin.

Eileen D. Adamson La Jolla Cancer Research Foundation, La Jolla, California 92037 (1)

I. B. Black Division of Developmental Neurology, Department of Neurology, Cornell University Medical College, New York, New York 10021 (161)

Igor B. Dawid Laboratory of Molecular Genetics, National Institute of Child Health and Human Development, National Institutes of Health, Bethesda, Maryland 20892 (261)

E. DiCicco-Bloom Division of Developmental Neurology, Department of Neurology, Cornell University Medical College, New York, New York 10021 (161)

C. F. Dreyfus Division of Developmental Neurology, Department of Neurology, Cornell University Medical College, New York, New York 10021 (161)

Martin Farber Department of Obstetrics and Gynecology, Albert Einstein Medical Center, Philadelphia, Pennsylvania 19141 (137)

Denis Gospodarowicz University of California Medical Center, Cancer Research Institute, San Francisco, California 94143 (57)

Richard T. Hamilton Department of Zoology, Iowa State University, Ames, Iowa 50011 (193)

Susan Heyner Department of Obstetrics and Gynecology, Albert Einstein Medical Center, Philadelphia, Pennsylvania 19141 (137)

F. Michael Hoffmann Department of Oncology, McArdle Laboratories, University of Wisconsin, Madison, Wisconsin 53706 (289)

Brigid L. M. Hogan Department of Cell Biology, Vanderbilt University, Nashville, Tennessee 37232 (219)

Lynn M. Matrisian Department of Cell Biology, Vanderbilt University, Nashville, Tennessee 37232 (219)

Albert J. T. Millis Center for Cellular Differentiation, Department of Biological Sciences, The University at Albany, State University of New York, Albany, New York 12222 (193)

Marc A. T. Muskavitch Programs in Genetics and Molecular, Cellular and Developmental Biology, Department of Biology, Indiana University, Bloomington, Indiana 47405 (289)

Marit Nilsen-Hamilton Molecular, Cellular and Developmental Biology Program, Department of Biochemistry and Biophysics, Iowa State University, Ames, Iowa 50011 (95)

Anna-Maija Partanen Institute of Dentistry, University of Helsinki, SF-00300 Helsinki, Finland (31)

Frédéric Rosa Laboratory of Molecular Genetics, National Institute of Child Health and Human Development, National Institutes of Health, Bethesda, Maryland 20892 (261)

I. Y. Rosenblum Pharmacology and Toxicology Section, Warner Lambert Company, Morris Plains, New Jersey 07950 (137)

Thomas D. Sargent Laboratory of Molecular Genetics, National Institute of Child Health and Human Development, National Institutes of Health, Bethesda, Maryland 20892 (261)

Preface

The history of embryology and cell biology contains many reports of factors required to support the growth of cells in culture or to regulate developmental events, but it has not been until the past 10 to 20 years, with the purification of these proteins and the advent of modern molecular biology and cell biology, that our understanding of growth factors has made rapid progress. The first growth factors to be purified were the epidermal growth factor and nerve growth factor. From extensive studies of these growth factors and others has come the realization that the regulation of proliferation is only part of the cellular response to growth factors.

Certain homeotic genes and other genes that regulate developmental events in invertebrates have been found homologous to mammalian genes that encode growth factors. This discovery opens the door to the exciting possibility of applying the extensive accumulated knowledge about the action of growth factors on isolated cells in culture to the understanding of vertebrate and invertebrate development at the molecular level. Conversely, our knowledge of developmental systems can now be used to augment our understanding of the mechanism of action of growth factors at the molecular and cellular levels. Of the large number of known growth factors, several representatives have been chosen for review in this volume. These growth factors have been studied extensively in cell culture systems. Each probably regulates different aspects of development. Current knowledge of the mechanism and nature of the action of each growth factor is discussed, and this information is related to what is known about the participation of the growth factor in specific developmental events.

Epidermal growth factor (EGF; Adamson, Chapter 1; Partanen, Chapter 2), fibroblast growth factor (FGF; Gospodarowicz, Chapter 3), and the insulinlike growth factors (Heyner *et al.*, Chapter 5) fit the traditional view of a growth factor which is a protein that stimulates cell growth and proliferation. However, the name growth factor has also been applied to some proteins that do not directly stimulate cell proliferation but that do regulate other cellular processes necessary for enhanced or continued proliferation. This situation has arisen because historically the term growth factor was applied to regulatory factors on the basis of any of a variety of assays both in cell culture and *in vivo*. Thus, nerve growth factor stimulates the growth of sympathetic neurons *in vivo*. However, when further analyzed with cultured cells, it seems that the function of this "growth factor" may be to enhance survival and differentiation of the sympathetic neurons *in vivo,* whereas other growth factors such as the insulinlike growth factors stimulate proliferation of these neurons (Black *et al.,* Chapter 6). Similarly, transforming growth factor type-β (TGF-β) stimulates colony formation of some cells in suspension culture, but, when tested on most cells in monolayer culture, inhibits their proliferation (Nilsen-Hamilton, Chapter 4). TGF-β also affects differentiation of some cells.

Many effects of TGF-β on cell proliferation and differentiation may be the consequence of its ability to regulate genes encoding proteins that contribute to, interact with, or degrade the extracellular matrix (ECM). Other growth factors such as FGF interact strongly with the ECM. Thus, an understanding of the role of growth factors in development is not complete without a discussion of the role of the ECM, its component proteins, proteoglycans, glycosaminoglycans, and the enzymes that degrade the ECM proteins and their inhibitors. The genes encoding these proteins are regulated in development and by growth factors in cultured cells (Hamilton and Millis, Chapter 7; Matrisian and Hogan, Chapter 8).

Growth factors also regulate the expression of genes encoding other secreted proteins that may participate in intercellular communication and coordination of embryonic development (Hamilton and Millis, Chapter 7). The lymphokine communication system of hematopoietic cells is a paradigm for what we believe happens in a developing organism.

Embryologists and cell biologists have long worked on the premise that all animal systems, from the primitive to the complex, are fundamentally similar in their developmental events and in the way that these are regulated. This concept of the unity of developmental regulation in all organisms is being realized through the study of growth factors. For example, homologs of mammalian growth factors have been identified in amphibians (Dawid *et al.,* Chapter 9) and invertebrates (Muskavitch and Hoffmann, Chapter 10).

This book is intended to provide the reader with an appreciation of the ubiquity and probable complexity of the action of growth factors in development, and to convey a sense of the rapidity with which we are approaching an understanding of the role of specific growth factors in development.

Marit Nilsen-Hamilton

Table of Abbreviations

In all chapters the gestational age is expressed as the number of days post-coitum with the day of coitus represented as day 0 or day 0.5.

AC	anchor cell
aFGF	acidic fibroblast growth factor
Ax	*Abruptex* alleles in *Drosophila melanogaster*
bf	basal forebrain
bFGF	basic fibroblast growth factor
BMP	bone morphogenetic protein
CAM	chick chorioallantoic membrane
CL	cathepsin L
CNS	central nervous system
ConA	concanavalin A
CRABP	cellular retinoic acid binding protein
crb	*crumbs* locus in *Drosophila melanogaster*
CSF-1	colony-stimulating factor, type 1 (same as M-CSF)
Dl	*Delta* locus
dpp	*decapentaplegic* locus in *Drosophila melanogaster*
DTC	distal tip cell
EC	embryonal carcinoma
EC_{50}	effective concentration that achieves 50% of the maximum response
ECDGF	embryonal carcinoma cell-derived growth factor
ECM	extracellular matrix
EGF	epidermal growth factor
EGF-R	epidermal growth factor receptor
ES	embryo stem cells
fa	*facet* allele of the *Notch* locus *split*
FGF	fibroblast growth factor

GAG	glycosaminoglycan
G-CSF	granulocyte colony-stimulating factor
GGF	glial growth factor
glp-1	(*germ line* proliferation-defective) locus of *Caenorhabditis elegans*
GM-CSF	granulocyte–macrophage colony-stimulating factor
HDL	high-density lipoprotein
[^{3}H]dT	[^{3}H]thymidine
HUE	human umbilical endothelial
IFN	interferon
IFN-α	interferon, type α
IFN-γ	interferon, type γ
IGF	insulinlike growth factor
IGF-I	insulinlike growth factor, type I
IGF-II	insulinlike growth factor, type II
IL-1	interleukin-1
IL-2	interleukin-2
IL-3	interleukin-3
IRF	insulin-related factor kDa
KS-FGF	Kaposi's sarcoma FGF
LAK	lymphokine-activated killer
LI	labeling index
lin-12	*lineage-defective* locus in *Caenorhabditis elegans*
LDL	low-density lipoprotein
M6P	mannose-6-phosphate
M6P-R	mannose-6-phosphate receptor
M-CSF	macrophage colony-stimulating factor
MEP	major excreted protein (same as CL)
MIF	mesoderm inducing factor
Mix	a gene encoding a homeodomain-containing protein
MMTV	mouse mammary tumor virus
MRP	mitogen-regulated protein (same as PLF)
N	*notch* locus in *Drosophila melanogaster*
N-CAM	neural cell adhesion molecule

nd	*notchoid*, allele of the *Notch* locus in *Drosophila melanogaster*
NGF	nerve growth factor
PA	plasminogen activator
PAI-I	type I inhibitor of plasminogen activator
PC13END	differentiated derivatives of embryonal carcinoma cells
PCR	polymerase chain reaction
PDGF	platelet-derived growth factor
PL-I	placental lactogen, type I
PL-II	placental lactogen, type II
PLF	proliferin (same as MRP)
PMA	phorbol myristate acetate or 12-*O*-tetradecanoyl phorbol acetate
PNS	peripheral nervous system
sli	*slit* locus in *Drosophila melanogaster*
spl	*split* allele of the *Notch* locus in *Drosophila melanogaster*
TH	tyrosine hydroxylase
TNF	tumor necrosis factor
TGF-α	transforming growth factor-α
TGF-β	transforming growth factor-β
TGF-βR	TGF-β receptor
TGF-βRI	type I TGF-β receptor
TGF-βRII	type II TGF-β receptor
TGF-βRIII	type III TGF-β receptor
TIMP	tissue inhibitor of metalloproteases
t-PA	plasminogen activator, tissue type
TPA	12-*O*-tetradecanoylphorbol-13-acetate phorbol ester
uEGF-1	locus of the sea urchin *Strongylocentrotus purpuratus*
u-PA	plasminogen activator, urokinase type
VSM	vascular smooth muscle
VU	ventral uterine precursor cell
VVGF	vaccinia virus growth factor
wg	*wingless* gene in *Drosophila melanogaster*
XTC-MIF	mesoderm inducing factor secreted by XTC cells

1

Developmental Activities of the Epidermal Growth Factor Receptor

Eileen D. Adamson
La Jolla Cancer Research Foundation
La Jolla, California 92037

I. Introduction

The two families of genes reviewed here that make up the mitogen–receptor system are those coding for epidermal growth factor and transforming growth factor-α (EGF/TGF-α) (Marquardt *et al.*, 1984) and for their common receptor, the EGF receptor (EGF-R) (Massagué, 1983).

Current Topics in Developmental Biology, Vol. 24

These genes are thought to be important for growth and development because (1) they are highly conserved throughout the evolutionary tree, (2) related forms appear in transformed cells in which growth may be rapid and/or aberrant, (3) they are normally expressed early in development, and (4) in some cases they exhibit a stage- and tissue-specific expression.

The EGF-R gene is similar to a more recently discovered transforming gene, *neu* (*erb*B2) (Drebin *et al.*, 1984). They are both members of the *src* group of oncogenes because they have a tyrosine protein kinase activity. Kinases that react with tyrosine residues are rare among cellular proteins, and this activity is now known to be essential for growth and transformation-related functions.

Ligands that bind to cellular EGF-Rs have quite similar biological activities in cell culture and *in vivo* (Smith *et al.*, 1985; Tam, 1985; Tam *et al.*, 1984). These ligands include EGF, TGF-α, urogastrone (the human form of EGF first found in urine), and vaccinia virus growth factor (Reisner, 1985; Brown *et al.*, 1985; Stroobant *et al.*, 1985). Current knowledge of the EGF-R can be found in several recent reviews (Kris *et al.*, 1985; Hollenberg and Armstrong, 1985; Herschman, 1985; Carpenter, 1987; Gill *et al.*, 1987). Reviews of EGF/TGF-α are found in Goustin *et al.* (1986) and Derynck (1988). Reviews discussing the developmental aspects referred to in this chapter are by Thorburn *et al.* (1981), Pratt (1984), Adamson, (1983, 1986a,b, 1987a,b), Jakobovits (1986), Pratt (1987), Mercola and Stiles (1988), and Nilsen-Hamilton (1989). This chapter is limited to consideration of the EGF-R and EGF/TGF-α families in early embryonic and fetal growth and development. More specific aspects of EGF-R involvement in tissue growth and function can be found in Chapter 2 in this volume.

II. EGF-R Activity in Mammalian Development

A. General Observations

Although EGF-Rs are expressed by a wide variety of adult cell types *in vivo* and cell lines in culture, EGF was so named because of its first-recognized activity in *in vivo* assay for epidermal maturation. Cohen (1962) injected EGF into neonatal mice to demonstrate its effectiveness in accelerating eye opening and tooth eruption. Recently, Zschiesche and Eckert (1988) demonstrated that EGF is normally involved in this developmental process. Antibodies to EGF injected into neonatal mice delayed eyelid opening and tooth eruption and inhibited weight gain in the first week of life. EGF affects the epidermal cell by stimulating proliferation and keratin formation. It is now known to affect a wide range of cell types of ectodermal, mesodermal, and endodermal origins in both epithelial and interstitial tissues. Most tissues—with some exceptions, such as parietal endoderm, mature skeletal muscle, and hematopoietic tissues—express EGF-Rs. However, the roles of the EGF-Rs in most tissues are not understood.

Tissues that continue to divide in order to renew themselves seem to have more EGF-R or to be more responsive to EGF than other tissues. These tissues include the epithelial lining of the gut and the epidermal layer of the skin. The role of the EGF-Rs here may be to aid proliferation. For example, EGF-R-positive cells line the intestinal tract and are exposed to EGF in milk (Shing and Klagsbrun, 1984), food, or saliva. These cells are continually regenerated as they slough off. Skin/epidermis is clearly another tissue that may depend on EGF/TGF-α for its survival and proliferation. Skin cells in culture seem to depend on EGF for proliferation. Keratinocytes themselves produce TGF-α in cell culture (Coffey *et al.*, 1987) that could stimulate their proliferation in an autocrine manner. In addition, EGF levels in mouse neonatal skin have been shown to be under the control of triiodothyronine prior to the onset of hormonal regulation of EGF production in the submaxillary salivary gland by androgens (Hoath *et al.*, 1983).

Hematopoiesis is another process in which continual cellular replacement occurs and in which EGF/TGF-α might participate. However, there are presently no data to support a role for EGF/TGF-α in hematopoiesis. Although mature blood cells do not seem to express EGF-Rs, this may not be true of their precursors or bone marrow stromal cells. Stromal cells could be stimulated either by autocrine factors (which have not been identified) or locally by macrophages known to produce TGF-α (Rappolee, 1988b). A further reason to believe that EGF-Rs may also be important for early hematopoietic cells is that their viral counterpart, v-*erb*B1, causes deregulated erythroblast proliferation and differentiation in birds (reviewed by Graf and Berg, 1983). This type of cell or its precursor must therefore contain the necessary signaling pathway, even though the truncated v-*erb*B1 protein does not bind or respond to extracellular EGF/TGF-α. This example also raises the possibility, however, that receptors for growth factors may be activated by intracellular mechanisms rather than by extracellular ligands. That intracellular receptors and ligands can induce changes in gene expression in normal or embryo cells is an interesting question. Although there is, as yet, no evidence for this with the EGF-R, there is evidence that platelet-derived growth factor (PDGF) and its receptor can interact productively inside the cell (Robbins *et al.*, 1985), although this has been refuted (Hannink and Donoghue (1988). The PDGF and EGF receptors are both tyrosine protein kinases. Intracellular interaction between EGF/TGF-α and EGF-R could be relevant to processes of development (see Section VI).

B. EGF Binding Activity in Fetal Tissues

The early searches for EGF-Rs in fetal tissues were triggered by the finding that differentiated embryonal carcinoma (EC) cells bind and respond to EGF, while parental EC cells do not bind EGF (Rees *et al.*, 1979). EC cells are the stem cells of murine teratocarcinomas. This finding suggested that fetal tissues would express EGF binding sites, while the earliest embryonic stem cells might not express the EGF-R. Part of this prediction was confirmed (Adamson *et al.*, 1981) when [^{125}I]EGF binding was recorded throughout gestation in the mouse and it was found that EGF binding activity in most tissues peaked at midgestation. These measurements represented averages from mixed cell types in dissected tissues. Extraembryonic tissues, amnion, and placenta had the highest EGF-binding capacity, while lungs, limbs, and brain had intermediate levels. Similar studies on human placenta tissues showed increasing numbers of EGF-Rs through gestation (Deal *et al.*, 1982; see Section V,C for a discussion of placental EGF-Rs). Earlier, Nexø *et al.* (1980) showed that the epithelial cells of the mouse secondary palate bound [^{125}I]EGF specifically, and, most significantly, they detected an EGF-like factor produced by embryos that could compete for EGF binding sites (see below; see also Proper *et al.*, 1982). A similar factor was described in rat fetuses (Matrisian *et al.*, 1982).

Are fetal EGF-Rs responsive to ligand binding and, if so, how do the cells respond? The addition of EGF to fetal organ cultures led to a dose-dependent increase in the incorporation of tritiated thymidine (Adamson *et al.*, 1981). The opposite effect was obtained *in vivo*. After exposure of fetal mice *in utero* to high concentrations of exogenous EGF, followed by the addition of tritiated thymidine 16 hours later, the tissues that were recovered from experimental fetuses after a further 2-hour incubation showed reduced incorporation of radioactivity into DNA compared to control tissues. In addition, when EGF was injected into the amniotic cavities of live fetuses *in utero*, [^{125}I]EGF binding measured subsequently in dissected tissues was depressed maximally 3–6 hours later (Adamson and Warshaw, 1981). These results suggest that the EGF-Rs were made less responsive to EGF by prior exposure to high levels of EGF (Adamson *et al.*, 1981). Similarly, Hoath *et al.* (1987) measured lower EGF binding activities in membranes prepared from 14-day-old suckling rats compared to membranes from 21-day fetal rat liver and from adult rats. The suckling rats that were administered parenteral EGF showed a 78% reduction in binding 2 hours later. This result demonstrated a correlation between the reduced responsiveness of the liver and the extent of EGF-induced down-regulation of the EGF-R. The results of these studies suggest that neonatal and fetal EGF-Rs are responsive to mitogenic signals that can down-regulate the EGF-R in the presence of EGF.

Measurements of [^{125}I]EGF binding and analysis by the methods of both Scatchard (1947) and Klotz (1982) revealed that the EGF-Rs in early fetal tissues occur in low numbers, but have a higher affinity than the more numerous EGF-Rs in older fetuses (Adamson and Meek, 1984). Infusion of excess EGF into neonatal rabbits led to increased liver growth and hepatic maturation at an earlier stage than in controls (Opleta *et al.*, 1987). While these results suggest that the EGF-R may function differently at different stages of gestation and may have multiple roles within one organ, the precise roles of EGF and the EGF-R remain obscure.

C. EGF-R Gene and Protein Structures

Progress in determining physiological roles for proteins is often rapid after the gene has been cloned and sequenced. In addition, if the protein can be purified and an antibody can be developed, studies of the protein structure, its distribution *in vivo*, and its biosynthesis may significantly illuminate the field of study.

cDNA fragments of the EGF-R were cloned and sequenced by several workers (Lin *et al.*, 1984; Simmen *et al.*, 1984; Downward *et al.*, 1984; Lax *et al.*, 1988), and genomic clones have been described (Ishii *et al.*, 1985, 1986; Hung *et al.*, 1986; Johnson *et al.*, 1988b). Rapid progress in characterizing the receptor was made after the protein was identified as the product of the protooncogene c-*erb*B, which has an intracellular domain homologous to the *src* gene product and which is also a tyrosine protein kinase. Figure 1 shows the main features of EGF-R protein. The tyrosine kinase activity of the EGF-R had been detected much earlier (Carpenter *et al.*, 1978; Carpenter, 1979; Cohen *et al.*, 1982), but the role that this activity plays in receptor function was clearly defined later using genetically engineered constructs (Honegger *et al.*, 1987a,b). This activity of the EGF-R probably underlies the pleiotropic effects of EGF.

The biochemical characterization of the EGF-R was made possible, in large part, by the existence of a human epidermoid carcinoma cell line, A431, which has large numbers of both normal and truncated receptors. Antibodies raised to EGF-R from A431 cells have been used to purify and to probe the structure and the mechanism of action of the EGF-Rs (Waterfield *et al.*,1982; Schreiber *et al.*, 1982; Rees *et al.*, 1984; Carpenter, 1984; Gullick *et al.*, 1985; Defize *et al.*, 1987; Lax *et al.*, 1988). Sequence studies of the rodent EGF-R have lagged behind, although antibodies to the purified mouse EGF-R have been useful in defining the molecular characteristics of the 170-kDa glycoprotein receptor (Cohen *et al.*, 1982; Weller *et al.*, 1987).

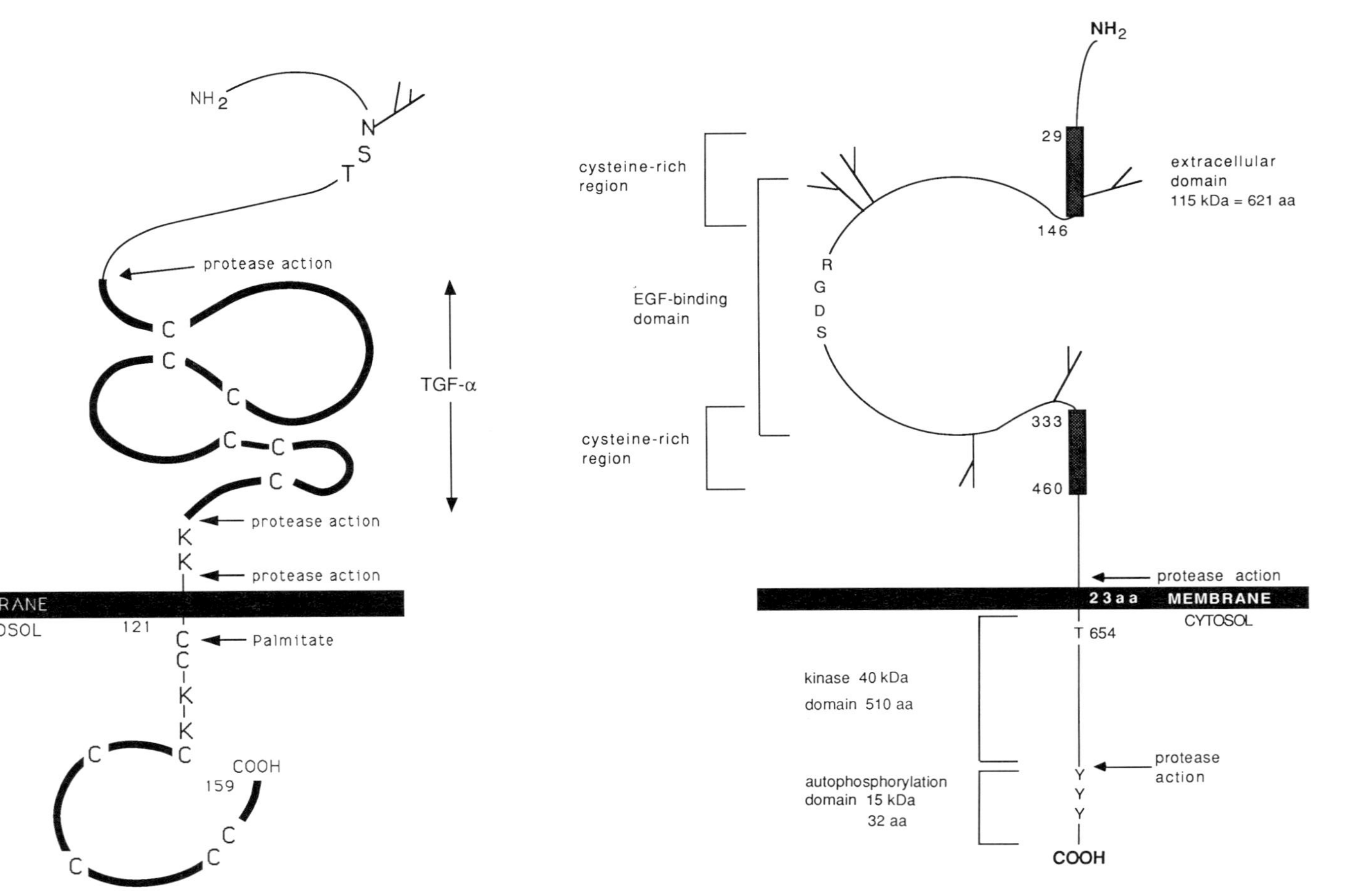
NH2
N
S
T
protease action
C
C
C
C
C
C
TGF-α
protease action
K
K
protease action
MEMBRANE
CYTOSOL
121
C
Palmitate
C
K
K
C
C
COOH
159
C
C
C
TGF-α precursor
NH2
29
cysteine-rich
region
extracellular
domain
115 kDa = 621 aa
146
R
G
D
S
EGF-binding
domain
cysteine-rich
region
333
460
protease action
23aa MEMBRANE
CYTOSOL
T 654
kinase 40 kDa
domain 510 aa
protease
action
Y
Y
Y
autophosphorylation
domain 15 kDa
32 aa
COOH
EGF receptor

D. EGF-R Tyrosine Kinase Activity

The EGF-R is characterized by the ability to phosphorylate itself in the well-known autophosphorylation activity. Detection of autophosphorylation indicates the presence of an activated EGF-R. Only one study that utilized the autophosphorylating activity to detect EGF-R in fetuses has been described (Hortsch *et al.,* 1983). The earliest stage at which the EGF-R kinase activity was detected was on the 10th day of gestation. The highest activities were found in the amnion, placenta, uterus, and skin, while lower activities were found in other tissues. In some tissues, such as visceral yolk sac and early liver, no EGF-R kinase activity was seen. This result conflicts with the results of the [^{125}I]EGF binding studies by Adamson and Meek (1984), in which EGF-R was detected throughout development. This discrepancy could have a number of explanations. The binding properties of the EGF-R may develop before detectable kinase activity develops. Alternatively, the kinase measurements may be less sensitive than the EGF-binding assay. The latter is a likely explanation for a number of reasons: In the study by Hortsch *et al.* (1983) the tissue lysates were immunoprecipitated before measuring kinase activity; the antibody used was raised against the human, not the rodent, receptor protein; and EGF was not used to stimulate the phosphorylation reaction. Therefore, the results of studies using a more sensitive assay with mouse-specific antibodies are needed before further conclusions regarding the developmental profile of the EGF-R can be made.

E. Roles of EGF-R in the Adult

As stated in Section I, adult tissues that continually proliferate and replace themselves could depend on EGF-Rs to provide mitogenic signals. A second major role for EGF-Rs in the adult is in healing or regeneration of damaged organs such as the liver. Although the number of EGF-Rs per cell has been reported to decrease between 8 and 36 hours after partial hepatectomy (Earp and O'Keefe, 1981), complex fluctuations in the EGF-R level are predictable in the regenerating liver. Two of the caveats in the interpretation of receptor binding measurements are that masked or down-regulated receptors give a low binding value, and normal liver tissue in rats is known to contain an intracellular compartment with a number of receptors equal to that on the cell surface (Dunn *et al.,* 1986). Presumably, this

Fig. 1 Some features of the EGF receptor and the TGF-α gene. aa, Amino acids; C, cysteine; Y, tyrosine; R, arginine; T, threonine; G, glycine; S, serine; D, aspartate; K, lysine; N, asparagine. Y-Shaped projections from the polypeptide chain are carbohydrate chains. (Modified from Bringman *et al.,* 1987.)

large intracellular pool of EGF-R exists because the intracellular receptors accumulate by continual endocytosis from the surface as this absorptive organ continually removes EGF from circulation. During liver regeneration, a high level of EGF produced by an unknown source appears in the plasma (Cornwell, 1985), which could account for the early period of low EGF binding. Later, the level of EGF-Rs increases due to EGF stimulated biosynthetic rates (see also Section V,A).

One very likely and clear role for EGF-Rs is the healing of skin lesions that have been coated with saliva administered by normal licking of the wounded area. The concentration of EGF is also higher in the saliva of mature male rodents, for whom combat wounds are more frequent. While only rodents are known to produce saliva that contains high concentrations of EGF, small amounts of EGF in the saliva of other species may well be enough to promote wound healing.

Constant exposure of living cells to EGF may be necessary for cellular viability, but this has by no means been proven. For instance, maintenance of the differentiated (but nondividing) state could depend on the novel effect that EGF has on increasing mRNA stability (Jinno *et al.,* 1988). Although measurable serum levels of EGF have been recorded many times in the literature (reviewed by Adamson, 1983), more recent measurements indicate that normal plasma levels of EGF may be much lower than originally thought because of the release of EGF-like material from activated platelets in serum samples (Bowen-Pope and Ross, 1983). The exact nature of the EGF-like material in human platelets (Oka and Orth, 1983) has not been established, but it occurs there together with TGF-α and PDGF and may be released simultaneously into the serum upon platelet activation. The adult organism, therefore, seems to have EGF-Rs present on most cell types that become activated only when EGF/TGF-α is released locally at wounds by platelets and macrophages (Rappolee *et al.,* 1988b). There may also be a continuing role for EGF-Rs in the gonads and the uterus (see Section II,G).

F. Roles of EGF-R in the Fetus

The precise roles of the EGF-R in the fetus have not been defined. During the gestation period, a predictable role would be to receive mitogenic signals to proliferate and produce the large number of new cells needed during development. The mitogenic activity of EGF/TGF-α is recognized now as only one of several of its actions that can influence cellular gene expression and behavior. Maturation of fetal lung, palate, and intestine are believed to be stimulated by EGF/TGF-α. The ability of EGF to stimulate expression of the differentiated phenotype has been recorded for pituitary and other cell types (e.g., Murdoch *et al.*, 1982). EGF-Rs could also initiate signals that direct cell behavior in more subtle ways, as described next.

One rapid response of cultured cells to EGF is a change in cell surface structure and cell shape (Chinkers *et al.*, 1981). The increased cell membrane ruffling and motility due to EGF (Barrandon and Green, 1987) may play a role in the cell migration that is characteristic of early embryonic development. Migrations such as trophoblast cell invasion, primitive streak formation, and mesodermal cell movements (Westermark and Blomquist, 1980) may be regulated by EGF/TGF-α. Later in gestation and also in the adult, EGF stimulates intestinal epithelial cell migration and renewal (Blay and Brown, 1985). It could be conjectured that EGF/TGF-α facilitates the changes in cell arrangements that occur when epithelial layers form and then bend into tubules or sacs to make lung, kidney, intestine, and glands of various kinds.

Cell motility and tissue shaping are important activities during development. Extracellular matrix and growth factors likely play important roles in tissue shaping (reviewed by Trelstad, 1984; see also Chapters 4, 7, and 8, this volume). Cells adhere to and migrate over substrates of fibronectin, collagen, laminin, and proteoglycans and interact with these extracellular matrix proteins via specific receptors called integrins (Ruoslahti and Pierschbacher, 1987). Fibronectin, collagen, and hyaluronic acid syntheses are all stimulated by EGF in cells in culture or *in vivo* (Chen *et al.*, 1978; Lembach, 1976; Silver *et al.*, 1984; Erickson and Turley, 1987; Sporn *et al.*, 1983). In addition, further modulation of cell motion and tissue shaping could occur through binding of the arginine-glycine-aspartate (RGD) (Fig. 1) motif in the EGF-R to integrin receptors on other cells. Cell–cell and cell–matrix interactions influenced by EGF/TGF-α seem to be important in oral cavity development (reviewed by Pratt, 1987; see also Chapter 2, this volume).

EGF may also be important in brain development. We noticed that the EGF binding activity in fetal brain increased toward the end of the gestation period (Adamson and Meek, 1984). EGF-immunoreactive material has been identified within neuronal fibers in the forebrain (Fallon *et al.*, 1984), and EGF enhances both survival and neurite outgrowth in primary cultures of subneocortical telencephalic neurons of neonatal rat brain in a dose-dependent manner (Morrison *et al.*, 1987). In addition, TGF-α mRNA has been detected in dentate gyrus, caudate nucleus, and other regions of the brain by Wilcox and Derynck (1988a). Therefore, these regions of the adult brain may also synthesize TGF-α. Although cultured glial cells express EGF-Rs, the evidence above suggests that neurons respond directly to EGF/TGF-α in a unique way that implies a specialized, but as yet undefined, role for EGF/TGF-α in neuronal development. Other growth factors that are important for neuronal development are described in Chapter 6.

G. Roles of EGF-R in Uterine and Germ Cell Development

The female uterine environment in the rat is prepared for pregnancy by a variety of hormones (especially estrogen) that are crucial at several stages for the development of a hospitable uterine environment for the embryo (Mukku and Stancel, 1985). The EGF binding activity of the uterus is responsive to pregnancy hormones. The level of EGF-R varies through pregnancy, with the highest level of binding occurring on day 7 (Chakrabarty *et al.*, 1988). Although the numbers of EGF-Rs increase from day 1 to day 7, the apparent affinity of the receptors declines over the same period. The increase in EGF binding was attributed primarily to the appearance of proliferating and differentiating (decidual) stromal cells, but it could also be brought about by the increase in progesterone or estrogen that occurs in pregnancy. The number of EGF receptors in the uterine membranes of immature rats was increased in response to estrogen but not in response to nonestrogenic steroids such as progesterone, dihydrotestosterone, or dexamethasone (Mukku and Stancel, 1985). The low level of EGF binding observed on day 1 could be the consequence of down-regulation of uterine receptors, because the highest concentrations of immunoreactive EGF are found in the uterus on that day (Chakrabarty *et al.*, 1988).

The production of mature oocytes in mouse ovaries is inhibited by EGF (Lintern-Moore *et al.*, 1981). This is an indirect effect due to the ability of EGF to inhibit the induction of luteinizing hormone receptors which usually appear in response to follicle-stimulating hormone (Mondschein *et al.*, 1981; Mondschein and Schonberg, 1981). The opposite result was found in rats, in which oocyte maturation was induced by EGF (Dekel and Sherizly, 1985). In addition, immunoreactive TGF-α has been found in the interstitial and thecal cells of ovaries of immature rats primed with diethylstilbestrol. This finding was supported by the presence of the 4.5-kb TGF-α mRNA in the ovaries of these animals (Kudlow *et al.*, 1987). Is this the same mRNA that is later found as maternal mRNA in the egg (Rappolee *et al.*, 1988a).?

A role for EGF in male reproductive function was suggested by the observation that EGF can activate steroid biosynthesis in Leydig tumor cells (Ascoli *et al.*, 1987). More direct evidence was obtained in a study that used sialoadenectomy (removal of the submaxillary saliva gland) to decrease the circulating levels of EGF in serum. Reductions of mature sperm, spermatids, and spermatocytes of 55%, 40–50%, and 20%, respectively, were demonstrated in sialoadenectomized animals. The reduced level of spermatogenesis could be reversed by the administration of EGF (Tsutsumi *et al.*, 1986). We have noted that antibodies to EGF-Rs bind to the plasma membrane of murine sperm (unpublished observations) and similar observations have been made in human sperm (B. Knowles, personal communication). Is the EGF-R present on sperm because it functions in fertilization, or does it reflect a role for the receptor during spermatogenesis?

H. Roles of EGF-R in Preimplantation Embryos

EGF-Rs have not yet been described in very early embryos but have been serologically detected on mouse blastocysts (Adamson, 1990). A significant recent finding in this area of research is the presence of stored maternal mRNA coding for growth factors in unfertilized eggs (Rappolee *et al.*, 1988a). TGF-α mRNA sequences were detected using the polymerase chain reaction procedure. In addition, a small amount of TGF-β1 mRNA and a larger amount of PDGF-A mRNA were detected, while mRNAs encoding EGF, basic fibroblast growth factor, nerve growth factor, and granulocyte colony-stimulating factor were undetectable at all stages of preimplantation development. Both TGF-α and PDGF-A mRNAs disappeared between the two and eight-cell stages and reappeared in early cavitation blastocysts. The abundance of PDGF-A mRNA was at least ten-fold greater in the blastocysts than in the oocytes. The growth factor transcripts in the blastocyst stage were also shown to be translated, since specific antibody staining was detected intracellularly. The presence of growth factor mRNA in mammalian eggs could indicate a role for growth factors in uterine/decidual preparation for implantation, as well as in early embryonic growth. The presence of PDGF-A mRNA has also been described in *Xenopus* oocytes (Mercola *et al.*, 1988), which suggests a role for growth factors in embryonic development itself. A TGF-like activity was also demonstrated by Rizzino (1985) in conditioned medium from mouse embryos. The presence of both TGF-α and TGF-β, which are known to be angiogenic (Folkman and Klagsbrun, 1987), would certainly correlate with the production of capillary beds at implantation sites in the uterus.

III. The EGF Gene and Its Product

Although it has generally been accepted that EGF production starts only in postnatal life, results obtained with more sensitive methods of detecting EGF suggest that this restriction may not hold true (see below). EGF-like genes and proteins have been detected in a wide range of species, including humans, rodents, amphibians, sea urchins, fruit flies, and birds (see Chapters 9 and 10, this volume). Such strong conservation in sequence generally implies an important biological role. Although its mitogenic activity is clearly useful to experimental biologists studying signal transduction, the role of EGF *in vivo*, like that of its receptor, is still obscure.

A. EGF/TGF-α Gene Structure

A cDNA prepared from male mouse submaxillary gland mRNA and encoding a large precursor of EGF was first described by Scott *et al.* (1983). The precursor contains seven related sequences, in addition to EGF and a membrane-spanning domain. Sequences similar to the EGF sequences were noted in pancreatic secretory trypsin inhibitor and in factors IX and X of the blood-clotting group of proteins (Doolittle *et al.*, 1984). In fact, the gene for preproEGF is made up of eight EGF-like exons and its overall structure is similar to that of the low-density lipoprotein receptor (Südhof *et al.*, 1985a,b). This receptorlike preproEGF may have specific functions apart from its relationship to EGF, since some tissues seem to be unable to process the membrane-bound form further (Rall *et al.*, 1985).

B. Expression of the EGF Gene and Its Protein Product

As expected from the presence of high levels of EGF protein, the male mouse submaxillary gland produces high levels of mRNA encoding preproEGF, and this organ produces a protease that specifically liberates EGF (6 kDa) from a 9-kDa precursor (Taylor *et al.*, 1970, 1974). An EGF/TGF-α-like activity is also found in platelets (Oka and Orth, 1983). However, the source of most of the large amount of heterogeneous EGF (originally called urogastrone) found in human (Gregory, 1975) and mouse urine is more likely to be the kidney than the submaxillary gland. The distal tubules of the mouse kidney contain high levels of mRNA encoding the precursor form of EGF compared with other tissues (Rall *et al.*, 1985). Immunohistochemical studies of the kidney confirmed the presence of EGF in the apical portions of cells lining the thick tubules of the loop of Henle and the distal convoluted tubules (Salido *et al.*, 1986).

The production of EGF by fetal tissues is controversial. In some cases measurements with different sensitivities or different techniques have given different results. For example, Popliker *et al.* (1987) were unable to detect any EGF mRNA in fetal mice, but after the mice were weaned, the male submaxillary glands contained detectable levels of EGF mRNA, which then increased until the mice reached adulthood. Female submaxillary glands had lower levels of EGF mRNA, as expected from their EGF protein content. The EGF mRNA appeared in the kidney after 2 weeks of age, and its level in female kidneys was slightly higher than in male kidneys (Gubits *et al.*, 1986). No EGF mRNA was detected by Northern blotting of RNA from fetal tissues (Popliker *et al.*, 1987). On the other hand, *in situ* hybridization using an oligonucleotide probe revealed EGF transcripts in developing teeth and lungs and the EGF protein was also observed by immunostaining (Snead *et al.*, 1989). Localized concentrations of specific mRNAs can be detected more readily by the *in situ* method than by Northern analyses. Similarly, immunodetection of the protein may be more sensitive than Northern analysis. Using three different antisera, Fallon *et al.* (1984) found a distinct distribution of EGF protein in adult and developing brain at all ages after the 14th day of gestation. Radioimmunoassay also confirmed the presence of EGF in extracts from whole fetuses following the 15th day of gestation (Pratt, 1987). Some of this EGF may be maternally derived (see Section III,C), but it seems that some EGF may also be produced by fetal cells and may be active in some fetal locations.

C. Does Maternal EGF Cross the Placenta?

A further discrepancy is apparent in the results of different studies of the ability of EGF to cross the placenta. Popliker *et al.* (1987) show that after injection of [^{125}I]EGF into pregnant females, a considerable proportion of the radioactivity appears in the fetuses. In this study the integrity of the EGF was not ascertained, but in a similar, more recent study intact [^{125}I]EGF was recovered from the fetuses (J. B. Warshaw and W. Stenzel, personal communication). In contrast, the conclusions of Di Augustine *et al.* (1987) were that [^{125}I]EGF does not cross the placenta. They showed that, after its injection into pregnant females, [^{125}I]EGF was stable in the placenta and the plasma for about 1 minute, but was largely degraded by 5 minutes to free iodine. The free iodine readily permeated the placenta and was found to be associated with fetal tissue. A half-life of less than 1 minute was measured for [^{125}I]EGF, while ^{125}I-labeled nerve growth factor was stable for up to 30 minutes.

If the placenta acts as a barrier to EGF transport, then it could do so by means of its numerous EGF-Rs. These receptors are known to occur on all surfaces of the plasma membrane of human placental syncytiotrophoblasts (Rao *et al.*, 1985; Ramani *et al.*, 1986; Chegini and Rao, 1986; Maruo and Mochizuki, 1987) and are also present in mouse placenta (Adamson and

Meek, 1984; Smith and Talamantes, 1986). In summary, it seems safe to say that a small amount of maternal EGF does reach the fetus, but it is still unknown if this is important to development.

IV. The TGF-α Gene and Its Product

This protein is currently regarded as the embryonic counterpart of EGF because it is produced by a range of cell types that includes transformed cells (hence its inappropriate name), tumor cells, and embryonic cells (Twardzik *et al.*, 1982, 1985). TGF-α binds to the same receptor as EGF, and currently it is the most likely candidate for interaction with the EGF-Rs in fetal and maternal tissues. TGF-α has also been reviewed by Massagué (1985) and by Derynck (1988).

A. Gene Structure

Rat (Lee *et al.*, 1985b) and human (Derynck *et al.*, 1984) TGF-α cDNA clones have been isolated and sequenced. Like EGF, these related genes are transcribed as large precursors yielding transmembrane proteins of 159 and 160 amino acids, respectively. The 50-amino acid TGF-α moiety is proteolytically derived from the 160-residue precursor. Carboxy-terminal to the mature TGF-α sequence is a long, hydrophobic region that could span the membrane. The carboxy-terminal regions in the human and rat precursors are virtually identical, which suggests that there is an important, but as yet unknown, biological function for the precursor. In addition to membrane insertion, the precursor is linked to the membrane through its carboxy terminus by means of a palmitic acid group which is covalently attached to cysteine (Bringman *et al.*, 1987).

It seems that the TGF-α precursor can be processed differentially, because TGF-α species of various molecular weights have been identified (Gentry *et al.*, 1987). A 17- to 20-kDa species which represents the 160-amino acid form is frequently found, as well as the 50-amino acid, 5-kDa form. The 17- to 20-kDa intermediate forms of TGF-α that are released by transformed cells are also bioactive and include the extracellular amino-terminal, glycosylated domain of 160 amino acids. This type of prohormone processing may also occur for preproEGF, vaccinia virus growth factor, and the related *Notch* gene in *Drosophila*. These genes have regions of amino acid sequence homology to mature TGF-α, as well as hydrophobic sequences that may act as membrane-spanning domains (Teixido *et al.*, 1987; see also Chapter 10, this volume). A rather unusual elastase type of cleavage (Ignotz *et al.*, 1986) between alanine and valine releases mature TGF-α from the extracellular domain of the membrane-bound form. Figure 1 shows the main characteristics and features of TGF-α.

B. TGF-α Expression in Developing Tissues

A TGF-α-encoding mRNA of 4.5 kb has been detected at relatively high levels during early embryogenesis. The highest level was detected on the 9th day of gestation in poly $(A)^+$ RNA preparations from whole rat conceptuses (Lee *et al.*, 1985a). No TGF-α mRNA was detected in 11th-day or older embryos and fetuses. This transient appearance of mRNA has not been reconciled with earlier reports of an EGF-like activity that was immunologically distinct from EGF, but that competed with EGF for binding to the EGF-R (Nexø *et al.*, 1980) and was found in mouse conceptuses (Proper *et al.*, 1982) and rat fetuses from the 12th day on (Matrisian *et al.*, 1982). A similar activity was found in human term placenta (Stromberg *et al.*, 1982). Using a sensitive and specific radioimmunoassay, Twardzik (1985) found the highest TGF-α level in day 7 conceptuses; this level declined by day 10 and rose to a second peak in day 13 fetuses. Therefore, there seems to be a high producing tissue early in gestation and then a later period of TGF-α production. This conclusion is also consistent with more recent *in situ* hybridization results. Han *et al.* (1987) showed that the maternal rat deciduum is a major source of TGF-α producing peak levels on day 8. The level of TGF-α mRNA then declined through day 15, when the deciduum is resorbed. Although Han *et al.* (1987) did not detect TGF-α mRNA in the fetal parts of the placenta or in the embryo, Wilcox and Derynck (1988b) detected TGF-α mRNA by the same procedure in the fetal portion of day 9 and day 10 placenta, in otic vesicle, oral cavity, pharyngeal pouch, first and second bronchial arches, and the developing kidneys. The same group also detected mRNA for TGF-α in the adult mouse brain (Wilcox and Derynck, 1988a). The production of a TGF-α-like protein by developing ovine kidneys was also recorded by Freemark and Comer (1987), who reported 14.5- and 9-kDa mitogenic and transformed growth-stimulating activities. Therefore, there is reason to believe that differences in the detection of mRNA for TGF-α (and EGF: see above) may be due to differing sensitivities of the assays. Again, these results need to be confirmed to make firm conclusions regarding the expression of the TGF-α gene in gestation.

C. Role for TGF-α in Implantation

In spite of the uncertainty as to the exact location of synthesis of TGF-α in the developing conceptus, there is agreement that TGF-α is produced in large amounts in extraembryonic tissues at least as early as the 7th day of gestation. The source could be the maternal placenta immediately adjacent to the invading trophoblast (Han *et al.*, 1987) or it could be the giant cells or syncytiotrophoblasts (Wilcox and Derynck, 1988b). Several intriguing questions emerge: Is the TGF-α released from the placental cells and does it diffuse to other locations? What are the target cells for the TGF-α produced by the embryonic and extraembryonic tissues? What are the roles for soluble and membrane-bound TGF-α?

Because TGF-α acts as a mitogen through EGF-Rs (although another, more specific, receptor has not been ruled out), the deciduum and the developing trophoblasts are possible targets. A mitogenic role for TGF-α in the early postimplantation period in development would certainly be supported by the rapid growth of trophoblasts and decidual cells during and following implantation. Proteases would also need to be present at this following implantation. Proteases would also need to be present at this time to provide the secreted version TGF-α. Plasminogen activator and cathepsin L are produced by trophoblast cells at the invasive stage (see Chapter 7, this volume). Plasminogen activator could produce active plasmin from plasminogen. EGF stimulates the production of plasminogen activator by HeLa cells (Lee and Weinstein, 1978) and of cathepsin L by 3T3 cells (Nilsen-Hamilton *et al.*, 1981; Denhardt *et al.*, 1986). It is possible that proTGF-α could similarly stimulate uterine epithelial cells to secrete proteases. Endogenous proteases that can process TGF-α are also present in many cell types (Teixido *et al.*, 1987). The regulation of protease production by growth factors and the expression of proteases in development are discussed in Chapters 4, 7, and 8 of this volume.

The precursor membrane-bound form of TGF-α may be a specific receptor or have a cell–cell interactive role. An additional intriguing idea is that the RGD-containing sequence found in the human EGF-R (residues 233–235; Xu *et al.*, 1984) can interact with the integrin family of receptors (for fibronectin and other matrix receptors) to assist in cell–cell interactions during this period of trophoblast cell invasion and migration.

V. Regulation of EGF-R Expression

A. Gene Regulation

The 5′ promoter region of the human EGF-R gene lacks the usual TATA and CAAT boxes and has some other unusual features. This region has a high G and C content with five CCGCCC repeats and four (TCC)TCCTCCTCC repeats that are close to or within an identified DNAse I-hypersensitive site in A431 cells (Ishii *et al.*, 1985). There are six transcription start sites that could give rise to heterogeneous transcripts. Several regulatory sites have been identified, including an SP-1 site (Kageyama *et al.*, 1988; Johnson *et al.*, 1988b).

Deregulation of the EGF-R gene may be an important factor in tumorigenesis. Several aberrant modes of overexpression are known, including amplification and rearrangements in carcinomas and gliomas (King *et al.*, 1985; Libermann *et al.*, 1985; Lin *et al.*, 1984). Despite the presence of a single EGF-R gene in normal cells, two distinctly sized mRNAs of approximately 10 and 6 kb are found in human, mouse, and rat cells. While differences in their proportions have been recorded in different cells, both of these mRNAs can give rise to EGF-R protein (Simmen *et al.*, 1984). Whether these two EGF-R mRNAs have different stabilities or other characteristics is not yet known.

During liver regeneration after partial hepatectomy in rats, the levels of the 6- and 10-kb EGF-R mRNAs change. Up to 12 hours after hepatectomy, the levels of EGF-R mRNAs decrease, but at 24–72 hours they are markedly increased (Johnson *et al.*, 1988a). This may be due to EGF-stimulated EGF-R synthesis brought about by the higher levels of EGF found in rat plasma after partial hepatectomy (Cornwell, 1985).

B. EGF-R Regulation *in Vitro*

The activity of the EGF-Rs can be modulated by PDGF, fibroblast growth factor, bombesin, mellitin, and tumor promoters (reviewed by Gill *et al.*, 1987). The EGF-R kinase activity is modulated by gangliosides (Bremer *et al.*, 1984) and by sphingosine (Faucher *et al.*, 1988), and these may be part of the regulatory mechanism of fetal EGF-Rs. Sphingosine activates protein kinase C, which phosphorylates the EGF-R at a number of sites and thereby reduces EGF binding activity (Faucher *et al.*, 1988). That the tyrosine phosphorylating activity of the EGF-R is absolutely necessary for the mitogenic activity of EGF/TGF-α was shown by studies with mutant recombinant receptors (Honegger *et al.*, 1987a,b; Livneh *et al.*, 1987). However, tyrosine autophosphorylation does not seem to be part of the mitogenic signal (Clark *et al.*, 1988).

Analysis of EGF binding data by Scatchard (1947) plots shows that there are two different affinities for EGF. However, there is no evidence for two EGF-R proteins. A mechanism involving EGF-induced receptor dimerization may explain the existence of high- and low-affinity EGF binding sites (Böni-Schnetzler and Pilch, 1987; Yarden and Schlessinger, 1987; Fanger *et al.*, 1989). It was also shown that EGF-R dimers have enhanced autophosphorylating activity. However, the mechanism underlying the existence of high- and low-affinity EGF binding sites remains obscure.

The regulation of EGF-R protein metabolism has been studied in cell cultures in great detail by several groups who have shown that the EGF-R kinase activity and EGF-R synthesis are stimulated by EGF (reviewed Decker, 1985). Similar results were reported for primary cultures of human cytotrophoblast cells (dePalo and Das, 1988). Low concentrations of EGF increased EGF-R synthesis, while high concentrations increased its degradation. This observation supports the hypothesis that the EGF-R has several roles in the placenta, which include the regulation of cellular activity and the provision of a barrier for the fetus by removing EGF from the surrounding fluids and thus preventing its general access to the fetus.

C. EGF-R Regulation in the Placenta

The placenta is an obvious subject for studying the regulation of EGF-Rs during development. The EGF binding sites in human placenta have been examined by Ramani *et al.* (1986) and by Chegini and Rao ((1986), who fractionated plasma membranes, lysosomes, smooth and rough endoplasmic reticula, and Golgi bodies and assessed EGF binding and receptor forms in these subcellular fractions by using [^{125}I]EGF cross-linking and sodium dodecyl sulfate–polyacrylamide gel electrophoresis. Two species of EGF-R, of 155 and 140 kDa in size, were demonstrated; their proportions varied in different intracellular organelles. The rough endoplasmic reticulum contained the greatest proportion of the 140-kDa form. Both species could be phosphorylated. Electron-microscopic evaluation of [^{125}I]EGF sites after internalization revealed the EGF-R in the syncytiotrophoblasts, with the order of binding as: plasma membrane > nuclei > lysosomes > Golgi bodies > rough endoplasmic reticulum. The high level of EGF-R found in the nucleus is intriguing, but whether EGF or EGF-R conveys the mitogenic signal directly to the nucleus is still unresolved. The large intracellular pool of EGF-Rs in the placenta probably reflects the highly absorptive activity of this organ. A similarly high proportion of intracellular EGF-R has been found in the liver (Dunn *et al.*, 1986), which is another highly absorptive organ.

Several reports are in agreement that both mouse and human placental EGF-Rs increase in number or in binding capacity from mid- to late gestation (Deal *et al.*, 1982). Some differences in detail have been recorded, such as whether there is a single affinity type of receptor (Adamson and Meek, 1984) or a heterogeneous one that presents a curvilinear Scatchard plot (Smith and Talamantes, 1986; Sissom *et al.*, 1987). But differences in purity of the membranes, the conditions of the assay, and recovery of bound [^{125}I]EGF may explain these variances. One very interesting study has shown that early (day 10) mouse placental membranes have essentially the same high number of EGF-Rs as late gestational placental membranes (day 17), while day 14 (midgestation) membranes have considerably fewer EGF-Rs (Adamson and Meek, 1984). The presence of the highest concentration of EGF-Rs in very early human syncytiotrophoblasts has also recently been shown by immunohistochemistry (Maruo and Mochizuki, 1987; Maruo *et al.*, 1987). Human chorionic gonadotropin and placental lactogen are also produced in very early syncytiotrophoblasts (Maruo *et al.*, 1987) and EGF stimulates primary cultures of these cells to release these hormones (Lai and Guyda, 1984). Therefore EGF/TGF-α could serve this early important function of stimulating fetal cells to secrete hormones that prepare the mother for pregnancy.

It is generally agreed that birth weights of newborns are directly related to placental weights. This relationship is multifaceted because of the essential role of the placenta to the development of the fetus. Sissom *et al.* (1987) showed that the large placentas produced by streptozotocin-induced diabetic rats did not mature in many respects. One sign of this immaturity was that there were fewer EGF-Rs in placentas from streptozotocin-induced diabetic rats than in placentas from untreated animals. In particular, there was a deficiency of the late-appearing, low-affinity–high-capacity receptor type that is observed in day 21 in normal rat placentas. Even at term, the large placentas of the streptozotocin-treated rats were still increasing in size due to cellular proliferation, whereas proliferation normally ceases in the last few days of pregnancy. Overall, the level of EGF binding per placenta may not be much different in diabetic and normal rats, but the delay of maturation of receptor types may be important to the disease.

On the basis of studies using an antibody that reacts with only the low-affinity population of EGF-R, Gregoriou and Rees (1984) suggested that high- and low-affinity receptors have different functions, namely to transduce a proliferative signal and down-regulate with removal of nearby EGF, respectively. If this applies to the placenta, then it supports the hypothesis that EGF-Rs respond mitogenically early in gestation, while at term they may have a predominantly absorptive role.

The autokinase activity of the EGF-R could be the function that is most relevant to development. This is certainly supported in a study of human placentas in patients of Yucheng (rice oil) disease, which occurs many years after exposure to polychlorinated biphenyls (PCBs) and dibenzofurans (dioxinlike compounds). Newborns delivered by these patients are always of low weight and this correlates with the level of PCBs found in the placenta, even 5 years after PCB exposure. Although there are no significant differences in the binding kinetics of EGF and in the numbers of EGF-Rs in the placentas of PCB- or dibenzofuran-exposed mothers, there is a 60% reduction in the EGF-stimulated receptor autophosphorylation activity of the term placenta that is correlated with the decreased birth weights and with the level of PCBs (Sunahara *et al.,* 1987). It would be interesting to determine whether the EGF-R kinase is defective throughout the gestation period in these patients. This would help to determine at which stage of gestation growth is retarded, to point to a possible mechanism by which PCBs retard fetal growth, and therefore better define the role of EGF and the EGF-R in development.

D. *neu* (*erb*B2)

An oncogene related to *c-erb*B1 and detected by antibody to cell surface proteins of a neuroblastoma cell line (Drebin *et al.,* 1984) has been described and is, so far, without a viral counterpart. The *neu* gene codes for a receptorlike protein of 185 kDa similar to the EGF-R (Ishii *et al.,* 1987) but whose ligand is as yet unknown. The *neu* gene, however, is not genetically linked to the EGF-R gene, and, although they are both expressed in A431 cells, *neu* is not coamplified with the EGF-R gene in these cells (Schechter *et al.,* 1985). Interestingly, when EGF is added to the mammary tumor cell line (SK-BR-3), the *neu* protein undergoes rapid phosphorylation. Therefore, the two receptors may have interconnected roles or activities (King *et al.,* 1988). The *neu* protein also has tyrosine kinase activity which, when down-regulated by anti-*neu* antibody, results in the reversion of the cell to a nontransformed phenotype (Drebin *et al.,* 1985).

The stage- and tissue-specific expression of the *neu* oncogene during rat development is similar to that of the EGF-R, with the highest levels of *neu* expressed in the nervous system, connective tissues, skin basal cells, and secretory epithelium. As for the EGF-R, lymphoid tissues do not contain detectable levels of *neu* (Kokai *et al.,* 1987).

VI. EC Cell Model Systems

EC cells have been derived both spontaneously (Stevens and Little, 1954) and experimentally by transplanting embryos on day 5 to 8 of gestation to sites such as the testis and the kidney in syngeneic adult hosts (Stevens, 1970). The process of tumor formation is strain dependent, but can give rise to teratocarcinomas that contain malignant stem cells (EC) among the differentiated tissues. More recently, embryo stem (ES) cells have been isolated and grown in culture by stimulating ectodermal cells of the blastocyst stage of embryos to proliferate using specialized culture conditions (reviewed by Silver *et al.,* 1983). ES cells have the most normal characteristics and are the most pluripotent of these cell types. They can take part in normal development with high frequency, as demonstrated in chimeric animals that were produced by introducing mixed ES and embryo cells into pseudopregnant mothers (reviewed by Robertson, 1987). This system provides an alternate method to microinjection into fertilized eggs for introducing exogenous gene sequences into embryos to create transgenic mice. The opportunity to test such sequences in EC and ES cells to determine their effects in cell culture is often desirable. Analysis of EC and ES cells as they grow as tumors in adult hosts or as differentiating systems in cell culture is a powerful approach to developmental studies of many kinds. These EC model systems have been reviewed by Silver *et al.* (1983).

From a survey of the literature, it will quickly become clear that there are as many patterns of cell behavior as there are individual EC cell lines. This may be because each cell line was isolated at different embryonic stages; PC13 (derived from the same tumor, OTT6050, as F9) and OC15 (derived from a C3H strain mouse) were the first EC lines shown to display EGF-Rs (Rees *et al.,* 1979). However, these cells only expressed EGF-Rs on the plasma membrane after they were induced to differentiate by retinoic acid (RA). RA also induces an increase in EGF-R numbers in fibroblasts (Adamson and Rees, 1981; Jetten, 1980, 1982), and this process may be important in development (see below).

RA is thought to be a natural morphogen (Maden and Summerbell, 1986) in developing tissues. The differential distribution of RA and its cellular RA binding protein (Eriksson *et al.,* 1987) together with the RA receptor could mediate its influence during normal development. It is possible that part of the influence of RA on development is due to RA induction of EGF-Rs, which leads to cell proliferation in the areas of highest concentrations of RA. The induction of inappropriate EGF-R expression could also explain why pharmacological doses of RA are teratogenic and cause cleft palate and other developmental defects (Abbott *et al.,* 1988).

Except for F9 cells, which do express low but detectable EGF binding activity, EC cells do not in general express cell surface EGF-Rs (Adamson and Hogan, 1984). A significant level of EGF-inducible 170-kDa autophosphorylation activity was detected in undifferentiated OC15 EC cells by using antibodies against mouse EGF-R. This activity could not be detected on the cell surface by radioiodination, but could be immunoprecipitated from [^{32}P]- or [^{35}S]-methionine-lebeled cells. It was concluded that OC15 EC cells have an intracellular compartment of EGF-Rs (Weller *et al.,* 1987). An EGF-R population that is totally intracellular has not been described in any other cell type. Several explanations for intracellular receptors are possible.

1. EGF/TGF-α is also produced by EC cells in sufficient quantities to mask receptors or to keep them intracellular by rapid endocytosis. No detectable EGF/TGF-α is secreted by OC15 EC cells, although TGF-α

production has recently been described for P19 EC cells, while PC13 cells were negative (Van Zoelen *et al.,* 1989a).

2. The EGF-R gene is "leaky." We have no quantitative information about this, although the EGF-R mRNA seems to be abundant in F9 EC cells (A. Russo and E. Adamson, unpublished observations).

3. EGF-Rs have an intracellular role. This could be a growth-related role that is similar to that of the truncated, largely intracellular viral *erb*B or it could be a different role that is specific to development. This has not yet been explored.

4. EGF-Rs are made and stored ready for differentiation. By analogy, embryo cells could have similar unusual gene regulation of EGF-R localization. These are all interesting possibilities, for which answers will be sought in the near future.

EC cells may also provide model systems for studying the interaction between growth factors and their receptors (see the review by Heath and Rees, 1985, for details). For example, the PC13 EC cell line produces and secretes a basic fibroblast growth factor (EGF) like factor called embryonal carcinoma-derived growth factor (ECDGF) (Heath and Isacke, 1984), which reduces the number of high-affinity EGF-Rs (Heath *et al.,* 1986). Combined with TGF-β, ECDGF has a profound effect on the development of mesodermal tissues in frogs (Slack *et al.,* 1987; see also Chapter 9, this volume). There is evidence that EC cells and their differentiated products can crossfeed each other. Differentiated teratocarcinoma cells express a variety of growth factor receptors, such as PDGF-R (Rizzino and Bowen-Pope, 1985), FGF-Rs (Mummery *et al.,* 1985), while EC cell-conditioned medium may contain ECDGF, PDGF, TGF-β and a set of unidentified factors (Jakobovits *et al.,* 1985; Jakobovits, 1986; Van Zoelen *et al.,* 1989a). In contrast, insulinlike growth factor receptors are present on F9 and other EC cell lines while their differentiated derivatives produce insulin-related mitogens (Heath and Shi, 1986; Nagarajan *et al.,* 1985; Van Zoelen *et al.,* 1989b). These findings stimulated searches for growth factor and receptor expression in preimplantation embryos by Werb and colleagues (Rappolee *et al.,* 1988a), as discussed earlier. Studies over the next few years should firmly establish definitive roles for EGF/TGF-α and EGF-Rs at all stages of embryonic development. Such roles will likely differ for each tissue at each stage, so that each of these genes can be finely regulated in the location and the timing of its expression during development.

VII. Summary

EGF-Rs are encoded by a single gene which produces two main transcripts that are translated and processed into a single polypeptide chain.

The membrane-inserted receptor kinase binds EGF or TGF-α at high and low affinities, but how these are related to the pleiotropic activities of the EGF-R is unknown.

The widespread distribution of fetal EGF-Rs suggests that they have many functions during mammalian development. The stage- and cell type-specific expression of receptors in tissues such as the placenta, together with the localized production of EGF/TGF-α, suggests that fetal EGF-Rs have specific activities and roles. The proliferation of the fetal trophoblast and the maternal deciduum is likely to provide the location for a major and necessary role of TGF-α and EGF-Rs, which probably act by autocrine and paracrine means to establish the placenta as rapidly as possible. There is evidence that if placental EGF-Rs malfunction, the fetus is at a disadvantage. This could be partly due to poor placental growth and development, as well as a reduced ability of the placenta to perform a barrier function.

The murine fertilized egg at preimplantation stages produces a number of growth factors, including TGF-α, but the significance of this is still uncertain. It is likely that several fetal and adult tissues produce low amounts of EGF/TGF-α for their self-maintenance. The precise roles for the putative EGF/TGF-α produced in the brain, kidney, tooth, and various head tissues are also obscure and will be subjects of close scrutiny in the future.

Acknowledgments

I am grateful for comments on the manuscript from Drs. S. A. Edwards and D. A. Mercola. This work was supported by U.S. Public Health Service grants CA 28427 and HD 18782.

References

Abbott, B. D., Adamson, E. D., and Pratt, R. M. (1988). *Development* **102,** 853–867.

Adamson, E. D. (1983). *In* "The Biological Basis of Reproductive and Developmental Medicine" (J. B. Warshaw, ed.), pp. 307–336. Elsevier, New York.

Adamson, E. D. (1986a). *In* "Cellular Endocrinology" (G. Serrero and J. Hayashi, eds.), pp. 159–174. Liss, New York.

Adamson, E. D. (1986b). *In* "Experimental Approaches to Mammalian Embryonic Development" (J. Rossant and R. Pedersen, eds.), pp. 326–364. Cambridge Univ. Press, London.

Adamson, E. D. (1987a). *Placenta* **8,** 449–446.

Adamson, E. D. (1987b). *Development* **99,** 449–471.

Adamson, E. D. (1990). *Mol. Reprod. Devel.* (in press).

Adamson, E. D., and Hogan, B. L. M. (1984). *Differentiation (Berlin)* **27,** 152–157.

Adamson, E. D., and Meek, J. (1984). *Dev. Biol.* **103,** 62–71.

Adamson, E. D., and Rees, A. R. (1981). *Mol. Cell. Biochem.* **34,** 129–152.

Adamson, E. D., and Warshaw, J. B. (1981). *Dev. Biol.* **90,** 430–434.

Adamson, E. D., Deller, M. J., and Warshaw, J. B. (1981). *Nature (London)* **291,** 656–659.

Ascoli, M., Euffa, J., and Segaloff, D. L. (1987). *J. Biol. Chem.* **262,** 9196–9203.

Barrandon, Y., and Green, H. (1987). *Cell (Cambridge, Mass.)* **50,** 1131–1137.

Blay, J., and Brown, K. D. (1985). *J. Cell. Physiol.* **124,** 107–112.

Böni-Schnetzler, M., and Pilch, P. F. (1987). *Proc. Natl. Acad. Sci. U.S.A.* **84,** 7832–7836.

Bowen-Pope, D. F., and Ross, R. (1983). *Biochem. Biophys. Res. Commun.* **114,** 1036–1041.

Bremer, E. G., Hakamori, S.-I., Bowen-Pope, D. F., Raines, E., and Ross, R. (1984). *J. Biol. Chem.* **259,** 6818–6825.

Bringman, T. S., Lindquist, P. B., and Derynck, R. (1987). *Cell* **48,** 429–440.

Brown, J. P., Twardzik, R., Marguardt, H., and Todaro, G. J. (1985). *Nature (London)* **313,** 491–492.

Carpenter, G. (1979). *J. Biol. Chem.* **254,** 4884–4891.

Carpenter, G. (1984). *Cell (Cambridge, Mass.)* **37,** 357–358.

Carpenter, G. (1987). *Annu. Rev. Biochem.* **56,** 881–914.

Carpenter, G., King, L., and Cohen, S. (1978). *Nature (London)* **276,** 409–410.

Chakrabarty, C., Tawfik, O. W., and Dey, S. K. (1988). *Biochem. Biophys. Res. Commun.* **153,** 564–569.

Chegini, N., and Rao, C. V. (1986). *J. Cell Sci.* **84,** 41–52.

Chen, L. B., Murray, A., Segal, R. A., Bushnell, A., and Walsh M. L. (1978). *Cell* **14,** 377–391.

Chinkers, M., McKanna, J. A., and Cohen, S. (1981). *J. Cell Biol.* **88,** 422–429.

Clark, S., Cheng, D. J., Hsuan, J. J., Haley J. D., and Waterfield, M. D. (1988). *J. Cell. Physiol.* **134,** 421–428.

Coffey, R. J., Derynck, R., Wilcox, J. N., Bringman, T. S., Goustin, A. S., Moses, H. L., and Pittelkow, M. R. (1987). *Nature (London)* **328,** 817–820.

Cohen, S. (1962). *J. Biol. Chem.* **237,** 1555–1562.

Cohen, S., Ushiro, H., Stoscheck, C., and Chinkers, M. (1982). *J. Biol. Chem.* **257,** 1523–1539.

Cornwell, R. P. (1985). *Am. J. Physiol.* **249,** 551–562.

Deal, C. L., Guyda, H. J., Lai, W. H., and Posner, B. I. (1982). *Pediatr. Res.* **16,** 820–826.

Decker, S. J. (1985). *In* "Cellular Regulation and Malignant Growth" (S. Ebashi, ed.), pp. 303–310. Springer-Verlag, Berlin.

Defize, L. H., Mummery, C. L., Moolenaar, W. H., and deLaat, S. W. (1987). *Cell Differ.* **20,** 87–102.

Dekel, N., and Sherizly, I. (1985). *Endocrinology (Baltimore)* **116,** 406–409.

Denhardt, D. T., Hamilton, R. T., Parfett, C. L. J., Edwards, D. R., St. Pierre, R., Waterhouse, P., and Nilsen-Hamilton, M. (1986). *Cancer Res.* **46,** 4590–4593.

dePalo, L., and Das, M. (1988). *Cancer Res.* **48,** 1105–1109.

Derynck, R. (1988). *Cell (Cambridge, Mass.)* **54,** 593–595.

Derynck, R., Roberts, A. B., Winkler, M. E., Chen, E. Y., and Goeddel D. V. (1984). *Cell (Cambridge, Mass.)* **38,** 287–297.

Di Augustine, R. P., Rosch, M. J., Lannon, D. E., Walker, M. P., and Pratt, R. W. (1987) *Endocrinology (Baltimore)* **120,** 1190–1196.

Doolittle, R. F., Fend, D. F., and Johnson, M. S. (1984). *Nature (London)* **307,** 558–590.

Downward, J., Yarden, Y., Mayes, E., Scrace, G., Totty, N., Stockwell, P., Ullrich, A., Schlessinger, J., and Waterfield, M. D. (1984). *Nature (London)* **307,** 521–527.

Drebin, J. A., Stern, D. F., Link, V. C., Weinberg, R. A., and Green M. I. (1984). *Nature (London)* **312,** 545–548.

Drebin, J. A., Link, V. C., Stern, D. F., Weinberg, R. A., and Greene, M. I. (1985). *Cell (Cambridge, Mass.)* **41,** 695–706.

Dunn, W. A., Connolly, T. P., and Hubbard, A. L. (1986). *J. Cell Biol.* **102,** 24–36.

Earp, H. S., and O'Keefe, E. J. (1981). *J. Clin. Invest.* **67,** 1580–1583.

Erickson, C. A., and Turley, E. A. (1987). *Exp. Cell Res.* **169,** 267–279.

Eriksson, V., Hansson, E., Nordlindes, H., Busch, C., Sundelin, J., and Peterson, P. A. (1987). *J. Cell. Physiol.* **133,** 482–490.

Fallon, J. H., Seroogy, K. B., Loughlin, S. E., Morrison, R. S., Bradshaw, R. A., Knaver, D. T., and Cunningham, D. D. (1984). *Science* **224,** 1107–1109.

Fanger, B. O., Stephens, J. E., and Staros, J. V. (1989). *FASEB J.* **3,** 71–75.

Faucher, M., Girones, N., Hannun, Y. A., Dell, R. M., and Davies, R. J. (1988). *J. Biol. Chem.* **263,** 5319–5327.

Folkman, J., and Klagsbrun, M. (1987). *Science* **235,** 442–447.

Freemark, M., and Comer, H. (1987). *Pediatr. Res.* **22,** 609–615.

Gentry, L. E., Twardzik, D. R., Lim, G. J., Ranchalis, J. E., and Lee, D. C. (1987). *Mol. Cell. Biol.* **7,** 1585–1591.

Gill, G. N., Bertics, P. J., and Santon, J. B. (1987). *Mol. Cell. Endocrinol.* **51,** 169–186.

Goustin, A. S., Leof, E. B., Shipley, G. D., and Moses, H. L. (1986). *Cancer Res.* **46,** 1015–1029.

Graf, T., and Berg, H. (1983). *Cell (Cambridge, Mass.)* **34,** 7–9.

Gregoriou, M., and Rees, A. R. (1984). *EMBO J* **3,** 929–937.

Gregory, H. (1975). *Nature (London)* **257,** 325–327.

Gubits, R. M., Shaw, P. A., Gresik, E. W., Onetti-Muda, A., and Barka, T. (1986). *Endocrinology (Baltimore)* **119,** 1382–1387.

Gullick, W. J., Downward, J., Parker, P. J., Whittle, N., Kris, R., Schlessinger, J., Ullrich, A., and Waterfield, M. D. (1985). *Proc. R. Soc. London Ser. B* **226,** 127–134.

Han, V. K. M., Hunter, E. S., Pratt, R. M., Zendegui, J., and Lee, D. C. (1987). *Mol. Cell. Biol.* **7,** 2335–2343.

Hannink, M., and Donoghue, D. J. (1988). *J. Cell Biol.* **107,** 287–298.

Heath, J. K., and Isacke, C. M. (1984). *EMBO J.* **3,** 2957–2962.

Heath, J. K., and Rees, A. R. (1985). *In* "Growth Factors in Biology and Medicine" (I. Eevered, ed.), pp. 3–22. Pitman, London.

Heath, J. K., and Shi, W.-K. (1986). *J. Embryol. Exp. Morphol.* **95,** 193–212.

Heath, J. K., Mahadevan, L. and Foulkes, J. G. (1986). *EMBO J.* **5,** 1809–1814.

Herschman, H. R. (1985). *In* "Control of Animal Cell Proliferation" (A. L. Boynton and H. L. Leffert, eds.), pp. 176–200. Academic Press, Orlando, Florida.

Hoath, S. B., Lakshmanan, J., and Fisher, D. A. (1983). *Life Sci.* **32,** 2709–2716.

Hoath, S. B., Pickens, W. L., Bucuvales, J. C., and Suchy, F. J. (1987). *Biochem. Biophys. Res. Commun.* **930,** 107–113.

Hollenberg, M. D., and Armstrong, G. D. (1985). *In* "Polypeptide Hormone Receptors" (B. I. Posner, ed.), pp. 201–226. Dekker, New York.

Honegger, A. M., Szapary, D., Schmidt, A., Lyall, R., van Obberghen, E., Dull, T. J., Ullrich, A., and Schlessinger, J. (1987a). *Mol. Cell. Biol.* **7,** 4568–4571.

Honegger, A. M., Dull, T. J., Felder, S., van Obberghen, E., Bellor, F., Szapary, D., Schmidt, A., Ullrich, A., and Schlessinger, J. (1987b). *Cell (Cambridge, Mass.)* **51,** 199-209.

Hortsch, M., Schlessinger, J., Gootwine, E., and Webb C. G. (1983). *EMBO J.* **2,** 1937–1941.

Hung, M.-C., Thompson, K. L., Chiu, I.-M, and Rosner, M. R. (1986). *Biochem. Biophys. Res. Commun.* **141,** 1109–1115.

Ignotz, R., Kelly, B., Davis, R., and Massagué, J. (1986). *Proc. Natl. Acad. Sci. U.S.A.* **83,** 6307–6311.

Ishii, S., Xu, Y.-H., Stratton, R. H., Roe, B. A., Merlino, G. T., and Pastan, I. (1985). *Proc. Natl. Acad. Sci. U.S.A.* **82,** 4920–4924.

Ishii, S., Kadonaga, J. T., Tjian, R., Brady, J. N., Merlino, G. T., and Pastan, I. (1986). *Science* **232,** 1410–1413.

Ishii, S., Imamoto, F., Yamanashi, Y., Toyoshima, K., and Yamamoto, T. (1987). *Proc. Natl. Acad. Sci. U.S.A.* **84,** 4376–4378.

Jakobovits, A. (1986). *In* "Oncogenes and Growth Control" (P. Kahn and T. Graf, eds.), pp. 9–17. Springer-Verlag, Berlin.

Jakobovits, A. J., Banda, M. J., and Martin, G. R. (1985) *In* "Cancer Cells, Growth Factors and Transformation" (J. Feramisco, B. Ozanne, and C. D. Stiles, eds.), Vol. 3, pp. 393–399. Cold Spring Harbor Laboratory, Cold Spring Harbor, New York.

Jetten, A. M. (1980). *Nature (London)* **284,** 626–629.

Jetten, A. M. (1982). *J. Cell. Physiol.* **110,** 235–240.

Jinno, Y., Merlino, G. T., and Pastan, I. (1988). *Nucleic Acids Res.* **16,** 4957–4966.

Johnson, A. C., Ishii, S., Jinno, Y., Pastan, I., and Merlino, G. T. (1988a). *J. Biol. Chem.* **263,** 5693–5699.

Johnson, A. C., Garfield, S. H., Merlino, G. T., and Pastan, I. (1988b). *Biochem. Biophys. Res. Commun.* **150,** 412–418.

Kageyama, R., Merlino, G. T., and Pastan, I. (1988). *J. Biol. Chem.* **263,** 6326–6329.

King, C. R., Kraus, M. H., and Aaronson, S. A. (1985). *Science* **229,** 974–976.

King, C. R., Borrello, T., Bellot, F., Comoglio, P., and Schlessinger, J. (1988). *EMBO J.* **7,** 1647–1651.

Klotz, I. M. (1982). *Science* **217,** 1247–1249.

Kokai, Y., Cohen, J. A., Drebin, J. A., and Greene, M. I. (1987). *Proc. Natl. Acad. Sci. U.S.A.* **84,** 8498–8501.

Kris, R. M., Libermann, T. A., Avivi, A., and Schlessinger, J. (1985). *Bio/Technology* **3,** 135–140.

Kudlow, J. E., Kobrin, M. S., Purchio, A. F., Twardzik, D. R., Hernandez, E. R., Asa, S. L., and Adashi, E. Y. (1987). *Endocrinology (Baltimore)* **121,** 1577–1579.

Lai, W. H., and Guyda, H. J. (1984). *J. Clin. Endocrinol. Metab.* **58,** 344–352.

Lax, I., Burgess, W. H., Bellot, F., Ullrich, A., Schlessinger, J., and Givol, C. D. (1988). *Mol. Cell. Biol.* **8,** 1831–1834.

Lee, D. C., Rochford, R., Todaro, G. J., and Villareal, L. P. (1985a). *Mol. Cell. Biol.* **5,** 3644–3646.

Lee, D. C., Rose, T. M., Webb, N. R., and Todaro, G. J. (1985b). *Nature (London)* **313,** 489–492.

Lee, L.-S., and Weinstein, I. B. (1978). *Nature (London)* **274,** 696–697.

Lembach, K. J. (1976). *Proc. Natl. Acad. Sci. U.S.A.* **73,** 183–187.

Libermann, T. A., Nussbaum, H. R., Razon, N., Kris, R., Lax, I., Soreq, M., Whittle, N., Waterfield, M. D., Ullrich, A., and Schlessinger, J. (1985). *Nature (London)* **313,** 144–147.

Lin, C. R., Chen, W. S., Kruiger, W., Stolarsky, L. S., Weber, W., Evans, R. M., Verma, I. M., Gill, G. N., and Rosenfeld, M. G. (1984). *Science* **224,** 843–848.

Lintern-Moore, S., Moore, G. P. M., Panaretto, B. A., and Robertson, D. (1981). *Acta Endocrinol. (Copenhagen)* **96,** 123–126.

Livneh, E., Reiss, N., Berent, E., Ullrich, A., and Schlessinger, J. (1987). *EMBO J* **6,** 2669–2676.

Maden, M., and Summerbell, D. (1986). *J. Embryol. Exp. Morphol.* **97,** 239–250.

Marquardt, H., Hunkapillar, M. W., Hood, L. E., and Todaro, G. J. (1984). *Science* **223,** 1079–1081.

Maruo, T., and Mochizuki, M. (1987). *Am. J. Obstet. Gynecol.* **156,** 721–727.

Maruo, T., Matsuo, H., Dishi, T., Hayashi, M., Nishimo, R., and Mochizuki, M. (1987). *J. Clin. Endocrinol. Metab.* **64,** 744–750.
Massagué, J. (1983). *J. Biol. Chem.* **258,** 13614–13620.
Massagué, J. (1985). *Trends Biochem. Sci.* **10,** 237–241.
Matrisian, L. M., Pathak, M., and Magun, B. E.(1982). *Biochem. Biophys. Res. Commun.* **107,** 761–769.
Mercola, M., and Stiles, C. D. (1988). *Development* **102,** 451–460.
Mercola, M., Melton, D. A., and Stiles, C. D. (1988). *Science* **241,** 1223–1225.
Mondschein, J. S., and Schonberg, D. W. (1981). *Science***211,** 1179–1180.
Mondschein, J. S., May, J. V., Ginn, E. B., and Schonberg, D. (1981). *In* "Dynamics of Ovarian Function" (N. B. Schwartz and B. Hunzicher-Dunn, eds.), pp. 83–100. Raven, New York.
Morrison, R. S., Kornblum, H. I., Leslie, F. M., and Bradshaw, R. A. (1987). *Science* **238,** 72–75.
Mukku, V. R., and Stancel, G. M. (1985). *J. Biol. Chem.* **260,** 9820–9826.
Mummery, C. L., Feijen, A., Vander Saag, P. T., van den Brink, C. E., and de Laat, S. W. (1985). *Dev. Biol.* **109,** 402–410.
Murdoch, G. H., Potter, E., Nicolaison, A. K., Evans, R. M., and Rosenfeld, M. G. (1982). *Nature (London)* **300,** 192–194.
Nagarajan, L., Anderson, W. B., Nissley, S. P., Rechler, M. M., and Jetten, A. M. (1985). *J. Cell. Physiol.* **124,** 199–206.
Nexø, E., Hollenberg, M. D., Figueroa, A., and Pratt, R. M. (1980). *Proc. Natl. Acad. Sci. U.S.A.* **77,** 2782–2785.
Nilsen,-Hamilton, M. (1989). *In* "Growth Factors in Early Development" (I. Y. Rosenblum and S. Heyner, eds.). CRC Press, Boca Raton, Florida. in press.
Nilsen-Hamilton, M., Hamilton, R. T., Allen, W. R., and Massoglia, S. L. (1981). *Biochem. Biophys. Res. Commun.* **101,** 411–417.
Oka, Y., and Orth, D. N. (1983). *J. Clin. Invest.* **72,** 249–259.
Opleta, K., O'Loughlin, E. V., Shaffer, E. A., Hayden, J., Hollenberg, M., and Gall, D. G. (1987). *Am. J. Physiol.* **253,** 622–626.
Popliker, M., Shatz, A., Avivi, A., Ullrich, A., Schlessinger, J., and Webb, C. G. (1987). *Dev. Biol.* **119,** 38–44.
Pratt, R. M. (1984). *In* "Issues and Reviews in Teratology" (H. Kalter, ed.). pp. 189–217. Plenum, New York.
Pratt, R. M. (1987). *Dev. Biol.* **22,** 175–193.
Proper, J. A., Bjornson, C. L., and Moses, H. L. (1982). *J. Cell. Physiol* **110,** 169–174.
Rall, L. B., Scott, J., Bell, G. I., Crawford, R. J., Penschow, J. D., Niall, H. D., and Coghlan, J. P. (1985). *Nature (London)* **313,** 228–231.
Ramani, N., Chegini, N., Rao, C. V., Woost, P. G., an Schultz, G. S. (1986). *J. Cell Sci.* **84,** 19–40.
Rao, C. V., Ramani, N., Chegini, N., Stadig, B. K., Carman, F. R., Wost, P. G., Schultz, G. S., and Cook, C. L. (1985). *J. Biol. Chem.* **260,** 1705–1710.
Rappolee, D. A., Brenner, C. A., Schultz, R., Mark, D., and Werb, Z. (1988a). *Science* **241,** 1823–1825.
Rappolee, D. A., Mark, D., Banda, M. J., and Werb, Z. (1988b). *Science* **241,** 708–712.
Rees, A. R., Adamson, E. D., and Graham, C. F. (1979). *Nature (London)* **281,** 309–311.
Rees, A. R., Gregoriou, M., Johnson, P., and Garland, B. (1984). *EMBO J.* **3,** 1843–1847.
Reisner, A. H. (1985). *Nature (London)* **313,** 801–803.
Rizzino, A. (1985). *In Vitro* **21,** 531–536.
Rizzino, A., and Bowen-Pope, D. F. (1985). *Dev. Biol.* **110,** 15–22.
Rizzino, A., Kuszynski, C., Ruff, C., and Tiesman, J. (1988). *Dev. Biol.* **129,** 61–71.

Robbins, K. C., Leal, F., Pierce, J. H., and Aaronson, S. A. (1985). *EMBO J.* **4,** 1783–1792.

Robertson, E. J. (1987). "Teratocarcinomas and Embryonic Stem Cells: A Practical Approach." IRL Press, Oxford.

Ruoslahti, E., and Pierschbacher, M. D. (1987). *Science* **238,** 490–497.

Salido, E. C., Barajas, L., Lechago, J., Laborde, N. P., and Fisher, D. A. (1986). *J. Histochem. Cytochem.* **34,** 1155–1160.

Scatchard, G. (1947). *Ann. N.Y. Acad. Sci.* **51,** 7609–7611.

Schechter, A. L., Hung, M.-C., Vaidyanathan, L., Weinberg, R. A., Yang-Feng, T. L., Francke, U., Ullrich, A., and Coussens, L. (1985). *Science* **229,** 976–978.

Schreiber, A. B., Libermann, T. A., Lax, I., Yarden, Y., and Schlessinger, J. (1983). *J. Biol. Chem.* **258,** 846–853.

Scott, J., Urdea, M., Quiroga, M., Sanchez-Pescador, R., Fong, N., Selby, M., Rutter, W. J., and Bell, G. I. (1983). *Science* **221,** 236–239.

Shing, Y. W., and Klagsburn, M. (1984). *Endocrinology (Baltimore)* **115,** 273–282.

Silver, L. M., Martin, G. R., and Strickland, S. eds. (1983) *Cold Spring Harbor Conf. Cell Proliferation* **10.**

Silver, M. H., Murray, C., Martin, G., and Pratt, R. M. (1984). *Differentiation (Berlin)* **18,** 141–150.

Simmen, F. A., Gope, M. L., Schulz, T. Z., Wright, D. A., Carpenter, G., and O'Malley, B. W. (1984). *Biochem. Biophys. Res. Commun.* **124,** 125–132.

Sissom, J. F., Stenzel, W. K., and Warshaw, J. B. (1987). *J. Clin. Invest.* **80,** 242–247.

Slack, J. M. W., Darlington, B. G., Heath, J. K., and Godsave, S. F. (1987). *Nature (London)* **326,** 197–200.

Smith, J. M., Sporn, M. B., Roberts, A. B., Derynck, R., Winkler, M. E., and Gregory, H. (1985). *Nature (London)* **315,** 515–516.

Smith, W. C., and Talamantes, F. (1986). *Placenta* **7,** 511–522.

Snead, M. L., Luo, W., Oliver, P., Nakamura, M., Don-Wheeler, G., Bessen, C., Bell, G. I., Rall, L. B., and Slavkin, H. C. (1989). *Dev. Bio.* **134,** 420–429.

Sporn, M. B., Roberts, A. B., Shull, J. H., Smith, J. M., Ward, J. M., and Sodek, J. (1983). *Science* **219,** 1329–1331.

Stevens, L. C. (1970). *J. Natl. Cancer Inst.* **44,** 923–940.

Stevens, L. C., and Little, C. C. (1954). *Proc. Natl. Acad. Sci. U.S.A.* **40,** 1080–1084.

Stromberg, K., Pigott, D. A., Ranchalis, J. E., and Twardzik, D. R. (1982). *Biochem. Biophys. Res. Commun.* **106,** 354–361.

Stroobant, P., Rice, A. P., Gullick, W. J., Cheng, D. J., Kerr, I. M., and Waterfield, M. D. (1985). *Cell (Cambridge, Mass.)* **42,** 383–393.

Südhof, T. C., Goldstein, J. L., Brown, M. S., and Russell, D. W. (1985a). *Science* **228,** 815–822.

Südhof, T. C., Russell, D. W., Goldstein, J. L., Brown, M. S., Sanchez-Pescador, R., and Bell, G. (1985b). *Science* **228,** 893–895.

Sunahara, G. J., Nelson, K. G., Wong, T. K., and Lucien, G. W. (1987). *Mol. Pharmacol.* **32,** 572–578.

Tam, J. P. (1985). *Science* **229,** 673–675.

Tam, J. P., Marquardt, H., Rosberger, D. F., Wong, T. W., and Todaro, G. J. (1984). *Nature (London)* **309,** 700–703.

Taylor, J. M., Cohen, S., and Mitchell, W. M. (1970). *Proc. Natl. Acad. Sci. U.S.A.* **67,** 164–171.

Taylor, J. M., Mitchell, W. M., and Cohen, S. (1974). *J. Biol. Chem.* **249,** 3198–3203.

Teixidó, J., Gilmore, R., Lee, D. C., and Massagué, J. (1987). *Nature (London)* **326,** 883–885.

Thorburn, G. D., Waters, M. J., Young, R., Dolling, M., Buntine, D., and Hopkins, P. S. (1981). "The Fetus and Independent Life," CIBA Foundation Symposium, 1986, pp. 172–198. Pitman, London.

Trelstad, R. L. (1984). "The Role of the Extracellular Matrix in Development." Liss, New York.

Tsutsumi, O., Kurachi, H., and Oka, T. (1986) *Science* **233,** 975–977.

Twardzik, D. R. (1985). *Cancer Res.* **45,** 5413–5416.

Twardzik, D. R., Ranchalis, J. E., and Todaro, G. J. (1982). *Cancer Res.* **42,** 590–593.

Twardzik, D. R., Kimball, E. S., Sherwin, S. A., Ranchalis, J. E., and Todaro, G. J. (1985). *Cancer Res.* **45,** 1934–1939.

Van Zoelen, E. J. J., Ward-van-Oostwaard, T. M. J., Nieuwland, R., Vander Burg, B., van den Eijnden-van Raaij, A. J. M., Mummery, C. L., and de Laat, S. W. (1989a). *Dev. Biol.* **133,** 272–283.

Van Zoelen, E. J. J., Koornneet, I., Holthuis, J. C. M., Ward-van Oostwaard, T. M. J., Feijen, A., de Poorter, T. L., Mummery, C. L., and van Buul-Offers, S. C. (1989b). *Endocrinology (Baltimore)* **124,** 2029–2041.

Waterfield, M. D., Mayer, E. L., Stroobant, P., Bennet, P. L. P., Young, S., Goodfellow, P. N., Banting, G. S., and Ozanne, B. (1982). **J. Cell. Biochem. 20,** 149–161.

Weller, A., Meek, J., and Adamson, E. D. (1987). *Development* **100,** 351–363.

Westermark, B., and Blomquist, E. (1980). *Cell Biol. Int. Rep.* **4,** 649–654.

Wilcox, J. N., and Derynck, R. (1988a). *J. Neurosci.* **8,** 1901–1904.

Wilcox, J. N., and Drynck, R. (1988b). *Mol. Cell. Biol.* **8,** 3415–3422.

Xu, Y.-H., Ishii, S., Clark, A. J. L., Sullivan, M., Wilson, R. K., Ma, D. P., Roe, B. A. Merlino, G. T., and Pastan, I. (1984). *Nature (London)* **309,** 806–810.

Yarden, Y., and Schlessinger, J. (1987). *Biochemistry***26,** 1443–1451.

Zschiesche, W., and Eckert, K. (1988). *Experientia* **44,** 249–251.

2

Epidermal Growth Factor and Transforming Growth Factor-α in the Development of Epithelial–Mesenchymal Organs of the Mouse

Anna-Maija Partanen
Institute of Dentistry
University of Helsinki
SF-00300 Helsinki, Finland

I. Introduction

The role of epidermal growth factor (EGF) in morphogenetic and differentiation events has been studied experimentally in several animal species. The main focus of this chapter is on the role of EGF and transforming growth factor type α (TGF-α) in organogenesis in the mouse. The chapter begins with a short general discussion of EGF and the related growth factor, TGF-α, then discusses specific morphogenetic events in which EGF/TGF-α may participate and that involve epithelial–mesenchymal interactions. A more extensive discussion of the basic aspects of expres-

Current Topics in Developmental Biology, Vol. 24

sion of EGF/TGF-α and the EGF receptor (EGF-R) in early development can be found in Chapter 1.

A. EGF and TGF-α

EGF is a 53-amino acid polypeptide with a molecular weight of 6045, which was first isolated by Cohen (1962) from extracts of the male mouse submandibular gland. Mouse EGF is identical to human urogastrone, a hormone which was isolated from human urine and inhibits gastric acid secretion (Gregory, 1975). EGF has been detected in several murine and human tissues and body fluids, where it is present at much lower concentrations than in male mouse submandibular glands (Byyny *et al.*, 1972; Frati *et al.*, 1976). Among body fluids, relatively high concentrations are present in urine, saliva, milk, and seminal fluid (Starkey and Orth, 1977; Hirata and Orth, 1979; Perheentupa *et al.*, 1985a; Pesonen *et al.*, 1987) compared with the considerably lower concentrations in plasma and serum (Perheentupa *et al.*, 1985b). The EGF in biological fluids appears to originate from the glands that secrete into these fluids, such as the salivary and mammary glands.

The presence of small amounts of immunoreactive EGF in various tissues is somewhat controversial (Kasselberg *et al.*, 1985; Beerstecher *et al.*, 1988). Immunoreactive human EGF/urogastrone has been detected in various human tissues (Kasselberg *et al.*, 1985).

By using cDNA probes, Rall *et al.* (1985) detected EGF precursor mRNA in adult mouse submandibular gland and kidney, whereas significantly lower levels were found in the lactating breast, pancreas, small intestine, ovary, spleen, lung, pituitary gland, and brain. The EGF in tissues appears to be locally produced and may function in a paracrine or autocrine manner.

TGF-α is an EGF-related growth-promoting polypeptide which was first discovered from cultures of murine sarcoma virus-transformed cells and was later isolated from cultures of various tumor cells (DeLarco and Todaro, 1978; Todaro *et al.*, 1980). EGF has not yet been found in tumor cells. TGF-α and EGF are homologous, with 35% identity in their sequence. Rodent (rat and mouse) TGF-α molecules have amino acid sequences nearly identical to human TGF-α (Derynck, 1987). TGF-α binds to the EGF-R molecule on the cell surface and has activity identical to that of EGF, but it is antigenically distinct from EGF. Particularly relevant to this discussion are the observations that TGF-α is expressed during the fetal development of mice (Wilcox and Derynck, 1988a), in neonatal and adult normal epidermal cells (Coffey *et al.*, 1987), and in brain cells (Wilcox and Derynck, 1988b).

B. EGF-R

The biological effects of polypeptide growth factors, including EGF and TGF-α, are mediated by an interaction with a specific cell surface receptor. The EGF-R is a transmembrane glycoprotein composed of 1186 amino acids with a molecular weight of 170,000. The receptor molecule consists of three structural elements. The extracellular domain binds TGF-α with affinity similar to that of EGF. The transmembrane region consists of hydrophobic amino acids. The cytoplasmic domain contains a protein tyrosine kinase which is activated by binding of EGF or TGF-α to the extracellular domain. The receptor can phosphorylate itself, and this autophosphorylation is apparently a crucial step in transduction of the mitogenic signal to the nucleus, although the exact mechanism of signal transduction is unknown. Intrinsic tyrosine kinase activity is a common feature shared by many growth factor receptors and various transforming proteins which are oncogene products (Hunter, 1987). The binding affinity of the EGF-R and its kinase activity are regulated by ligand molecules and also by occupation of other growth factor receptors that activate protein kinase C (Schlessinger, 1986). After binding the ligand, the receptor complex is internalized and both EGF and the receptor are degraded by lysosomal enzymes.

The crucial role of the receptor in mediating the action of EGF or TGF-α implies that only cells that express the receptor are responsive to the growth factor. EGF-Rs are present in many cell types derived from all three germ layers (Carpenter and Cohen, 1979).

C. Biological Activities of EGF and TGF-α

EGF was initially discovered by the ability of submandibular gland extracts to induce precocious eyelid opening and incisor tooth eruption when injected into newborn mice. It was suggested that these effects resulted from stimulation of epithelial proliferation and keratinization by EGF (Cohen, 1962; Cohen and Elliot, 1963). The results of numerous studies of cells in culture have established that EGF is a potent mitogen for many cell types of ectodermal, mesodermal, and endodermal origin (Carpenter and Cohen, 1979). EGF also stimulates proliferation of embryonic cells in culture (Kaplowitz *et al.*, 1982; Yoneda and Pratt, 1981) and during morphogenetic events (Goldin and Opperman, 1980; Pratt, 1980).

The presence of functional EGF-Rs in rodent embryonic tissues (Adamson *et al.*, 1981; Hortsch *et al.*, 1983; Adamson and Meek, 1984) indicates that EGF or EGF-related factors are involved in embryonic development. High levels of EGF-like activity were measured in mouse embryos by Nexø *et al.* (1980), using a radioreceptor assay, while significantly lower levels were detected using a radioimmunoassay. However, synthesis of EGF at the mRNA level was not detected until 2 weeks postnatally (Popliker *et al.*, 1987). On the other hand, TGF-α which binds to the same receptor as EGF, is present in placenta and embryonic tissues (Matrisian *et al.*, 1982; Proper *et al.*, 1982; Twardzik *et al.*, 1982; Twardzik, 1985; Han *et al.*, 1987; Wilcox and Derynck, 1988a). Accordingly, it is probable that TGF-α represents an embryonic species of a family of EGF-related growth factors.

Because preimplantation embryos express TGF-α (Rappolee *et al.*, 1988), it is likely that TGF-α is involved in mammalian development from the very early stages on. EGF-related molecules and the EGF-R also have long evolutionary histories. The EGF-R appears to have been well conserved both structurally and functionally through evolution, because a gene homologous to human EGF-R gene was detected in *Drosophila melanogaster* (Livneh *et al.*, 1985) which is expressed in association with cell proliferation during *Drosophila* development (Kammermeyer and Wadsworth, 1987). Furthermore, the products of two developmentally important genes, the *lin-12* gene of *Caenorhabditis* and the *Notch* gene of *Drosophila*, were found to contain several EGF-homologous sequences (Greenwald, 1985; Wharton *et al.*, 1985). These EGF-related proteins, as well as the precursors for EGF and TGF-α are apparently transmembrane peptides (Rall *et al.*, 1985; Teixidó *et al.*, 1987). It was also shown recently that transmembrane TGF-α precursors are able to activate EGF-Rs on adjacent cells (Brachmann *et al.*, 1989; Wong *et al.*, 1989). Thus, it is possible that the family of EGF-related proteins could mediate cell–cell interactions while in the form of transmembrane proteins by binding to an appropriate receptor on another cell and thus transmit developmental information between adjacent cells.

Besides stimulation of cell proliferation, various other effects of EGF on cellular functions have been described. EGF influences cell differentiation (Sun and Green, 1976; Johnson *et al.*, 1980), the organization of cytoskeletal elements (Keski-Oja *et al.*, 1981; Schlessinger and Geiger, 1981), and cell migration (Barrandon and Green, 1987). EGF also affects the synthesis and turnover of many extracellular matrix molecules, such as fibronectin (Chen *et al.*, 1977), collagens (Hata *et al.*, 1984), laminin (Panneerselvam *et al.*, 1985), and glycosaminoglycans (Turley *et al.*, 1985; Erickson and Turley, 1987). The biological activities induced by EGF are also shared by TGF-α, and in many responses TGF-α is even a more potent agent than EGF. TGF-α accelerates eyelid opening, incisor eruption, and wound healing (Smith *et al.*, 1985; Tam, 1985; Schultz *et al.*, 1987). EGF and TGF-α enhance bone resorption by promoting calcium release from bone (Tashjian and Levine, 1978; Ibbotson *et al.*, 1986), and they also stimulate angiogenesis (Schreiber *et al.*, 1986).

Sequence studies on growth factors and their receptors have revealed interesting connections with oncogene products. The transforming protein encoded by an avian erythroblastosis virus oncogene, v-*erb*B, was found to be structurally similar to a truncated EGF-R. It lacks most of the extracellular domain of the EGF-R molecule and the major autophosphorylation site at the intracellular portion (Downward *et al.*, 1984). It is possible that the truncated receptor molecule causes continuous proliferation signals, since the regulation of the receptor activity by binding of the ligand is lost. TGF-α is produced by tumor cells and may play a role in the development and growth of neoplasia through an autocrine mechanism. EGF-Rs have also been found to be overexpressed in various tumors (Derynck *et al.*, 1987). Thus, it seems that EGF-R is linked with cancer by several mechanisms.

II. Effects of Exogenous EGF on Morphogenesis and Differentiation

Organogenesis comprises the processes of morphogenesis and accompanying differentiation of organ-specific cell types. Morphogenesis is a result of locally active cell proliferation and simultaneous movements of cell populations. Most organs consist of tissues of diverse developmental origins, an ectoderm- or endoderm-divided epithelial component, and a mesoderm-derived connective tissue. The differentiated epithelial tissue often forms the functional part of the organ, as in the lung, kidney, and various glands. During development, both morphogenesis and cell differentiation are controlled by interactions between epithelial and mesenchymal tissues. The primary trigger of differentiation can be either the mesenchyme or the epithelium, but the advancing development is regulated by a chain of reciprocal tissue interactions.

A. Teeth

Tooth development is a good model for morphogenesis and differentiation of an epithelial–mesenchymal organ. In few other organs do both tissue components contribute so substantially to organ-specific cell differentiation and production of specific extracellular materials. Odontogenesis is divided into several successive steps that are recognized according to specific morphological features: dental lamina, bud, cap, and bell stages (Fig. 1). Tooth development starts by thickening of the presumptive dental epithelium of the first branchial arch, which subsequently proliferates and buds at the sites of future teeth. The neural crest-derived mesenchymal cells condense around the dental epithelial bud and are programmed to the

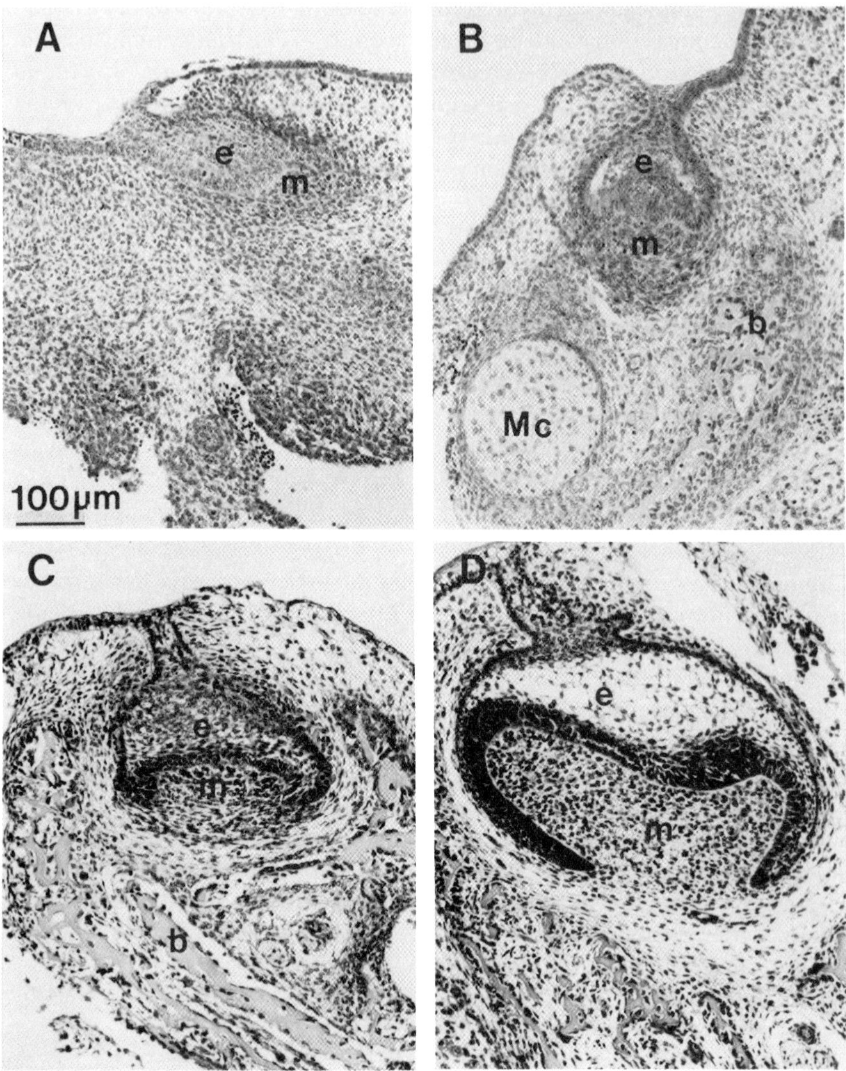

Fig. 1 Light micrographs of embryonic mandibular first molar teeth at various developmental stages. (A) In day 13 mouse embryo (day 0 represents the day of vaginal plug) the mandibular first molar tooth is in the bud stage of development. An area of condensed dental mesenchymal cells (m) surrounds the dental epithelial bud (e). (B) The day 14 mandibular first molar tooth is in the early cap stage of development. The dental epithelium (e) covers the dental mesenchyme (m) in a caplike structure. Formation of mandibular bone (b) has started. Mc, Meckel's cartilage. (C) The day 15 mandibular first molar tooth is in the late cap stage. The dental epithelium (e) has begun to grow around the dental mesenchymal papilla (m). The amount of mandibular bone has markedly increased. (D) The day 16 mandibular first molar tooth has reached the bell stage of development. The dental epithelium (e), which has developed into an enamel organ, now encloses the dental mesenchymal papilla (m).

lineage of dental mesenchymal cells. These are subsequently enclosed by the growing dental epithelium, first in a caplike, and then in a belllike, structure. After crown morphogenesis occurs, then specific dental cells terminally differentiate; these are the mesenchymal odontoblasts and the epithelial ameloblasts, which secrete the mineralizing matrices of dentin and enamel, respectively.

In mouse embryos tooth development starts between days 9 and 11 of gestation. The form of the tooth crown of the lower first molar tooth, which has been the subject of most experimental studies, is established between days 12 and 16, and the first overtly differentiated odontoblasts are visible at day 18. The whole process of morphogenesis, dental cell differentiation, and secretion of matrix molecules proceeds in a specific temporal and spatial pattern and is continuously controlled by reciprocal interactions between the mesenchyme and the epithelium (Kollar and Baird, 1970; Slavkin, 1974; Thesleff and Hurmerinta, 1981; Ruch *et al.*, 1983).

We have examined the development of embryonic tooth germs under controlled conditions in organ culture. The use of a chemically defined culture medium, which supports tooth morphogenesis in organ culture, enabled analysis of the specific effects of various supplemented growth factors because numerous undefined serum components were not present (Partanen *et al.*, 1984). Representatives from various growth factor families (Mercola and Stiles, 1988) were tested, and their influence on morphogenesis, cell proliferation, and cell differentiation was analyzed during culture. EGF inhibited early tooth morphogenesis and dental cell differentiation, while fibroblast growth factor and platelet-derived growth factor, which are also potent mitogens for various cell types (Ross *et al.*, 1986; Gospodarowicz *et al.*, 1986; see also Chapter 3, this volume), did not affect cell proliferation or morphogenesis (Partanen *et al.*, 1985). EGF significantly stimulated cell proliferation in tooth explants when measured as the incorporation of [^{3}H]thymidine into DNA (Fig. 2). However, this stimulation was accompanied by inhibition of morphogenesis and cell differentiation. Localization of [^{3}H]thymidine-labeled cells in histological tissue sections by autoradiography revealed that the various cell populations present in a tooth explant responded to EGF with diverse proliferation rates. EGF stimulated the proliferation of dental epithelial cells and nondental jaw mesenchyme, but prevented proliferation of the dental mesenchymal cells (Fig. 2) (Partanen *et al.*, 1985). These differences in cell proliferation were already visible after 2 days of culture, but were dramatic after 6 days, when inhibition of morphogenesis was also evident (Fig. 3).

TGF-α appears to have similar effects on tooth development. Sarcoma growth factor, which is composed of TGF-α and β, prevented tooth morphogenesis and caused a more massive stimulation of vascular tissues in cultured embryonic tooth explants than did EGF (Thesleff *et al.*, 1983). In

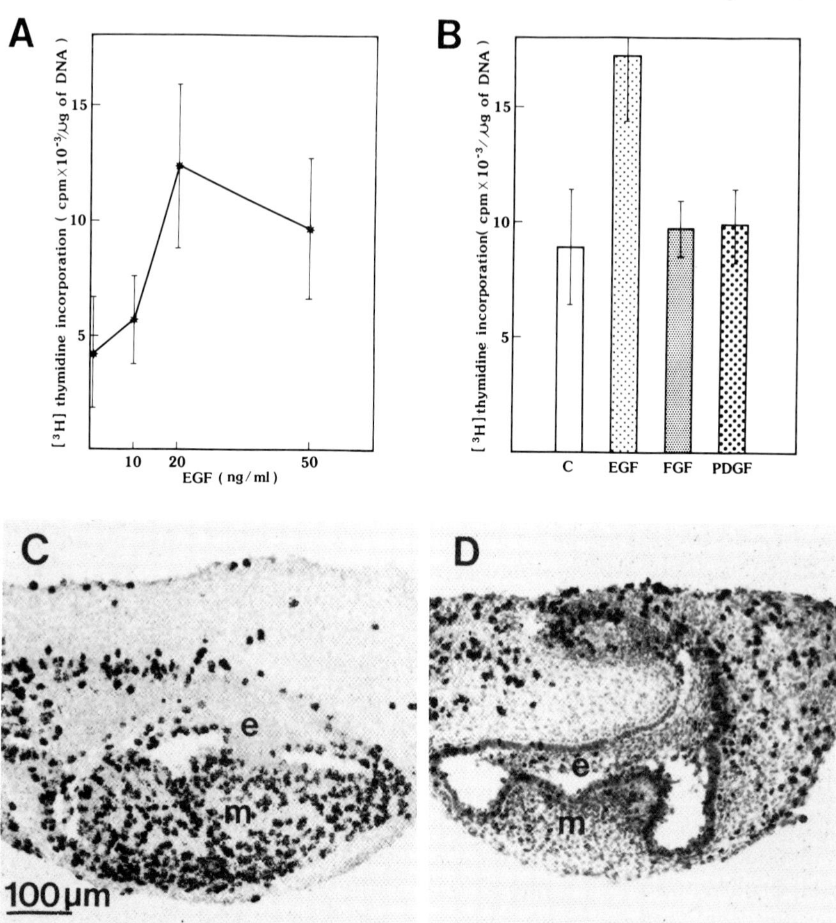

Fig. 2 Effect of EGF on incorporation and autoradiographic localization of [^{3}H]thymidine in day 14 tooth explants. (A) Effect of increasing concentrations of EGF in a chemically defined culture medium on [^{3}H]thymidine incorporation in day 14 early cap stage teeth after 2 days of culture. Incorporation of [^{3}H]thymidine was stimulated in a dose-dependent manner by concentrations of EGF up to 20 ng/ml, but decreased with 50 ng/ml EGF. (B) Effect of 20 ng/ml of EGF, 100 ng/ml of fibroblast growth factor (FGF), and 5 ng/ml of platelet-derived growth factor (PDGF) on [^{3}H]thymidine incorporation by day 14 early cap stage teeth after 2 days of culture. Growth factors were added to the culture medium at the onset of culture. EGF increased incorporation significantly, while FGF or PDGF had no effects. C, Control culture in chemically defined culture medium containing 50 μg/ml of transferrin. (C) Autoradiographic localization of [^{3}H]thymidine in day 14 tooth explants after 2 days of culture in the control medium. The tooth has grown in size, and cuspal morphogenesis has advanced slightly. Active cell proliferation is evident especially in the dental mesenchyme (m). e, Dental epithelium. (D) Autoradiographic localization of [^{3}H]thymidine in day 14 tooth explants after 2 days of culture in medium containing 20 ng/ml EGF. Cell proliferation in the dental mesenchyme (m) has been inhibited and there is more incorporation by cells in the mesenchymal tissue around the tooth germ than in control cultures. e, Dental epithelium. (A and B from Partanen *et al.*, 1985.)

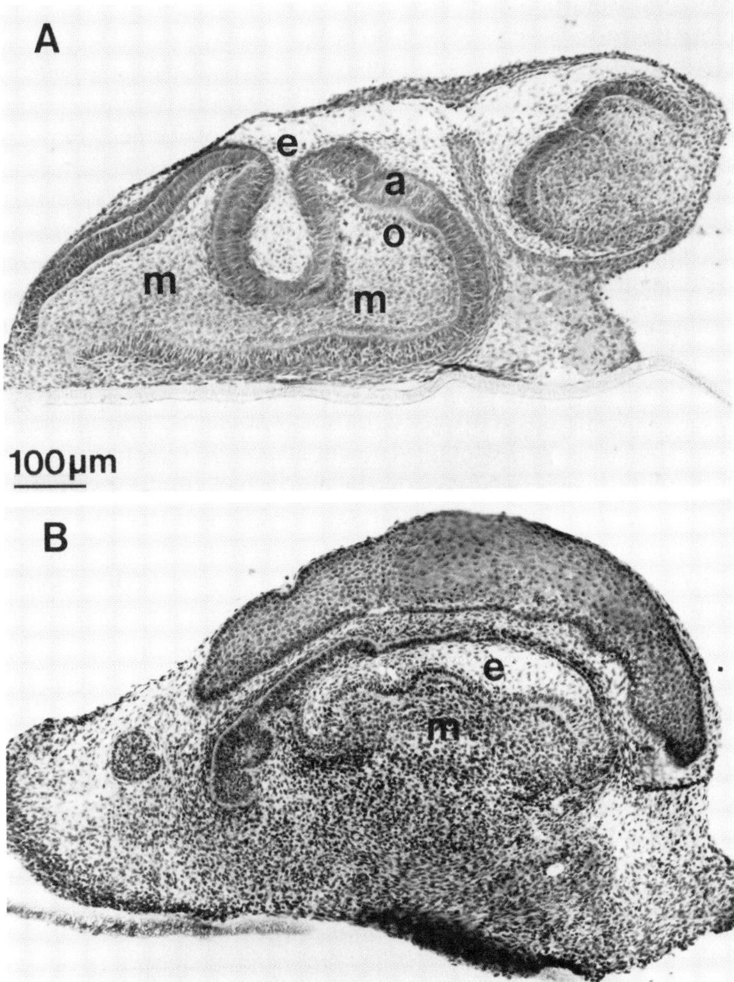

Fig. 3 Effect of EGF on morphogenesis and cell differentiation of early cap stage day 14 tooth germs after 9 days of culture. (A) In the control medium the first mandibular molar tooth has undergone overt cuspal morphogenesis. Polarization of mesenchymal odontoblasts (o) and epithelial ameloblasts (a) is evident. The second mandibular molar tooth (right) is at the bell stage of development. (B) The presence of 20 ng/ml of EGF in the culture medium has prevented tooth development. The tooth has grown in size, but cuspal morphogenesis has not proceeded. Stimulation of surrounding jaw mesenchyme is prominent. e, Dental epithelium; m, dental mesenchyme.

EGF-treated tooth explants the stimulation of mesenchymal tissue surrounding the tooth germ is obviously at least partly due to the presence of vascular elements, which are stimulated by EGF (Gospodarowicz *et al.*, 1978; McAuslan *et al.*, 1985). TGF-α is also a more potent angiogenic factor than is EGF *in vivo* (Schreiber *et al.*, 1986). Hence, EGF-related factors may function in the regulation of angiogenesis during embryonic development.

It is apparent that EGF prevents tooth morphogenesis by decreasing cell proliferation in the dental mesenchyme. Thus, factors that affect proliferation may have adverse effects on normal morphogenesis and differentiation. During tooth development, the proliferation rates of dental cells are tightly regulated by epithelial–mesenchymal cell interactions (Thesleff and Hurmerinta, 1981; Ruch *et al.*, 1983). Disturbances in proliferation may lead to impaired tissue interactions and inhibit morphogenesis. EGF also inhibits normal development of palate and hair follicles in the mouse by maintaining cell proliferation in the epithelium (Pratt, 1980; Moore *et al.*, 1983; discussed in more detail in Sections III and IV).

The inhibitory effect of exogenous EGF on tooth development in organ culture was restricted to early developmental stages; EGF inhibited further development at the early cap stage, but did not have marked effects during the late cap stage or bell stage. Thus, dental tissues are able to respond to exogenous EGF at the early cap stage, but not at a later stage. Apparently, a proper combination and temporal appearance of growth factors, both stimulatory and inhibitory, are required for normal tooth development *in vivo*.

B. Other Organs

In contrast to its inhibitory effects on tooth, palate, and hair follicle development, EGF hastens certain developmental events. EGF stimulates the branching morphogenesis of tracheal epithelium to form supernumerary buds in organ culture of embryonic chick lung (Goldin and Opperman, 1980). It also enhances maturation of lung epithelium by stimulating the differentiation of type II pneumocytes (Sundell *et al.*, 1975; Catterton *et al.*, 1979). EGF and TGF-α stimulate proliferation of mouse mammary epithelial cells and promote ductal morphogenesis as well as lobuloalveolar growth in developing mammary glands in organ culture (Turkington, 1969; Tonelli and Sorof, 1980; Taketani and Oka, 1983) and *in vivo* (Vonderhaar, 1987; Coleman *et al.*, 1988). Vonderhaar (1987) showed the TGF-α was a more potent agent than EGF for developing mammary glands because the stimulatory effect of EGF required simultaneous treatment with estradiol and progesterone, while TGF-α alone was sufficient to promote growth. Apparently, EGF-like factors have a physiological role in mammary gland development. An EGF-like growth factor, called mammary-derived growth factor, has been detected in mammary tissue. This binds to EGF-Rs, but is immunologically distinct from EGF (Vonderhaar, 1984).

III. Expression of EGF Receptors in Developing Organs

A. Teeth

The results of studies of the presence and quantity of EGF-Rs in developing tissues have indicated a role for EGF/TGF-α in morphogenetic and differentiation events. Because the responsiveness of embryonic dental tissues to EGF was found to be stage dependent, we studied the quantity and localization of EGF-Rs in tooth germs at various developmental stages using [^{125}I]EGF. Binding of [^{125}I]EGF was quantitated by measuring tissue-incorporated radioactivity and localized by autoradiography from histological tissue sections. The amount of incorporated [^{125}I]EGF was relatively high in mouse embryonic teeth, and there was no significant change in the level of EGF binding from the early cap stage, which is responsive to exogenous EGF, to the bell stage, which does not respond to EGF in organ culture. However, localization of EGF binding cells by autoradiography revealed a dramatic change in the distribution of receptors in the dental tissues during tooth development, which correlated with the loss of EGF responsiveness (Fig. 4) (Partanen and Thesleff, 1987). In bud stage teeth the dental epithelium bound EGF, while the condensed dental mesenchymal cells around the epithelial bud had only a few EGF-Rs. At early cap stage the number of EGF-Rs had decreased in the dental epithelium. Only the outer epithelial cells bound EGF, whereas the epithelial cells near the epithelial–mesenchymal interface lacked receptors. At this stage the dental mesenchymal EGF-Rs were uniformly distributed in the dental papilla. EGF binding decreased markedly from the early to the late cap stage, and had almost totally disappeared from the dental epithelium and dental mesenchyme at the bell stage.

In the nondental mesenchyme around the tooth, the binding of EGF was more intense than in the dental mesenchyme and increased in intensity from the bud stage to the cap stage. At the bell stage abundant EGF binding was observed, especially in the cells of the dental follicle, which consists of condensed mesenchymal cells intimately surrounding the tooth germ. The abundance of EGF-Rs in the dental follicle was still evident in erupting teeth (Thesleff *et al.*, 1987a; Topham *et al.*, 1987). Besides being in the dental sac, EGF binding was also observed in the apical mesenchy-

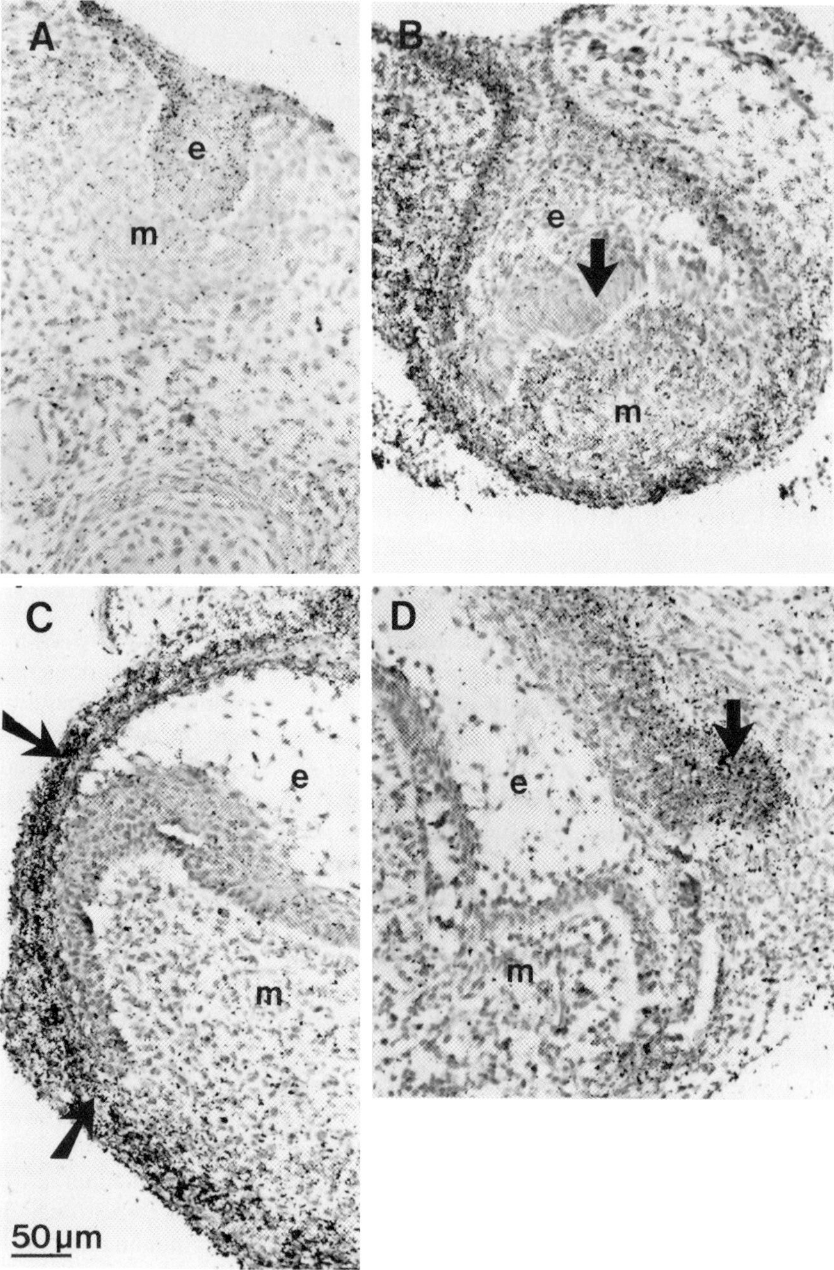

Fig. 4 Autoradiographs of [^{125}I]EGF binding in developing mouse mandibular molar tooth germs. (A) In the bud stage first mandibular molar tooth from a day 13 mouse embryo, the

mal tissue, in the cervical loop epithelium, and around the blood vessels (Thesleff *et al.*, 1987a).

Previous studies have suggested that the appearance and the amount of EGF-Rs in various embryonic tissues are related to the developmental stage of each organ (Adamson *et al.*, 1981; Hortsch *et al.*, 1983; Adamson and Meek, 1984). The developing tooth is a particularly suitable model to analyze how the expression of EGF-Rs is related to the developmental stage of the organ or to embryonic age. This is because the development of different teeth starts at different embryonic ages, and thus various stages of tooth development can be studied in the same embryo. Our results show that the pattern of EGF binding was specific to the developmental stage of tooth and did not depend on the age of the embryo. For example, the distribution of receptors was similar in bud stage teeth from day 13 to day 17 and newborn mice (Fig. 4A and D).

B. Kidney

As well as being found in the epithelial tooth bud, EGF-Rs were found in the ureter buds in embryonic kidney anlage, while the surrounding mesenchymal condensations did not bind EGF. Also, the branching epithelium in embryonic submandibular salivary gland had large numbers of EGF-Rs (Fig. 5B). Here, the stimulatory effect of EGF seems to converge on the receptor-bearing cells.

It is notable that in both developing tooth and kidney, EGF-Rs appeared in the mesenchyme with advancing morphogenesis, but they were lost from differentiating mesenchymal cells (Figs. 4 and 6). It cannot be concluded at the moment that the expression of the EGF-R in the mesenchyme is induced by the action of EGF on the epithelium, as is the case in the induction of hormone receptor expression in the developing mammary

---

epithelial tooth bud (e) binds [^{125}I]EGF, whereas the condensed dental mesenchyme (m) around the bud is sparsely labeled. (B) In the early cap stage first mandibular molar tooth from a day 14 mouse embryo, the cells of the dental mesenchymal papilla (m) are labeled by bound [^{125}I]EGF, while in the tooth epithelium (e) only the outermost cells are labeled and the epithelial cells at the epithelial–mesenchymal interface are totally unlabeled (arrow). The surrounding jaw mesenchyme is heavily labeled by [^{125}I]EGF. (C) In the bell stage day 17 first mandibular molar tooth, binding of [^{125}I]EGF has also decreased in the dental mesenchyme (m), but the mesenchymal cells of the dental follicle surrounding the tooth germ show abundant binding (arrows). e, Dental epithelium. (D) In newborn mouse the second mandibular molar tooth (left) is undergoing cuspal morphogenesis and the third molar is at the bud stage. The second molar shows sparse labeling of bound [^{125}I]EGF, but the epithelial bud of the third molar is intensely labeled (arrow). e, Dental epithelium; m, dental mesenchyme. (From Partanen and Thesleff, 1987.)

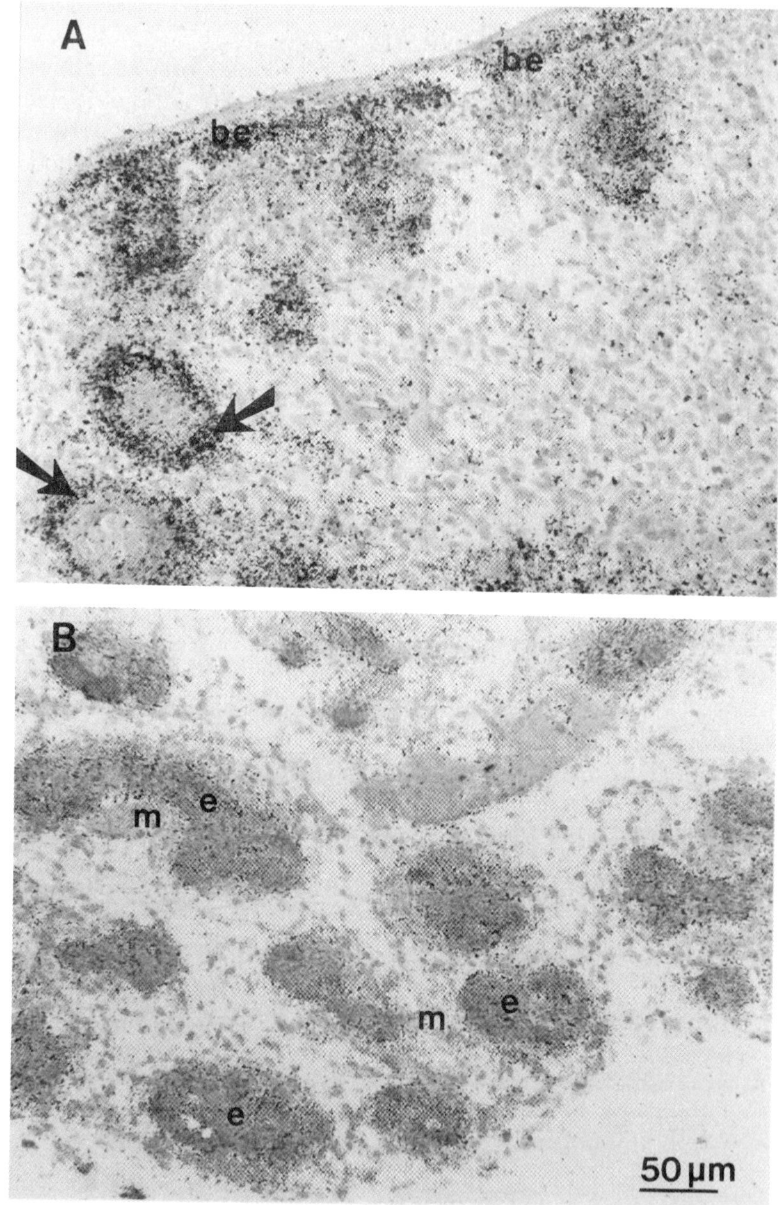

Fig. 5 Autoradiographs showing the binding of [^{125}I]EGF in mouse embryonic skin and submandibular gland. (A) In the tissue section of skin from the upper lip of day 16 mouse embryo, several transverse sections of hair follicles are visible. In hair follicles the outer root sheath and the mesenchymal cells surrounding the outer epithelium show intense binding of [^{125}I]EGF (arrows), while the dermal papilla and the inner epithelium are nearly unlabeled. In

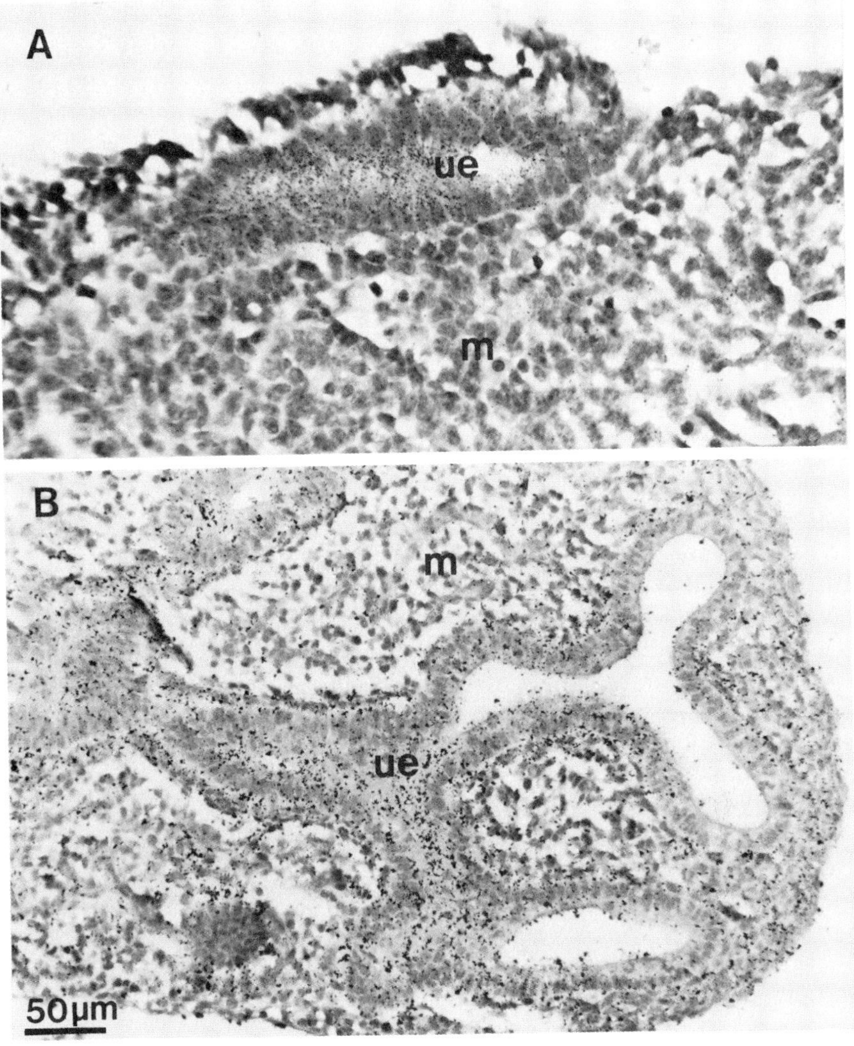

Fig. 6 Autoradiographs of [^{125}I]EGF binding in mouse embryonic kidney. (A) In the kidney rudiment of a day 11 mouse embryo, the epithelium of the ureter bud (ue) binds [^{125}I]EGF, but the metanephric mesenchyme (m) is unlabeled. (B) In a day 13 kidney the ureter epithelium is undergoing extensive branching. The epithelium of the ureter branches (ue) and the mesenchymal cells near the ureter epithelium bind [^{125}I]EGF, while the mesenchymal stroma (m) shows sparse labeling. (From Partanen and Thesleff, 1987.)

---

epidermis the basal cells (be) are heavily labeled, whereas the upper cell layers are unlabeled The dermal tissue is sparsely labeled. (From Partanen and Thesleff, 1987.) (B) In the developing submandibular gland from a day 14 mouse embryo, the branching epithelial strands (e) show abundant binding of [^{125}I]EGF. There is light label of bound [^{125}I]EGF in the mesenchymal cells (m).

gland (Kratochwil and Schwartz, 1976). The appearance of EGF-Rs in the mesenchyme may at least partly be related to vascularization of the organ, since both EGF and TGF-α stimulate angiogenesis (Gospodarowicz *et al.*, 1978; Thesleff *et al.*, 1983; Schreiber *et al.*, 1986).

It is interesting that Wilcox and Derynck (1988a) detected expression of TGF-α by *in situ* hybridization in the oral cavity and the developing kidney of 9- to 10-day mouse embryos. The probable production of TGF-α and the expression of the EGF-Rs in these tissues suggest local action of TGF-α during tooth and kidney morphogenesis.

C. Hair Follicles and Skin

The structure of the hair follicle resembles that of the developing tooth. In both organs the mesenchymal papilla is enclosed by the epithelium, and the organ is surrounded by a layer of condensed mesenchymal cells. In both organs the mesenchymal papilla exerts an inductive effect on the enclosing epithelium. Also, we found that binding of EGF in a day 16 mouse embryonic hair follicle was analogous to that in a day 16 bell stage tooth germ. Large numbers of EGF-Rs were found in the outer epithelial root sheath and in the connective tissue sheath of hair follicles (Fig. 5A), which parallels the location of the EGF-R in the outer dental epithelium and the dental follicle around the tooth germ (Fig. 4C) (Partanen and Thesleff, 1987).

Inhibition of hair follicle development by EGF, with subsequent delay in hair growth, has been believed to be caused by prolonged stimulation of cell division in the epidermis of neonatal mice (Moore *et al.*, 1983). The intense binding of EGF in the basal cells of the epidermis (Fig. 5A) is related to the proliferative capacity of these cells. There are many fewer EGF-Rs in the differentiating cells of the upper epidermis. Our results of EGF binding in mouse embryonic skin are in agreement with the results of studies of [^{125}I]EGF binding in neonatal rat skin by Green *et al.* (1983). The presence of TGF-α mRNA and protein in human neonatal epidermis suggests that TGF-α functions in an autocrine or paracrine manner (Coffey *et al.*, 1987).

The abundance of EGF-Rs in skin epithelium is probably related to the capacity of TGF-α and EGF to enhance epithelial wound healing (Buckley *et al.*, 1985; Brown *et al.*, 1986; Schultz *et al.*, 1987).

D. General Aspects of EGF/TGF-α Action in Morphogenesis

In all embryonic organs that we studied, the amount of EGF-Rs appeared to be highest during the developmental stages when cell proliferation is most active and to decrease significantly during advancing morphogenesis and differentiation (Partanen and Thesleff, 1987). For example, EGF-Rs decreased in the dental epithelium and the dental mesenchyme with advancing morphogenesis and declining cell proliferation, and totally disappeared with dental cell differentiation, in parallel with the differentiation of epidermal cells. Thus, EGF/TGF-α may stimulate or maintain proliferation of undifferentiated cells rather than promote differentiation.

IV. EGF and TGF-α in Epithelial–Mesenchymal Tissue Interactions

A. Teeth

In most epithelial–mesenchymal organs morphogenesis is initiated by budding of ectodermal or endodermal epithelium which, as a consequence of cell divisions and interactions with the mesenchymal tissue, intrudes into the mesenchymal stroma and undergoes morphogenesis. In several organs, such as the lung, kidney, and various glands, morphogenesis involves extensive branching of the epithelium. The abundance of EGF-Rs during both budding and branching of the epithelium suggests that EGF-like factors stimulate epithelial proliferation in these processes (Partanen and Thesleff, 1987; Coleman *et al.*, 1988). The distribution of [^{125}I]EGF binding and particularly the shifts in EGF binding patterns between the epithelium and the mesenchyme, with advancing development in different organs, suggest that tissue interactions are involved in the action of EGF on organogenesis (Partanen and Thesleff, 1987).

During the cap stage of tooth development, the effect of EGF on cell proliferation seems to be modified by epithelial–mesenchymal tissue interactions. In the early cap stage tooth, which responds with increased proliferation to exogenous EGF in organ culture, the distribution of EGF-Rs in the dental epithelium and the dental mesenchyme did not correlate with the response of these tissues to EGF. The cells of the dental epithelium were stimulated to proliferate by EGF, but did not bind EGF, while the cells of the dental mesenchyme bound EGF, but their proliferation was inhibited by EGF. Thus, the dental mesenchymal cells obviously are the primary target of EGF, and they regulate the proliferation of epithelial cells.

Other evidence for the occurrence of cellular interactions in tissue formation came from a comparison of the results of studies of dispersed primary cell cultures and whole tooth explants. EGF markedly stimulated proliferation of disaggregated dental papilla cells that were grown as monolayers (Brownell and Rovero, 1980; Steidler and Reade, 1981; Partanen *et al.*, 1985). However, cell proliferation in the dental papilla of

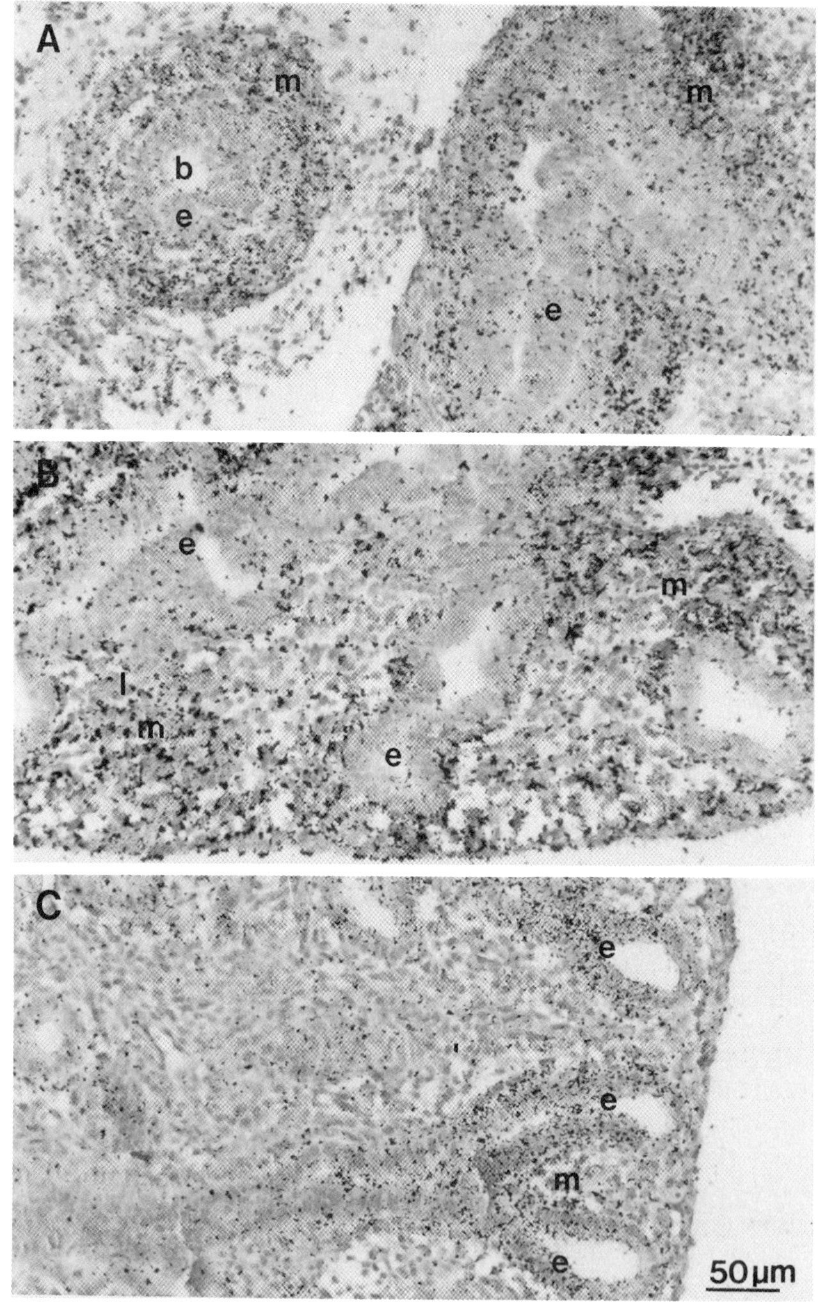

Fig. 7 Autoradiographs of [^{125}I]EGF binding in mouse embryonic lung. (A) In the lung of a day 13 mouse embryo there is heavy labeling by bound [^{125}I]EGF in the lung mesenchyme, especially in the concentrically arranged mesenchymal cells (m) around the bronchus (b) and

whole tooth explants in culture was decreased by EGF (Partanen *et al.*, 1985). Hence, the responses of both the dental epithelium and the dental mesenchyme are apparently modified by tissue interactions.

Tissue interactions also control the responsiveness to EGF during palate development in mouse embryos. EGF inhibits palate fusion by maintaining cell proliferation in the medial epithelium of palatal shelves; this requires the presence of the underlying mesenchyme (Tyler and Pratt, 1980).

B. Lungs

In lung morphogenesis, the epithelium originating from tracheal epithelial buds undergoes extensive branching and forms tubular structures. EGF stimulates cell proliferation in lung epithelium (Goldin and Opperman, 1980). At the stage of active epithelial branching in day 13 mouse embryo, we observed large numbers of EGF-Rs in the mesenchyme near the epithelium, but there were markedly fewer receptors in the epithelium. EGF binding decreased dramatically with advancing morphogenesis, and in day 14 embryonic lung only the most distal epithelial branches and the neighboring mesenchymal cells bound EGF (Fig. 7). This suggests that EGF has a role in the branching morphogenesis of the lung, and this effect may be mediated by the mesenchyme.

It is notable that the pattern of glucocorticoid binding in the mouse embryonic lung (Beer *et al.*, 1984) resembles the pattern of EGF binding. Thus, at the early stages of lung development, the mesenchyme seems to be the primary target tissue for hormone and growth factor responses. Coleman *et al.* (1988) have used [^{125}I]EGF binding in developing mammary gland to localize the EGF-R. During ductal growth, the highest concentration of epithelial receptors was in the cap cells of end buds, which are the primary sites of ductal cell proliferation. However, the mesenchymal stroma adjacent to ductal epithelium had even more EGF-Rs. The authors suggested that the mammary epithelium may induce receptors in nearby stromal cells. This epithelium has been shown to induce receptors for testosterone during fetal development of the mammary gland (Heuberger

---

the mesenchymal cells near the proximal epithelial tubuli (e). The lung epithelium in both the bronchi and the proximal tubuli is markedly less labeled than the mesenchyme. (B) In a day 13 lung the peripheral mesenchyme (m) also shows intense binding of [^{125}I]EGF, while the branching distal epithelial tubuli (e) are only lightly labeled. (C) In the lung of a day 14 mouse embryo, branching of lung epithelium has advanced and the binding of [^{125}I]EGF has dramatically decreased. Only the most distal epithelial branches (e) and some surrounding mesenchymal cells (m) bind [^{125}I]EGF. Other parts of the lung are unlabeled. (From Partanen and Thesleff, 1987.)

et al., 1982). A similar interaction may occur in the embryonic kidney and the lung, in which we observed a high number of EGF-Rs in the mesenchymal cells that intimately surround the epithelial tubular structures. The cells around bronchi in the lung and around the ureter in the kidney will later differentiate into smooth muscle cells.

C. Extracellular Matrix in Development of Epithelial–Mesenchymal Organs

Several studies have shown that morphogenetic and differentiation events during the development of epithelial–mesenchymal organs such as the tooth and kidney are accompanied by specific changes in the composition or organization of extracellular matrix molecules (Thesleff and Hurmerinta, 1981; Ruch *et al.*, 1983; Ekblom, 1984; Aufderheide *et al.*, 1987; Thesleff *et al.*, 1987b, 1988). The biological functions of growth factors and their receptors in tissue interactions could be intimately linked with the extracellular matrix. Matrix molecules may bind growth factors and thus anchor them in tissues. Hydrolysis of the extracellular matrix during morphogenetic events (Bernfield *et al.*, 1984; Gospodarowicz *et al.*, 1986) could result in the local release of growth factors and stimulation of proliferation of specific cell populations. On the other hand, EGF has been shown to affect the production or turnover of numerous matrix molecules, and could thus control cell–matrix interactions by regulating the composition of the extracellular matrix. Furthermore, the presence of EGF-like sequences in various matrix molecules may be associated with interactions on the cell surface (Krusius *et al.*, 1987; Sasaki *et al.*, 1987; Jones *et al.*, 1988; Pearson *et al.*, 1988). Further discussions on the role of growth factors in regulating the expression of the components of the extracellular matrix and of secreted proteases and their inhibitors can be found in Chapters 4, 7, and 8 of this volume.

Interesting connections were observed recently between the pattern of the expression of a cell surface heparan sulfate proteoglycan, syndecan, and the distribution of EGF binding during tooth development (Thesleff *et al.*, 1988). The expression of the cell surface proteoglycan in the dental epithelium and the dental mesenchyme changes concomitantly with the reciprocal epithelium–mesenchyme interactions which direct tooth development. The distribution of EGF binding coincides with syndecan expression at the cap and bell stages of tooth development (Fig. 8). The proteoglycan binds interstitial matrix molecules and may function as a matrix receptor on the cell surface (Koda *et al.*, 1985; Saunders and Bernfield, 1988), but the possible functional relationship of EGF binding to cell–matrix interactions remains obscure.

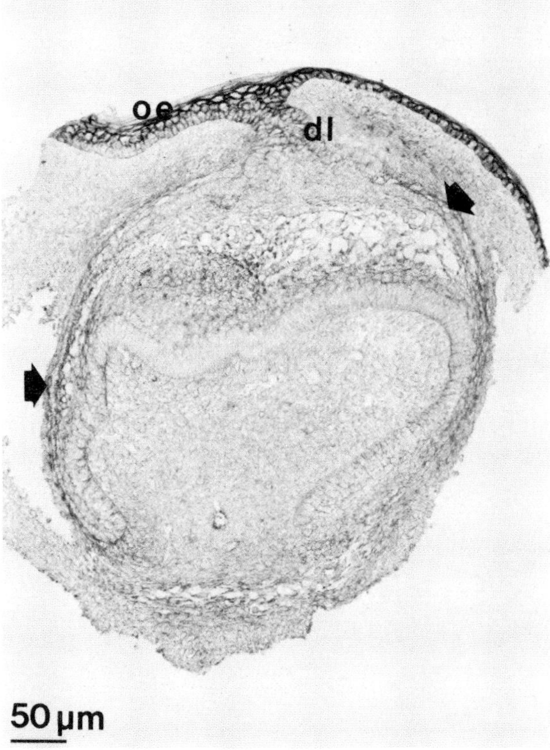

Fig. 8 Immunoperoxidase localization of the cell surface proteoglycan syndecan, with the monoclonal antibody in the bell stage first mandibular molar of a day 17 mouse embryo. The staining is most intense in the oral epithelium (oe). The epithelial cells of the dental lamina (dl) connecting the tooth germ to oral epithelium, as well as the mesenchymal cells of the dental follicle surrounding the tooth germ, are moderately stained. The distribution of staining resembles that of [^{125}I]EGF binding in the bell stage tooth shown in Fig. 4C. (From Thesleff *et al.*, 1988, with permission.)

V. Summary

Taken together, there is a substantial amount of evidence that EGF-like growth factors have a physiological role in organ development and that the action of EGF or TGF-α in the development of epithelial–mesenchymal organs is associated with tissue interactions that guide morphogenesis and differentiation. The functions of growth factors in these interactions are not known at present, but they can be speculated in light of recent data.

EGF and TGF-α might act as paracrine mediators of tissue interactions during organ development, as has been suggested for TGF-β, which, together with fibroblast growth factor, acts as a morphogen to induce differentiation of embryonic tissue that is normally induced by tissue interactions (Kimelman and Kirschner, 1987). By *in situ* hybridization, TGF-β mRNA was shown to be expressed by epithelial cells in many epithelial–mesenchymal organs (Lehnert and Akhurst, 1988), whereas by immunolocalization the TGF-β protein was found in the mesenchymal stroma (Heine *et al.*, 1987). Although there have been some studies of the localization of EGF and the EGF-R in the embryo, which are discussed in Chapter 1 of this volume, there is a need for more detailed studies of the relative distribution of cells that synthesize the receptor and its ligand at various stages of organogenesis. The use of appropriate cDNA probes and the *in situ* hybridization technique will enable the localization of sites of EGF or TGF-α synthesis in relation to sites of receptor expression in developing organs and thus provide a deeper understanding of how EGF/TGF-α coordinates epithelial–mesenchymal interactions throughout development.

References

Adamson, E. D., and Meek, J. (1984). *Dev. Biol.* **103,** 62–70.

Adamson, E. D., Deller, N. J., and Warshaw, J. B. (1981). *Nature (London)* **291,** 656–659.

Aufderheide, E., Chiquet-Ehrismann, R., and Ekblom, P. (1987). *J. Cell Biol.* **105,** 599–608.

Barrandon, Y., and Green, H. (1987). *Cell (Cambridge, Mass.)* **50,** 1131–1137.

Beer, D. C., Butley, M. S., Cunha, G. R., and Malkinson, A. M. (1984). *Dev. Biol.* **105,** 351–364.

Beerstecher, H. J., Huiskens-Van Der Mej, C., and Warnaar, S. O. (1988). *J. Histochem. Cytochem.* **36,** 1153–1160.

Bernfield, M., Banerjee, S. D., Koda, J. E., and Rapraeger, A. C. (1984). *In* "The Role of Extracellular Matrix in Development" (R. L. Trelstad, ed.), pp. 545–572. Liss, New York.

Brachmann, R., Lindquist, P. B., Nagashima, M., Kohr, W., Lipari, T., Napier, M., and Derynck, R. (1989). *Cell (Cambridge, Mass.)* **56,** 691–700.

Brown, G. L., Curtsinger, L., Brightwell, J. R., Ackerman, D. M., Tobin, G. R., Folk, N. C., George-Nascimento, C., Valenzuela, P., and Schultz, G. S. (1986). *J. Exp. Med.* **163,** 1319–1324.

Brownell, A. G., and Rovero, L. J. (1980). *J. Dent. Res.* **59,** 1075–1080.

Buckley, A., Davidson, J. M., Kamerath, C. D., Wolt, T. B., and Woodward, S. C. (1985). *Proc. Natl. Acad. Sci. U.S.A.* **82,** 7340–7344.

Byyny, R. L., Orth, D. N., and Cohen, S. (1972). *Endocrinology (Baltimore)* **90,** 1261–1266.

Carpenter, G., and Cohen, S. (1979). *Annu. Rev. Biochem.* **48,** 193–216.

Catterton, W. Z., Escobedo, M. B., Sexson, W. R., Gray, M. E., Sundell, H. W., and Stahlman, M. T. (1979). *Pediatr. Res.* **13,** 104–108.

Chen, L. B., Gudor, R. C., Sun, T.-T., Chen, A. B., and Mosesson, M. W. (1977). *Science* **197,** 776–778.

Coffey, R. J., Jr., Derynck, R., Wilcox, J. N., Bringman, T. S., Goustin, A. S., Moses, H. L., and Pittelkow, M. R. (1987). *Nature (London)* **328,** 817–820.
Cohen, S. (1962). *J. Biol. Chem.* **237,** 1555–1562.
Cohen, S., and Elliot, G. A. (1963). *J. Invest. Dermatol.* **40,** 1–5.
Coleman, S., Silberstein, G. B., and Daniel, C. W. (1988). *Dev. Biol.* **127,** 304–315.
DeLarco, J. E., and Todaro, G. J. (1978). *Proc. Natl. Acad. Sci. U.S.A.* **75,** 4001–4005.
Derynck, R. (1987). *In* "Oncogenes, Genes and Growth Factors" (G. Guroff, ed.), pp. 133–163. Wiley, New York.
Derynck, R., Goeddel, D. V., Ullrich, A., Gutterman, J. U., Williams, R. D., Bringham, T. S., and Berger, W. H. (1987). *Cancer Res.* **47,** 707–712.
Downward, J., Yarden, Y., Mayes, E., Scrace, G., Totty, N., Stockwell, P., Ullrich, A., Schlessinger, J., and Waterfield, M. D. (1984). *Nature (London)* **307,** 521–527.
Ekblom, P. (1984). *In* "The Role of Extracellular Matrix in Development" (R. L. Trelstad, ed.), pp. 173–206. Liss, New York.
Erickson, C. A., and Turley, E. A. (1987). *Exp. Cell Res.* **169,** 267–279.
Frati, L., Cenci, G., Sbaraglia, G., Teti, D. V., and Covelli, I. (1976). *Life Sci.* **18,** 905–912.
Goldin, G. V., and Opperman, L. A. (1980). *J. Embryol. Exp. Morphol.* **60,** 235–243.
Gospodarowicz, D., Brown, K. D., Birdwell, C. R., and Zetter, B. R. (1978). *J. Cell Biol.* **77,** 774–788.
Gospodarowicz, D., Neufeld, G., and Schweigerer, L. (1986). *Cell Differ.* **9,** 1–17.
Green, M. R., Basketter, D. A., Couchman, J. R., and Rees, D. A. (1983). *Dev. Biol.* **100,** 506–512.
Greenwald, I. (1985). *Cell (Cambridge, Mass.)* **43,** 583–590.
Gregory, H. (1975). *Nature (London)* **257,** 325–327.
Han, V. K. M., Hunter, E. S., III, Pratt, R. M., Zendegui, J. G., and Lee, D. C. (1987). *Mol. Cell. Biol.* **7,** 2335–2343.
Hata, R.-I., Hori, H., Nagai, Y., Tanaka, S., Kondo, M., Hiramatsu, M., Utsumi, N., and Kumegawa, M. (1984). *Endocrinology (Baltimore)* **115,** 867–876.
Heine, U. I., Munoz, E. F., Flanders, K. C., Ellingsworth, L. R., Lam, H.-Y. P., Thompson, N. L., Roberts, A. B., and Sporn, M. B. (1987). *J. Cell Biol.* **105,** 2861–2876.
Heuberger, B., Fitzka, I., Wasner, G., and Kratochwil, K. (1982). *Proc. Natl. Acad. Sci. U.S.A.* **79,** 2957–2961.
Hirata, Y., and Orth, D. N. (1979). *Endocrinology (Baltimore)* **105,** 1382–1387.
Hortsch, M., Schlessinger, J., Gootwine, E., and Webb, C. G. (1983). *EMBO J.* **2,** 1937–1941.
Hunter, T. (1987). *Cell (Cambridge, Mass.)* **50,** 823–829.
Ibbotson, K. J., Harrod, J., Gowen, M., D'Souza, S. M., Smith, D. D., Winkler, M. E., Derynck, R., and Mundy, G. R. (1986). *Proc. Natl. Acad. Sci. U.S.A.* **83,** 2228–2232.
Johnson, L. K., Baxter, J. D., Vlodavsky, I., and Gospodarowicz, D. (1980). *Proc. Natl. Acad. Sci. U.S.A.* **77,** 394–398.
Jones, F. S., Burgoon, M. P., Hoffman, S., Crossin, K. L., Cunningham, B. A., and Edelman, G. M. (1988). *Proc. Natl. Acad. Sci. U.S.A.* **85,** 2186–2190.
Kammermeyer, K. L., and Wadsworth, S. C. (1987). *Development* **100,** 201–210.
Kaplowitz, P. B., D'Ercole, A. J., and Underwood, L. E. (1982). *J. Cell. Physiol.* **112,** 353–359.
Kasselberg, A. G., Orth, D. N., Gray, M. E., and Stahlman, M. T. (1985). *J. Histochem. Cytochem.* **33,** 315–322.
Keski-Oja, J., Lehto, V.-P., and Virtanen, I. (1981). *J. Cell Biol.* **90,** 537–441.

Kimelman, D., and Kirschner, M. (1987). *Cell (Cambridge, Mass.)* **51,** 869–877.
Koda, J. E., Rapraeger, A. C., and Bernfield, M. R. (1985). *J. Biol. Chem.* **260,** 8157–8162.
Kollar, E. J., and Baird, G. R. (1970). *J. Embryol. Exp. Morphol.* **24,** 159–171.
Kratochwil, K., and Schwartz, P. (1976). *Proc. Natl. Acad. Sci. U.S.A.* **73,** 4041–4044.
Krusius, T., Gehlsen, K. R., and Ruoslahti, E. (1987). *J. Biol. Chem.* **262,** 13120–13125.
Lehnert, S. A., and Akhurst, R. J. (1988). *Development* **104,** 263–273.
Livneh, E., Glazer, L., Segal, D., Schlessinger, J., and Shilo, B.-Z. (1985). *Cell (Cambridge, Mass.)* **40,** 599–607.
McAuslan, B. R., Bender, V., Reilly, W., and Moss, B. A. (1985). *Cell Biol. Int. Rep.* **9,** 175–182.
Matrisian, L. M., Pathak, M., and Magun, B. E. (1982). *Biochem. Biophys. Res. Commun.* **107,** 761–769.
Mercola, M., and Stiles, C. D. (1988). *Development* **102,** 451–460.
Moore, G. P. M., Panaretto, B. A., and Robertson, D. (1983). *Anat. Rec.* **205,** 47–55.
Nexø, E., Hollenberg, M. D., Figueroa, A., and Pratt, R. M. (1980). *Proc. Natl. Acad. Sci. U.S.A.* **77,** 2782–2785.
Panneerselvam, M., Sahai, A., and Salomon, D. S. (1985). *Arch. Dermatol. Res.* **277,** 377–383.
Partanen, A.-M., and Thesleff, I. (1987). *Dev. Biol.* **120,** 186–197.
Partanen, A.-M., Thesleff, I., and Ekblom, P. (1984). *Differentiation (Berlin)* **27,** 59–66.
Partanen, A.-M., Ekblom, P., and Thesleff, I. (1985). *Dev. Biol.* **111,** 84–94.
Pearson, C. A., Pearson, D., Shibahara, S., Hofsteenge, J., and Chiquet-Ehrismann, R. (1988). *EMBO J.* **7,** 2677–2981.
Perheentupa, J., Lakshmanan, J., and Fisher, D. A. (1985a). *Pediatr. Res.* **19,** 428–432.
Perheentupa, J., Lakshmanan, J., Hoath, S. B., Beri, U., Kim, H., Macaso, T., and Fisher, D. A. (1985b). *Am. J. Physiol.* **248,** E391–E396.
Pesonen, K., Viinikka, L., Koskimies, A., Banks, A. R., Nicolson, M., and Perheentupa, J. (1987). *Life Sci.* **40,** 2489–2494.
Popliker, M., Shatz, A., Avivi, A., Ullrich, A., Schlessinger, J., and Webb, C. G. (1987). *Dev. Biol.* **119,** 38–44.
Pratt, R. M. (1980). *In* "Development in Mammals" (M. H. Johnson, ed.), pp. 203–231. Elsevier/North-Holland, New York.
Proper, J. A., BJornson, C. L., and Moses, H. L. (1982). *J. Cell. Physiol.* **110,** 169–174.
Rall, L. B., Scott, J., Bell, G. I., Crawford, R. A., Penschow, J. D., Niall, H. D., and Coghlan, J. P. (1985). *Nature (London)* **313,** 228–231.
Rappolee, D. A., Brenner, C. A., Schultz, R., Mark, D., and Werb, Z. (1988). *Science* **241,** 1823–1825.
Ross, R., Raines, E. W., and Bowen-Pope, D. F. (1986). *Cell (Cambridge, Mass.)* **46,** 155–169.
Ruch, J. V., Lesot, H., Karcher-Djuricic, V., Meyer, J. M., and Mark, M. (1983). *J. Biol. Buccale* **11,** 173–193.
Sasaki, M., Kato, S., Kohno, K., Martin, G. R., and Yamada, Y. (1987). *Proc. Natl. Acad. Sci. U.S.A.* **84,** 935–939.
Saunders, S., and Bernfield, M. R. (1988). *J. Cell Biol.* **106,** 423–430.
Schlessinger, J. (1986). *J. Cell Biol.* **103,** 2067–2072.
Schlessinger, J., and Geiger, B. (1981). *Exp. Cell Res.* **134,** 273–279.
Schreiber, A. B., Winkler, M. E., and Derynck, R. (1986). *Science* **232,** 1250–1253.
Schultz, G. S., White, M., Mitchell, R., Brown, G., Lynch, J., Twardzik, D. R., and Torado, G. J. (1987). *Science* **235,** 350–352.
Slavkin, H. C. (1974). *In* "Oral Science Reviews" (A. H. Melcher, and G. A. Zarb, eds.), Vol. 4, pp. 1–136. Munksgaard, Copenhagen.

Smith, J. M., Sporn, M. B., Roberts, A. B., Derynck, R., Winkler, M. E., and Gregory, H. (1985). *Nature (London)* **315,** 515–516.

Starkey, R. H., and Orth, D. N. (1977). *J. Clin. Endocrinol. Metab.* **45,** 1144–1153.

Steidler, N. E., and Reade, P. C. (1981). *J. Dent. Res.* **60,** 1977–1982.

Sun, T. T., and Green, H. (1976). *Cell (Cambridge, Mass.)* **9,** 511–521.

Sundell, H., Serenius, F. S., Barthe, P., Friedman, Z., Kanarek, K. S., Escobedo, M. B., Orth, D. M., and Stahlman, M. T. (1975). *Pediatr. Res.* **9,** 371–376.

Taketani, Y., and Oka, T. (1983). *FEBS Lett.* **152,** 256–260.

Tam, J. P. (1985). *Science* **229,** 673–675.

Tashjian, A. H., and Levine, L. (1978). *Biochem. Biophys. Res. Commun.* **85,** 966–975.

Teixidó, J., Gilmore, R., Lee, D. C., and Massague, J. (1987). *Nature (London)* **326,** 883–885.

Thesleff, I., and Hurmerinta, K. (1981). *Differentiation (Berlin)* **18,** 75–88.

Thesleff, I., Ekblom, P., and Keski-Oja, J. (1983). *Cancer Res.* **43,** 5902–5909.

Thesleff, I., Partanen, A.-M., and Rihtniemi, L. (1987a). *Eur. J. Orthod.* **9,** 24–32.

Thesleff, I., Mackie, E., Vainio, S., and Chiquet-Ehrismann, R. (1987b). *Development* **101,** 289–296.

Thesleff, I., Jalkanen, M., Vainio, S., and Bernfield, M. (1988). *Dev. Biol.* **129,** 565–572.

Todaro, G. J., Fryling, C., and DeLarco, J. E. (1980). *Proc. Natl. Acad. Sci. U.S.A.* **77,** 5258–5262.

Tonelli, Q. J., and Sorof, S. (1980). *Nature (London)* **285,** 250–252.

Topham, R. T., Chiego, D. J., Jr., Gattone, V. H., II, Hinton, D. A., and Klein, R. M. (1987). *Dev. Biol.* **124,** 532–543.

Turkington, R. W. (1969). *Exp. Cell Res.* **57,** 79–85.

Turley, E. A., Hollenberg, M. D., and Pratt, R. M. (1985). *Differentiation (Berlin)* **28,** 279–285.

Twardzik, D. R. (1985). *Cancer Res.* **45,** 5413–5416.

Twardzik, D. R., Ranchalis, J. E., and Todaro, G. J. (1982). *Cancer Res.* **42,** 590–593.

Tyler, M. S., and Pratt, R. M. (1980). *J. Embryol. Exp. Morphol.* **58,** 93–106.

Vonderhaar, B. K. (1984). *In* "Control of Cell Growth and Proliferation" (C. M. Veneziale, ed.), pp. 11–33. Van Nostrand–Reinhold, Princeton, New Jersey.

Vonderhaar, B. K. (1987). *J. Cell. Physiol.* **132,** 581–584.

Wharton, K. A., Johansen, K. M., Xu, T., and Artavanis-Tsakonas, S. (1985). *Cell (Cambridge, Mass.)* **43,** 567–581.

Wilcox, J. N., and Derynck, R. (1988a). *Mol. Cell. Biol.* **8,** 3415–3422.

Wilcox, J. N., and Derynck, R. (1988b). *J. Neurosci.* **8,** 1901–1904.

Wong, S. T., Winchell, L. F., McCune, B. K., Earp, H. S., Teixidó, J., Massagué, J., Herman, B., and Lee, D. C. (1989). *Cell (Cambridge, Mass.)* **56,** 495–506.

Yoneda, T., and Pratt, R. M. (1981). *Science* **213,** 563–565.

3

Fibroblast Growth Factor and Its Involvement in Developmental Processes

Denis Gospodarowicz
University of California Medical Center
Cancer Research Institute
San Francisco, California 94143

I. Introduction

In recent years growth factors have been shown to influence the proliferation and differentiation of various cell types in culture (Sporn *et al.*, 1987). It has been postulated that they could play an important role in local control mechanisms *in vivo* that involve either autocrine or paracrine

Current Topics in Developmental Biology, Vol. 24

regulation of cell proliferation and/or differentiation (Sporn *et al.*, 1987; Goustin *et al.*, 1986). Through their ability to modulate each other's activity, they are well suited to control the complex morphogenetic events that take place in various organs during embryonic development or in organs such as ovaries during the adult phase (Gospodarowicz, 1976; Gospodarowicz *et al.*, 1986a,b, 1987).

Among the growth factors that could be relevant to the development and functions of various mesoderm-derived tissues are fibroblast growth factor (FGF) and its modulator, transforming growth factor type β (TGF-β) (Gospodarowicz *et al.*, 1987). FGF exists in two closely related forms, basic (bFGF) and acidic FGF (aFGF), which interact with a common cell surface receptor (Neufeld and Gospodarowicz, 1986). This ability to share a receptor enables aFGF and bFGF to exert similar biological effects on a wide range of mesodermal and neuroectodermal cells to control both their proliferation and differentiation (Gospodarowicz, 1987) (Table I). This wide range of FGF-responsive cells is best explained by the observation that FGF is probably a vegetalizing factor responsible (in combination with TGF-β) for ventral mesenchyme induction in early embryos (Slack *et al.*, 1987, 1988; Kimelman and Kirschner, 1987; Kimelman *et al.*, 1988). One would therefore expect that during the ontogeny of development, FGF would affect the proliferation and differentiation of most tissues derived from the primary and secondary mesenchyme.

The bioactivity of both bFGF and aFGF can be positively or negatively regulated by TGF-β, depending on the cell type (Fràter-Schröder *et al.*, 1986; Baird and Durkin, 1986; Globus *et al.*, 1988). Therefore, the ability of various tissues to synthesize FGFs, or TGF-β, and the relative concentrations of these growth factors in the microenvironment would determine whether cell proliferation and differentiation were selectively enhanced or repressed by FGF.

This review concentrates on the role of FGF in early development and its putative role in the developmental and functional aspects of various organs that have been shown to contain predominantly bFGF.

II. Molecular Characterization of the FGF Genes, mRNA, and Protein Products

A. FGF Genes

The high degree of structural homology (55%) between aFGF and bFGF suggests that they are derived from a common ancestral gene (Esch *et al.*, 1985a,b). The FGF genes have been cloned and complementary DNA sequences of both bFGF and aFGF have been synthesized. The localiza-

Table I Cell Types for Which FGFs Are Mitogenic or Which Affect Their Differentiation[a]

	bFGF	aFGF
Normal diploid cells		
Glial and astroglial cells	+(D)	+
Oligodendrocytes	+(D)	+
Schwann cells	+	?
Trabecular meshwork cells	+	?
Endothelial cells from capillaries, large vessels, and endocardium	+(D)	+(D)
Corneal endothelial cells	+(D)	+(D)
Fibroblasts	+	+
Myoblasts	+(D)	+(D)
Vascular smooth muscle	+	+
Chondrocytes	+(D)	+(D)
Osteoblasts	+	+
Blastema cells	+	?
Adrenal cortex cells	+	+
Granulosa cells	+	+
Prostatic epithelial cells	+	+
Mesothelial cells	+	+
Neuronal cells	+	?
Established cell lines		
Rat fibroblast-1	+	+
BALB/c 3T3	+	+
Swiss 3T3	+	+
BHK-21	+	+
A-204 rhabdomyosarcoma	+	?
PC-12	(D)	(D)

[a] (D), Induces differentiation; +, positive effect on cell proliferation; ?, effect on cell proliferation not determined.

tion and organization of the bFGF and aFGF genes have been reported (Abraham *et al.*, 1986a,b, 1987). The bFGF gene is located on human chromosome 4, and the aFGF gene is on chromosome 5 (Abraham *et al.*, 1987; Jaye *et al.*, 1986). The separation of the bFGF and aFGF genes through gene duplication is probably an ancient evolutionary event. The bFGF gene has a size greater than 38 kb. It encodes three exons widely separated by two large introns: The first intron separates codons 60 and 61; the second separates codons 94 and 95 (Abraham *et al.*, 1986a). The aFGF gene has a similar organization, with two large introns located in the identical positions in the coding sequence once the bFGF and aFGF genomic sequences are properly aligned (Mergia *et al.*, 1989). Southern blot analysis of human genomic DNA has shown that there is only one bFGF and one aFGF gene. Therefore, most, if not all, of the characterized or uncharacterized heparin-binding endothelial cell mitogens related to bFGF or aFGF are probably the products of the bFGF or aFGF gene (Abraham *et al.*, 1986a,b, 1987). In various cultured cells and tissues, the bFGF gene gives rise to two polyadenylated mRNAs, with approximate lengths of 3.7 and 7.0 kb (Schweigerer *et al.*, 1987b). The aFGF gene appears to encode a single mRNA species, with an approximate length of 4.1 kb (Schweigerer *et al.*, 1988; Jaye *et al.*, 1986).

B. Various Forms of FGF

The primary translation product for either bFGF or aFGF is composed of 155 amino acids (Abraham *et al.*, 1986a,b; Jaye *et al.*, 1986) and has an apparent molecular weight of 18,000. Proteolytic cleavage from the precursor molecule of the first nine amino acids for bFGF or 15 residues for aFGF results in the generation of shorter forms, which can then be cleaved further in homologous positions to give the NH_2-truncated form of bFGF (des.1–15) or aFGF (des.1–6). (Gospodarowicz *et al.*, 1985; Gospodarowicz, 1987; Esch *et al.*, 1985b). Despite the fact that both bFGF and aFGF have been shown to interact with high-affinity cell surface receptors (Neufeld and Gospodarowicz, 1986; Friesel *et al.*, 1986; Olwin and Hauschka, 1986) and are thus presumed to be secreted, the 155-residue forms of these two factors possess no obvious conventional secretion signals (Jaye *et al.*, 1986; Abraham *et al.*, 1986a,b). This apparent lack of a signal peptide is consistent with the observation that cultured bFGF-producing cells release into the culture medium little of the bFGF that they make (Gospodarowicz *et al.*, 1987; Schweigerer *et al.*, 1987b, 1988).

Larger bFGF forms with apparent molecular weights of 25,000 have also been recently reported (Moscatelli *et al.*, 1987), together with 22,000, 23,000, and 24,000 molecular weight forms (Florkiewicz and Sommer, 1989; Prats *et al.*, 1989). While translation of the 18,000 molecular weight form of bFGF is initiated at an AUG codon, translation of the higher forms of bFGF (22,000, 23,000, and 24,000 molecular weight) are initiated at a CUG codon (Florkiewicz and Sommer, 1989). This predicts that the primary transcript of the bFGF gene is processed by alternative splicing or that there are two alternative transcriptional start sites in the bFGF gene. Because the genomic organization of the aFGF gene is much like that of the bFGF gene, one would suspect the aFGF gene also contains a fourth exon located upstream from the three exons already identified.

The identification of two forms of bFGF which are derived from alternative translational initiation codons is not unusual. A similar observation has been made for the c-*myc* protein that exists in two forms that have no precursor–product relationship, but derive instead from alternative translational initiation in which an AUG codon is used to initiate translation of the shorter form and a CUG codon initiates translation of the larger form (Hann *et al.*, 1988). The shorter form of bFGF, which is initiated at an AUG codon, as well as the larger form of bFGF lacks a secretory signal peptide (Florkiewicz and Sommer, 1989; Prats *et al.*, 1989).

bFGF seems to have been extremely well conserved through evolution. For example, bovine and human bFGF differ in only two of their 146 amino acids and have an overall amino acid sequence homology of 98.7% (Abraham *et al.*, 1986a). Avian and bovine bFGF have the same amino acid composition and avian bFGF cross-reacts on an equimolar basis with bovine bFGF in a radio immunoassay using rabbit anti-bFGF polyclonal antibodies. Thus, homologous epitopes are well conserved (Gospodarowicz *et al.*, 1987). The deduced amino acid sequence from the bFGF cDNA clone coding for *Xenopus laevis* shows an 84% homology with the human bFGF (Kimelman *et al.*, 1988). aFGF seems to be less well conserved, and the bovine form differs from the human form by 11 of 140 amino acids (Abraham *et al.*, 1986a,b).

C. Oncogenes in the FGF Family

Various oncogenes are structurally related to FGF (Delli-Bovi *et al.*, 1987; Taira *et al.*, 1987; De Lapeyrière *et al.*, 1989; Dickson *et al.*, 1984; Dickson and Peters, 1987; Zhan *et al.*, 1988). These oncogenes are a diverse group and have been identified in Kaposi's sarcoma (*KS3* oncogene), human stomach cancer (*hst* oncogene), mouse mammary cancer (*int-2* oncogene), and bladder cancer (*FGF-5* oncogene). The *KS3* oncogene (Delli-Bovi *et al.*, 1987) appears to be the same as the *hst* oncogene, which was previously isolated from human stomach cancers and also from normal stomach tissue (Taira *et al.*, 1987). Both proteins encoded by the *hst* and *KS3* (also called *KS-FGF*) oncogenes contain 206 amino acids. Once properly aligned, the sequences of these oncogenes are about 45% identical with the sequence of bFGF and show less resemblance to the sequence of aFGF (Delli-Bovi *et al.*, 1987; Taira *et al.*, 1987). By screening genomic libraries with an *hst* probe at reduced stringency, a gene with strong homology with *hst* was also isolated (De Lapeyrière *et al.*, 1989) and named *FGF-6*.

The protein product of *int-2*, an oncogene that was originally detected in mouse mammary cancers caused by the mouse mammary tumor virus (Dickson *et al.*, 1984), also belongs to the FGF family. Although one substantial gap has to be introduced to maximize the alignment, it too resembles (with 46% homology) bFGF more closely than aFGF (Dickson and Peters, 1987). The *FGF-5* oncogene isolated from human bladder cancer cells (Zhan *et al.*, 1988) has a 44% sequence identity with bFGF, with a lesser degree of homology with aFGF.

These results are intriguing in view of findings that the FGFs not only stimulate the division of mesoderm- or neuroectoderm-derived cells, but are also potent angiogenic agents that foster the growth of new blood vessels (Gospodarowicz *et al.*, 1987). Such new blood vessel formation is essential if solid tumors are to develop to a significant size (Folkman, 1986; Folkman and Klagsbrun, 1987). Production of the FGFs or related proteins might therefore contribute to the development of solid cancers because of the proteins' effects on cell division and angiogenesis. There is also evidence implicating *int-2* as a developmental control gene (Jakobovits *et al.*, 1986). Complex patterns of accumulation of *int-2* RNA have been reported in embryonic and extraembryonic tissues that suggest multiple roles for *int-2* in development, which may include regulation of the migration of early mesoderm and induction of the otocyst (Wilkinson *et al.*, 1988). The precise functions of the genes that gave rise to the other FGF-related oncogenes are currently unknown.

III. Mesoderm Induction in Early Embryos

In early embryonic development the basic body plan arises because cells in different regions of the egg become programmed to follow different pathways (Nieuwkoop, 1969; Slack, 1983). During oogenesis, differences arise between the animal and vegetal halves of the eggs. Fertilization results in a subdivision of the vegetal half into a dorsovegetal and a ventrovegetal region. Mesoderm is then induced from the animal hemisphere by signal(s) originating from the vegetal region of the egg (Nieuwkoop, 1969; Slack, 1983; Smith and Slack, 1985). This induction is an instructive phenomenon that suppresses epidermal differentiation of cells from the animal pole and directs them instead to differentiate into mesodermal cells. Signals originating from the dorsovegetal region lead to the formation of dorsal-type mesoderm, mostly consisting of notochord and somites, while signals originating from the ventrovegetal region lead to the formation of ventral-type mesoderm that consists primarily of blood cells, mesenchyme, and mesothelium. It has been proposed that this process of regional specification arises from the action of inducing factors or morphogens (Smith *et al.*, 1985). Until recently, the chemical natures of developmental morphogens were unknown, because only minute amounts of the substances that cause mesodermal induction can be isolated from an early-stage embryo. However, agents that cause induction have been isolated from more abundant sources, such as late-stage chick embryo or guinea pig bone marrow, and have been characterized as 13,000 molecular weight polypeptides with basic p*I* (Tiedmann, 1982, Born *et al.*, 1972). An in-depth discussion of the role of morphogens in amphibian development is found in Chapter 9 of this volume.

In recent studies Slack and colleagues (1987) have investigated the possibility that bFGF mimics the effect of the ventrovegetal signal(s) responsible for the formation of ventral mesoderm. When explants of ectoderm cut from the animal pole of stage 8 *Xenopus* blastulae were exposed to bFGF, the cells differentiated into mesodermal structures, instead of differentiating into epidermis or remaining undifferentiated. At low concentrations of bFGF, the induced differentiation closely resembled ventral mesoderms formed by explants of ventrovegetal regions combined with animal poles. They consisted of concentric arrangements of loose mesenchyme, mesothelium, and blood cells within an epidermal jacket. At higher bFGF concentrations most of the explants contained significant numbers of muscle blocks. The inducing effect of bFGF seems to be highly specific, because it could not be mimicked by other growth factors, such as TGF-β; TGF-α; tumor necrosis factor (TNF); the interferons (IFN), IFN-γ or IFN-α; insulin; interleukin 1a or 1b; or the granulocyte or granulocyte–macrophage colony-stimulating factors.

These results have been confirmed and expanded by Kimelman and Kirschner (1987), who reported the presence of an mRNA encoding a protein highly homologous to bFGF in *Xenopus* embryos. FGF mRNA levels were high in the oocyte and dropped by 25-fold during oocyte maturation and then abruptly increased at the midblastula transition, which is a stage during which expression of vegetalizing factor would be expected. It was also reported that the relatively weak effect of bFGF on muscle formation observed earlier by Slack *et al.* (1987) could be potentiated by TGF-β1 (Kimelman and Kirschner, 1987). Interestingly, Weeks and Melton (1987) have also recently reported that a maternal mRNA called Vg1, which is localized to the vegetal hemisphere of frog eggs, encodes a member of the TGF-β family. More recently, Kimelman *et al.* (1988) isolated a cDNA clone present in the *Xenopus* oocyte and newly transcribed in the neurula stage of development. This mRNA encodes a 155-amino acid protein which is 84% identical to human bFGF. Immunoblots indicate that the oocyte and early embryo contain a store of FGF at a high enough concentration to induce mesoderm (Kimelman *et al.*, 1988). A similar conclusion was reached by Slack and Isaacs (1989), who purified a mesoderm-inducing activity in *Xenopus* embryos, eggs, or whole ovary which was neutralized by anti-bFGF antibodies. The concentration in the embryo of this bFGF-like mesoderm-inducing activity was estimated to be 7 ng/ml, which is sufficiently high for it to be active as an endogenous inducer of ventral mesoderm (Slack and Isaacs, 1989). In further studies, it was established that the appearance of FGF receptors closely parallel the developmental competence of animal pole cells to respond to FGF (Gillespie *et al.,* 1989). The mesoderm-inducing properties of bFGF are also shared by Int-2 and k-FGF: two oncogenes encoded growth factors related to bFGF (Paterno *et al.,* 1989).

Recent studies compared the effects of the two subclasses of TGF-β on muscle formation and it was found that TGF-β2 induces somites, while TGF-β1 does not (Rosa *et al.,* 1988). In addition, the inducing activity was present in conditioned medium from XTC cells, which is a cell line derived from *Xenopus* that was shown in earlier studies to induce animal caps to form various mesodermal derivatives (Smith, 1987). The XTC-mesoderm-inducing factor (XTC-MIF) activity can be specifically abolished by neutralizing anti-TGF-β2 antibodies and has been shown to be closely related to TGF-β2 (Smith *et al.,* 1988); Rosa *et al.,* 1988). This suggests that TGF-β2 could be the dorsovegetalizing factor, while FGF, which preferentially induced ventral mesoderm, could be the ventrovegetalizing factor.

The Xenopus homeobox gene xhox-3 is one of the first genes to be transcribed in the early embryo, and is expressed in a graded fashion along the anterior posterior axis in the axial mesoderm (Ruiz i Altaba and Melton, 1989a). This suggests that xhox-3 is involved in interpreting positional information in the axial mesoderm along the antero posterior axis. Studies by Ruiz i Altaba and Melton (1989b) have shown that high doses of bFGF increase xhox-3 mRNA, while high doses of XTC-MIF decrease it. This suggests that these agents, through their ability to modulate the expression of xhox-3, could induce a state that enables mesodermal cells to acquire a specific dorso ventral and antero posterior fate during gastrulation.

Therefore, bFGF can act as a differentiation factor in early embryos and instruct tissues destined to form ectodermal structures to differentiate into mesoderm instead. This is in close agreement with the results of previous studies of cells in culture which showed that FGF has a transforming activity and acts as a morphogen as well as a mitogen on practically all mesoderm-derived cells studied to date (Gospodarowicz *et al.,* 1987). Nevertheless, one cannot conclude that FGF will only induce the proliferation and differentiation of mesodermal and neuroectodermal cells, because a few of the cell types shown to respond to FGF are of ectodermal origin; these include lens (Gospodarowicz *et al.,* 1977a) and glial cells (Gospodarowicz *et al.,* 1987; Ferrara *et al.,* 1988; Morrison *et al.,* 1985; Pettmann *et al.,* 1985, Eccleston and Silberberg, 1985). In addition, ectodermal cells such as pituitary-derived follicular cells, although not FGF sensitive, are known to express the bFGF gene and to contain bioactive bFGF (Ferrara *et al.,* 1987).

IV. Muscle Formation in Early Embryos

The FGF levels in whole embryo and limb buds during chick development have been analyzed (Munaim *et al.*, 1988; Seed *et al.*, 1988). First detected in both the yolk and the white of unfertilized chick eggs, the level of FGF in the embryonic chick body is fairly constant from days 2–6. Thereafter, the level increases, so that by day 13, the embryo contains sevenfold more FGF than on days 2–6. In contrast, the level of FGF in the limb bud is higher than in the rest of the body until day 5, when it undergoes a transient decrease between days 5 and 7 (Seed *et al.*, 1988). It is tempting to speculate that there may be a correlation between the decrease in the FGF level observed during days 5–7 in the limb bud and the extensive myotube formation which occurs during this period (Marchok and Herrmann, 1967). Consistent with previous observations (Gospodarowicz *et al.*, 1976b) that FGF stimulates the proliferation of myoblasts and delays their differentiation, it was found that FGF delays the onset of differentiation of days 4–12 embryonic chick wing bud myoblasts (Seed and Hauschka, 1988). However, at an earlier stage (days 4–5), FGF seems to be required for the myogenic differentiation of myoblasts (Seed and Hauschka, 1988). The limited period during which FGF-dependent myoblasts are found in the limb bud suggests they may play a role in early muscle morphogenesis, and also suggests that FGF may affect muscle development differently during various phases of embryogenesis (Seed and Hauschka, 1988).

In some established myoblast cell lines, bFGF and aFGF can inhibit the synthesis of creatine phosphokinase or actin mRNA (Lathrop *et al.*, 1985a,b). These inhibitory effects of FGF on differentiation have been attributed to the ability of FGF to maintain myoblasts as fast-growing populations which would be prevented from entering into a stage of terminal differentiation (Wice *et al.*, 1987; Clegg *et al.*, 1987).

V. Development of the Nervous System

In view of the wide range of target cells for the FGFs, it is not so surprising that they affect nerve cells as well. Togari *et al.* (1983, 1985) first reported that bFGF acts as a differentiation factor for a rat pheochromocytoma (PC-12) cell line by inducing both neurite outgrowth and ornithine decarboxylase activity. Later, it was shown that aFGF has similar properties (Neufeld *et al.*, 1987a; Wagner and D'Amore, 1986). Similarly, bFGF can increase both the survival and neurite outgrowth of highly purified populations of fetal rat hippocampal neurons grown in well-defined, serum-free cell culture conditions (Walicke *et al.*, 1986). Furthermore, the addition of bFGF to cultured rat cerebral cortical neurons markedly enhances their survival and the elaboration of neurites (Morrison *et al.,* 1986). These results suggest that bFGF may function as a neurotropic agent in the central nervous system (CNS). In addition to its effects on CNS cholinergic neurons, bFGF has similar effects on two other defined CNS neuronal populations (i.e., dopaminergic and gabaergic neurons) when tested on fetal mesencephalic neurons in cell culture (Ferrari *et al.,* 1989). Growth factors that enhance survival and stimulate neurite outgrowth (nerve growth factor) or proliferation (insulinlike growth factor) of specific neuronal populations are discussed further in Chapter 6 of this volume.

Among other types of neurons shown to be responsive to FGF are embryonic chick ciliary ganglia neurons, in which bFGF can induce choline acetyltransferase activity and whose survival is enhanced by bFGF to a degree similar to that observed in response to the ciliary neurotrophic factor (Unsicker *et al.,* 1987). FGF also enhances the long-term survival of embryonic chick spinal cord neurons, including motor neurons that were identified *in vivo* by labeling with rhodamine isothiocyanate which was taken up into the cell body through the axon by retrograde transport (Unsicker *et al.,* 1987). In addition, nerve cells from the peripheral or central nervous system (Pettmann *et al.,* 1986; Janet *et al.,* 1988), as well as astrocytes (Ferrara *et al.,* 1988; Hatten *et al.,* 1988), contain bFGF. Neuroblasts that later express cholinergic differentiation proliferate in response to bFGF (Gensburger *et al.,* 1987). Therefore, bFGF is not only a morphogen for nerve cells, but a mitogen as well. All of these effects point toward a possible role for bFGFs in peripheral (PNS) and CNS development. Indeed, studies have shown that FGF promotes the survival of adult rat retinal ganglion cells *in vivo* after transection of the optic nerve (Seivers *et al.,* 1987) and protects adult sensory neurons from lesion-induced death (Otto *et al.,* 1987). In the CNS FGF prevents the death of cholinergic neurons in the medial septum and diagonal band of broca following transection of their axons (Anderson *et al.,* 1988). This indicates a possible role for FGF in the normal support of basal forebrain cholinergic neurons.

FGF could also have pronounced effects *in vivo* on CNS-derived astrocytes and oligodendrocyte proliferation and differentiation (Pettmann *et al.,* 1985; Morrison *et al.,* 1985; Eccleston and Silberberg, 1985) by influencing their properties during normal development or their responses to specific pathogenic events. In turn, astroglial cells, which are known to synthesize FGF (Ferrara *et al.,* 1988), could be an endogenous source of FGF for the stimulation of cerebellar granule neurons and other neuronal cell populations. As well as nerve cells, chromaffin cells respond to bFGF by undergoing neuronal differentiation and cell proliferation and becoming NGF dependent (Stemple *et al.,* 1988). Claude *et al.* (1988) have reported similar effects of aFGF on chromaffin cells. FGF has been reported to induce the neural specific gene *SCG-10* (Stein *et al.*, 1988), which is also induced in the neuronal cell line PC-12 by nerve growth factor (Leonard *et al.*, 1987). bFGF has also been reported to be a survival factor, both *in vivo* and *in vitro,* for neural crest derived nonneuronal cells during the early stage of development of sensory ganglia (Kalcheim 1989).

In addition to its effects on nerve and glial cells, bFGF could influence PNS and CNS development through its angiogenic properties. The early anlagen of the mesencephalon and telencephalon do not contain blood vessels, but are surrounded by a primitive perineural vascular plexus (Evans, 1909) from which vascular sprouts radially penetrate into the neural tissue at a defined time in development. In the chick this takes place around day 4 of embryonic development and correlates well with the onset of neuroectodermal proliferation. It has been suggested that brain-derived FGF could be responsible for this capillary ingrowth *in vivo* (Risau, 1986). In the embryonic chick brain FGF-like activity is present in mesencephalic and telencephalic brain structures from day 3 to day 18 of embryonic development, and the activity increases up to 700-fold in parallel with the increase in neural tissue mass until days 14–16, when the activity reaches a plateau (Risau, 1986). This change in FGF-like activity correlates with the ingrowth of stem vessels into the brain.

VI. Possible Role of FGF in Cartilage and Bone Formation

In tissues such as cartilage bFGF has been reported to promote chondrossification (Jentzch *et al.*, 1980), and its presence in bone matrix indicates that it plays a role in the development and growth of osseous tissue (Hauschka *et al.*, 1986). However, studies on the effect of FGF on bone formation and chondrossification *in vivo* have been limited and most of our knowledge is derived from experiments with cultured cells.

With cultured chondrocytes bFGF can act as both a mitogen (Gospodarowicz *et al.*, 1977b) and a morphogen (Kato and Gospodarowicz, 1985a,b). While costal chondrocytes grown in the absence of bFGF soon assume a fibroblast appearance and lose their ability to synthesize and release chondroitin sulfate proteoglycans and collagen type II, the same cells grown in the presence of bFGF retain these capabilities and at confluence become embedded in a thick extracellular matrix (ECM) that has all of the characteristics of the ECM present in cartilage (Kato and Gospodarowicz, 1985a,b). Interestingly, these cells will express their chondrocyte phenotype only if exposed to bFGF when dividing actively; when added to confluent layers of dedifferentiated and resting chondrocytes, bFGF can no longer reverse its phenotype (Kato and Gospodarowicz, 1985a). In addition, cartilage tissues are known to express the bFGF gene and to contain bioactive bFGF (Lobb *et al.*, 1986). Therefore, bFGF may be an autocrine growth factor for chondrocytes *in vivo*.

Both bFGF and aFGF are mitogenic for bone cells (Globus *et al.*, 1988; Rodan *et al.*, 1987; Canalis *et al.*, 1988). The effect of bFGF is potentiated by TGF-β, which has a minimal effect by itself (Globus *et al.*, 1988). bFGF can also influence the bone cell phenotype because it increases the osteocalcin content of the cell (Canalis *et al.*, 1988; Rodan *et al.*, 1987) and decreases alkaline phosphatase activity and collagen production (Globus *et al.*, 1988). As expected from previous reports showing that mineralized bone matrix contains both aFGF and bFGF, osteoblasts are capable of producing both mitogens and were found to produce tenfold more bFGF than aFGF when analyzed by specific and sensitive radioimmunoassays (Globus *et al.*, 1989). The bone cell-derived bFGF is stored in an active form in the ECM. This observation suggests that bone-derived bFGF may function as an autocrine or paracrine mitogen via its deposition into the bone ECM (Globus *et al.*, 1989).

VII. Limb Regeneration

Certain amphibian species have a well-developed capacity to regenerate lost appendages. The dependence of limb regeneration on nerves was reported as early as 1823 (Todd, 1823) and the observations made by Singer (1974) have clarified and extended the concept of neurotrophic control in this process. Denervation of an adult newt limb at the time of amputation or prior to the formation of the regeneration blastema effectively blocks the regeneration process. However, if denervation is delayed until after a blastema has formed, then differentiation of the blastema cells and morphogenesis of new limb parts occur despite the lack of nerves (Powell, 1969; Singer and Craven, 1948). This finding implies that the neurotrophic effect is needed for the initial cell proliferation involved in blastema formation, but not for the later events of regeneration, which include differentiation of blastema cells into muscle, cartilage, and other tissues of the new limb. The molecular basis of neurotrophic phenomena is poorly understood, but the available evidence suggests that such control is mediated by means of neurosecretion product(s) not related to nerve impulses of neurotransmitters (Dresden, 1969; Gutmann, 1976).

Blastema cells are thought to originate from either dedifferentiating myoblasts or chondrocytes (Hay, 1974), two cell types for which FGF has been shown to be a potent mitogen (Gospodarowicz *et al.*, 1976b, 1978b,c; Gospodarowicz and Mescher, 1977). Infusion of FGF promotes the resumption of mitotic activity in denervated newt forelimb blastemas (Mescher and Gospodarowicz, 1979), and is as effective as an optimal dose of brain extract in promoting [^{3}H]thymidine incorporation (Mescher and Loh, 1981), [^{14}C]amino acid incorporation, and mitotic activity (Carlone and Foret, 1979). bFGF has also been shown to maintain total acetylcholinesterase activity in cultured newt triceps muscle above that in untreated contralateral controls when measured after 1 week (Carlone *et al.*, 1981). It has also been reported (Gospodarowicz *et al.*, 1975) that administration of FGF promotes heterotrophic growth of amputated adult frog (*Rana pipiens*) forelimbs comparable to that observed by others after surgical augmentation of the nerve supply (Singer, 1954).

Two other groups of investigators have identified "trophic" factors with chemical properties similar to those reported for FGF. Jennings *et al.* (1979) reported purification of a mitogenic polypeptide with a p*I* of 9.5–9.8 and a molecular weight of 11,000 from neonatal calf spinal cord. A similar basic protein (13,500 molecular weight) which stimulates protein synthesis in cultured regeneration blastemas has been partially purified from embryonic chick brain by Choo *et al.* (1981). The exact relationship of these proteins to FGF remains to be determined.

Also intriguing is the relationship between FGF and glial growth factor (GGF) (Gospodarowicz *et al.*, 1987). GGF has a basic p*I* and an apparent molecular weight of 31,000 and has been purified from pituitary and brain tissue (Brockes, 1984, 1987) using a purification scheme similar to that developed for bFGF. GGF has been shown to play a role in nerve-dependent proliferation in the blastema (Brockes and Kintner, 1986), but a lack of its structural characterization prevents the establishment of its possible structural relationship (if any) with bFGF. Because GGF was mitogenic for Schwann cells, while bFGF was believed not to be, the former was at first claimed to be distinct from bFGF on the basis of its biological properties. Recent data have, however, established that bFGF is mitogenic for Schwann cells (Eccleston *et al.*, 1987; Ratner *et al.*, 1988).

VIII. Ovarian Follicular Morphogenesis

A. Granulosa Cell Proliferation and Differentiation

The ovarian follicle is one of the most rapidly proliferating normal tissues *in vivo*. Granulosa cell proliferation accounts for the majority of follicular growth (Gougeon, 1982). Previous studies have shown that bFGF is mitogenic for granulosa cells maintained in culture (Gospodarowicz *et al.*, 1977b) and delays their terminal differentiation (Gospodarowicz and Bialecki, 1978). This is likely to reflect the ability of bFGF to keep granulosa cells actively cycling (Gospodarowicz and Bialecki, 1978), thereby preventing them from entering the G_0 phase. bFGF could therefore play a role in the initiation of follicular morphogenesis by controlling the growth of granulosa cells in ovarian follicles prior to their preantral stage, when hormonal control would take over (Savion and Gospodarowicz, 1980). At the same time that FGF acts as an autocrine growth factor for granulosa cells, it could also regulate their metabolic activity by controlling the release of cellular products into the liquor folliculi and regulating the delivery of nutrients to oocytes (Savion and Gospodarowicz, 1980). The ability of FGF to act as an autocrine growth factor and as a morphogen for granulosa cells can be influenced by TGF-β which is produced by theca cells (Skinner *et al.*, 1986) and which can positively or negatively modulate the biological activity of FGF, depending on the conditions and environment of the cells. This interplay between FGF and TGF-β could explain, in part, the developmental coordination of the various tissues present within preantral follicles.

B. Interaction with Other Hormones and Growth Factors

In addition to affecting the proliferation and differentiation of granulosa cells, bFGF also influences their hormonal response by inhibiting the follicle-stimulating hormone (FSH)-mediated induction of the luteinizing hormone receptor (Mondschein and Schomberg, 1981), reversibly attenuating the FSH-induced aromatase activity (Mondschein and Schomberg, 1981; Adashi *et al.*, 1988), and stimulating progesterone biosynthesis (Baird and Hsueh, 1986). This suggests that FGF may play an inhibitory cytodifferentiative role in the ontogeny of granulosa cells. The capacity of FGF to interrupt a specific steroidogenic pathway (i.e., estrogen formation) in granulosa cells and promote another (i.e., progesterone formation) might be linked to the hormonal events that precede corpus luteum formation and follicular development.

TGF-β regulates FSH-induced aromatase activity (Adashi and Resnick, 1986) in a mode diametrically opposed to bFGF. Thus, the presence of TGF-β, produced by theca cells (Skinner *et al.*, 1986), in the microenvironment of granulosa cells could modulate the effects of FGF. Steroid production could therefore be finely controlled by the ratio of TGF-β to FGF, expressed by the theca and granulosa cells, respectively, during follicular development.

C. Ovulation

At the time of ovulation, extensive degradation of the follicular wall is necessary for the ovum to escape from the Graafian follicle. A specific biochemical mechanism for ovulation has been proposed (Beers *et al.*, 1979). According to this hypothesis, plasminogen activator (PA) is responsible for disruption of the follicle. bFGF is among the growth factors known to stimulate protease and collagenase activity in responsive cells. Although these activities have not yet been studied using granulosa cell cultures, FGF stimulates production of PA and collagenase and decreases the production of a PA inhibitor by vascular endothelial cells and various tumor cells (Montesano *et al.*, 1986; Saksela *et al.*, 1987). TGF-β influences PA expression induced by bFGF and can inhibit the production of secreted proteases as well as increase the production of a protease inhibitor (Saksela *et al.*, 1987; Thalacker and Nilsen-Hamilton, 1987). Since both TGF-β and bFGF are present in ovarian follicles, one could speculate that these factors could ultimately play a role in modulating PA activity as well as that of other proteolytic enzymes and collagenase, which plays an important role in the extensive degradation of the follicular wall at the time of ovulation.

D. Development of the Corpus Luteum

Through its angiogenic properties, bFGF could also be an important regulator in the early phase of corpus luteum development, when angiogenesis plays a critical role. This is discussed further in Section IX,D,2.

IX. Vascular Development

A. Vascular Endothelial Cell Proliferation

1. FGF Requirement

As early as 1976, it was reported that bFGF was a potent mitogen for vascular endothelial cells derived from large vessels (Gospodarowicz, 1976). This effect was first described with vascular endothelial cells derived from bovine fetal aortic arch, or from fetal endocardium, bovine umbilical vein, and calf aortic arch (Gospodarowicz *et al.*, 1978b). The ability of FGF to act as a survival agent when cells were maintained at clonal density allowed the establishment of the first clonal vascular endothelial cell strains, which were strongly dependent on FGF (Gospodarowicz *et al.*, 1976a, 1978b) and exhibited increased life spans when maintained in its presence (Gospodarowicz *et al.*, 1978b). In 1978 it was reported that bFGF was mitogenic for human umbilical vascular endothelial cells (Gospodarowicz *et al.*, 1978a). These cells, in contrast to their bovine counterparts, are also sensitive to epidermal growth factor (EGF) (Gospodarowicz *et al.,* 1978a). The proliferative effect caused by either EGF or FGF could be potentiated by thrombin (Gospodarowicz *et al.,* 1978a).

The response of capillary-derived endothelial cells to FGF is identical to that of endothelial cells derived from large vessels (Gospodarowicz *et al.,* 1986c,d). The discovery of the proliferative response of endothelial cells to FGF has led to the long-term establishment in culture of vascular endothelial cell strains derived from the microvasculature of various organs as different as testis, fetal ovarian cortex, corpus luteum, adrenal cortex, brain, lung, thymus, and retina (Gospodarowicz *et al.,* 1987).

aFGF has much of the same effect as its basic counterpart. This reflects the interaction of both mitogens with the same cell surface receptor (Neufeld and Gospodarowicz, 1986). Interestingly, they differ by their potency, which, for aFGF, can be 30- to 100-fold less than that of bFGF, depending on the endothelial cell strain (Gospodarowicz *et al.,* 1986c,d).

2. Other Growth Requirements

Growth factors require progression factors in order to support cell proliferation. In the case of vascular endothelial cells, the mitogenic effect of FGF was reported to depend on the serum or plasma concentration to which the cells were exposed (Gospodarowicz, 1976). This suggests that progression factors present in plasma or serum complement the biological effects of FGF and that therefore, by limiting the concentrations of the progression factors, one could limit the effect of FGF even at its optimally effective concentration. In 1980 it was reported that these progression factors were transferrin and high-density lipoproteins (HDLs) (Tauber *et al.,* 1980). In their presence bovine vascular endothelial cells exposed to FGF can be serially passaged under serum-free conditions and exhibit all of the properties of counterpart cultures passaged in the presence of serum (Tauber *et al.,* 1981).

The requirement for transferrin is related to the fact that iron is an essential requirement for the enzyme ribonucleotide reductase, whose activity in turn is strongly related to the rate of DNA synthesis and is greatly increased during the S phase of the cell cycle (Thelander and Reichard, 1979). The requirement for HDLs was shown in later studies to be related to its ability to stimulate the cellular enzyme HMG hydroxymethylglutaryl–coenzyme A reductase (Cohen *et al.,* 1982a,b; reviewed by Gospodarowicz *et al.,* 1982), which results in increased mevalonate synthesis. The mevalonate is used for the synthesis of isopentenyl adenosine, ubiquinone, dolichols, and yet unidentified isoprenoid pyrophosphate compounds. Recent evidence suggests that cultured cells incorporate these unidentified isoprenoid groups into unique proteins that could play an important role in the maintenance of cell shape as well as in DNA synthesis (Schnitzer-Polokoff *et al.*, 1982; Sinensky and Logel, 1985). Thus, it is clear that changes in the synthesis of isoprenoid compounds could have an impact on cellular metabolism at many different levels. In addition to its ability to activate HMG CoA reductase, HDLs may also support cell growth by providing choline and fatty acids (Cohen and Gospodarowicz, 1985).

3. Factors That Modulate FGF-Stimulated Proliferation

Among the agents that modulate the mitogenic effect of FGF on vascular endothelial cells are heparin, TGF-β, TNF, and IFN-γ.

a. Heparin. Heparin and its closely related glycosaminoglycan, heparan sulfate, have both negative and positive effects on cell growth, depending on the cell type tested. Heparin potentiates by 100-fold the mitogenic activity of aFGF when tested on human umbilical endothelial cells (Gospodarowicz *et al.*, 1986c) and in this way makes aFGF as potent as bFGF. The ability of heparin to potentiate the mitogenic effect of aFGF on these cells could reflect its ability to stabilize the tertiary structure of aFGF. It also reflects the lack of a direct growth-inhibitory effect of heparin on that cell type. However, when cells are growth-inhibited by heparin, such as in the case of capillary endothelial cells, heparin does not potentiate the mitogenic effect of aFGF (Gospodarowicz *et al.*, 1986c). Instead, strong inhibitory effects are observed that probably reflect a direct effect of heparin on cell metabolism.

Heparin protects bFGF and aFGF from acid or heat inactivation (Gospodarowicz and Cheng, 1986), as well as from proteolytic degradation (Saksela *et al.*, 1988). It has been proposed that the inherent lability of bFGF or aFGF to denaturing conditions could originate in the fact that none of the cysteine residues identified in their primary sequence (Gautschi-Sovi *et al.*, 1986) participates in disulfide bridging. Because bFGF and aFGF have extremely high affinities for heparin, one could speculate that, at a physiological salt concentration, one molecule of glycosaminoglycan could bind to the two heparin binding domains of FGF; this would result in cyclization of the FGF molecule and would stabilize its tertiary structure, thus making it both heat and acid resistant (Gospodarowicz and Cheng, 1986). The protective effect of heparin on the biological activity of FGF could have physiological significance. In previous studies it has been shown that, even at 37°C and at neutral pHs, the half-life of FGF *in vitro* when incubated in tissue culture medium and in the absence of cells was only 24 hours (Westall *et al.*, 1983). Interaction of heparin or heparan sulfate with aFGF or bFGF should therefore greatly extend its biological half-life as it has been shown to do (Flaurmenhaft *et al.*, 1989).

When bFGF is bound to either heparin or heparan sulfate, it is also protected against degradation by trypsin or plasmin (Saksela *et al.*, 1988). Heparin has also been shown to protect aFGF from plasmin degradation (Sommer and Rifkin, 1989). Heparin interaction may be important in stabilizing bFGF to proteases generated during wound healing and tumor growth, processes in which bFGF may play a role (Saksela *et al.*, 1988; Sommer and Rifkin, 1989).

b. TGF-β. Depending on the cell type, TGF-β can either inhibit or potentiate FGF activity. This reflects the multifunctional properties of TGF-β, which has been shown to both inhibit and stimulate cell proliferation or differentiation (Sporn *et al.*, 1986). In the case of vascular endothelial cells, TGF-β is a potent inhibitor of the actions of both bFGF and aFGF (Fràter-Schröder *et al.*, 1986; Baird and Durkin, 1986). This effect is both dose dependent and characteristic of a noncompetitive interaction. These observations of cells in culture contrast with reports that TGF-β has angiogenic properties *in vivo* (Roberts *et al.*, 1986). This latter response could, however, be an indirect effect of TGF-β, due to induced fibrosis as well as to the chemotactic effect of TGF-β on human peripheral blood monocytes (Wahl *et al.*, 1987), which may subsequently release their own angiogenic factors, among which is bFGF (Baird *et al.*, 1985a). The above studies, which demonstrate that TGF-β and FGF can interact at the cellular level to modulate vascular endothelial cell growth, also suggest that many of the biological activities of FGF observed in cell culture and *in vivo* may be regulated by the presence of TGF-β and related proteins in the local cellular milieu.

c. TNF. TNF is known to induce hemorrhagic necrosis of solid tumors. When tested on capillary endothelial cells, TNF inhibited the proliferation of cells exposed to serum alone but was not cytotoxic. In contrast, when added to cells stimulated by bFGF, TNF had a considerable cytotoxic effect in addition to arresting growth (Schweigerer *et al.*, 1987a; Fráter-Schröder *et al.*, 1987). The inhibitory and cytotoxic effect of TNF on cultured capillary endothelial cells stimulated to proliferate by FGF contrasts with its angiogenic properties *in vivo* (Fràter-Schröder *et al.*, 1987). These, however, may be due to the ability of TNF to act as a chemoattractant for leukocytes, as reflected by the inflammatory response that is seen in the cornea after implantation of a source of TNF (Fràter-Schröder et al., 1987). The susceptibility of proliferating, tumor-associated cells versus the relative resistance of normal, nonproliferating capillary endothelial cells toward the cytotoxic effect of TNF might allow the selective, hemorrhagic necrosis of tumor capillaries. This would provide an effective means to control tumor angiogenesis and eventually to inhibit further tumor growth.

d. IFNs. IFN also inhibits the proliferative response of vascular endothelial cells to aFGF (Friesel *et al.*, 1987). This is in agreement with previous studies which showed that IFN-γ is a potent antiproliferative agent for normal and transformed cells in culture (Ucer *et al.*, 1985). Interestingly, FGF has been reported to stimulate IFN-γ production (Johnson and Torres, 1985). This suggests that IFN-γ could regulate the proliferation of bFGF-sensitive cells in an autocrine fashion.

4. Expression of FGF by Endothelial Cells

Vascular endothelial cells express the bFGF gene and produce bioactive bFGF (Schweigerer *et al.*, 1987b; Moscatelli *et al.*, 1986; Vlodavsky *et al.*, 1987b). In contrast, these cells do not express the aFGF gene, nor do they produce bioactive aFGF (Schweigerer *et al.*, 1987b; Winkles *et al.*, 1987). Therefore, bFGF, but not aFGF, can act as an autocrine growth factor for capillary endothelial cells and might contribute to the formation of new capillaries. Recent studies have confirmed the autocrine activities of bFGF in vascular endothelial cells. Sato and Rifkin (1988), using neutralizing antibodies against bFGF, were able to block movement, PA synthesis, and DNA synthesis in vascular endothelial cells. Using similar antibodies, Sakaguchi *et al.* (1988) were able to block the basal proliferation of vascular endothelial cells exposed to serum alone. These results suggest that the endothelial cells proliferated in response to bFGF produced by themselves rather than in response to a serum-derived growth factor.

B. Vascular Endothelial Cell Differentiation

FGF was the first growth factor shown to be both a mitogen and a morphogen (Gospodarowicz *et al.*, 1979b). Until then, it was widely believed that both effects were mutually exclusive. The morphogenetic effects of FGF were first described in vascular endothelial cells (Vlodavsky and Gospodarowicz, 1979; Vlodavsky *et al.*, 1979).

1. Morphology and ECM of FGF-Treated Cells

Upon reaching confluency, vascular endothelial cells grown in the presence of FGF adopt the morphology of a cell monolayer composed of tightly packed, flattened cells. As in the vascular endothelium *in vivo*, this cell layer has a polarity of cell surfaces, with a nonthrombogenic apical cell surface and a basal cell surface involved in the synthesis of a highly thrombogenic ECM. When examined by immunofluorescence, this ECM is composed in part of collagen types III and IV (Vlodarsky *et al.*, 1979; Vlodavsky and Gospodarowicz, 1979; Gospodarowicz *et al.*, 1979b). The results of chemical analysis of collagens produced by cultures of bovine vascular endothelial cells that were grown and maintained in the presence of FGF (conditions under which the cells express their normal phenotype and proliferate actively) showed that they synthesize primarily interstitial collagen type III and basement membrane collagen type IV and type V at a ratio of 10 : 1 : 3 (Vlodavsky and Gospodarowicz, 1979; Gospodarowicz *et al.*, 1979b; Tseng *et al.*, 1982). Two glycoproteins involved in cell adhesion, laminin and fibronectin, are also associated with the ECM produced by vascular endothelial cells. While fibronectin is associated with both apical and basal cell surfaces as well in regions of cell–cell contact in actively growing cells, a dramatic redistribution of the cell surface-associated population of this glycoprotein occurs when the cells reach confluence: Disappearing from the apical cell surface, fibronectin preferentially accumulates in close association with the basal cell surface, where it becomes an integral component of the ECM (Birdwell *et al.*, 1978; Gospodarowicz *et al.*, 1979b). In parallel with the redistribution of fibronectin, the appearance of a new cell surface protein, CSP-60, can also be observed (Vlodavsky and Gospodarowicz, 1979; Gospodarowicz *et al.*, 1979b) as the cells reorganize into a nonoverlapping cell monolayer.

2. Morphology and ECM of FGF-Deprived Cells

In contrast to cultures grown in the presence of FGF, vascular endothelial cells that were maintained in its absence and passaged at low cell density lost, within three passages, their ability to form at confluence a monolayer of closely apposed, flattened cells. Instead, the cultures adopted a multilayer configuration consisting of large, overlapping cells that were no longer contact-inhibited (Vlodavsky *et al.*, 1979). Parallel to these changes in cell morphology, a loss of cell surface polarity was observed. Both the apical and the basal cell surfaces became covered with an ECM that strongly reacted when analyzed by immunofluorescence with purified antibodies against collagen types I, III, and IV (Gospodarowicz *et al.*, 1979b; Vlodavsky *et al.*, 1979). The biochemical analysis of the collagens produced by such cultures indicates that cells have increased their rate of collagen production twofold and synthesize predominantly collagen types I and III, but also make basement membrane collagen types IV and V. The ratio of collagen types I : III : IV : V was 3 : 7 : 0.1 : 1.5 (Gospodarowicz *et al.*, 1979b; Vlodavsky *et al.*, 1979; Tseng *et al.*, 1982). The appearance of an ECM on the apical surface of endothelial cells grown in the absence of FGF correlates with their loss of nonthrombogenic properties, which is reflected by their newly acquired ability to bind platelets (Gospodarowicz *et al.*, 1979b; Vlodavsky *et al.*, 1979). Similarly, marked changes in the distribution and the appearance of cell surface proteins such as fibronectin and CSP-60 can also be observed in vascular endothelial cells cultured without FGF: CSP-60 does not appear on the surfaces of the cells, even at late confluence (Vlodavsky and Gospodarowicz, 1979; Vlodavsky *et al.*, 1979). Fibronectin, which is detected only in the basal cell surface of confluent, highly organized cultures grown in the presence of FGF, is present on both basal and apical cell surfaces of cells grown in its absence (Vlodavsky *et al.*, 1979).

On the basis of the results just described that used immunoprecipitation to detect specific proteins, it was calculated that sparse or confluent cultures maintained in the absence of FGF secreted 30- and 50-fold more fibronectin per cell into the medium than did sparse or confluent cells grown in the presence of FGF (Vlodavsky *et al.*, 1979; Gospodarowicz *et al.*, 1979b). Thus, vascular endothelial cells maintained in the absence of FGF exhibit, in addition to a much slower growth rate, morphological as well as structural alterations that mostly involve changes in the composition and the distribution of the ECM (Greenburg *et al.*, 1980). These changes result in a loss of phenotypic expression, because, in the absence of FGF, cells are not contact-inhibited and develop a thrombogenic apical cell surface. In contrast, vascular endothelial cell cultures, previously maintained without FGF, will regain their characteristic phenotypic expression if reexposed to it in sparse or subconfluent cultures. However, highly confluent cultures that exhibit altered phenotypes due to FGF deprivation showed no response to the addition of FGF (Vlodavsky *et al.*, 1979; Greenburg *et al.*, 1980). It could therefore be concluded that the addition of FGF to growing cultures of vascular endothelial cells stabilizes their phenotypic expression. FGF can also participate in ECM remodeling through its ability to increase PA and collagenase activity while decreasing PA inhibitor synthesis and to repress collagen type I and fibronectin expression while enhancing collagen type III and type IV expression. This results from the ability of FGF to control the expression of various ECM components at the pre- and posttranslational levels. More discussion of the ability of growth factors to regulate the expression of ECM components can be found in Chapters 4, 7, and 8 of this volume.

3. Cellular Processes Characteristic of Angiogenesis

bFGF can stimulate processes that are characteristic of angiogenesis *in vivo;* these include endothelial cell migration, invasion, and PA production. For example, it causes capillary-derived endothelial cells to invade a three-dimensional collagen matrix and promotes their organization into tubules that resemble vascular capillaries (Montesano *et al.,* 1986). Concomitantly, bFGF stimulates vascular endothelial cells to produce PA, a protease that has been implicated in the breakdown of the microvascular basement membrane during the formation of new capillaries. TGF-β, which has been reported to be growth inhibitory for vascular endothelial cells (Fràter-Schröder *et al.,* 1986; Baird and Durkin, 1986), also inhibits bFGF-induced motility of vascular endothelial cells in collagen matrices (Muller *et al.,* 1987), the FGF-dependent increase in PA (Saksela *et al.,* 1987), and the induction of angiogenesis by FGF in cell culture (Muller *et al.,* 1987).

C. FGF Expression in Other Cellular Components of the Vascular Tree

Because bFGF is present in capillary endothelial cells for which it acts as an autocrine growth factor as well as a morphogen, it could be involved in the development of the vascular tree. Recent studies have shown that bFGF is also present in other cellular elements of the vascular tree, the vascular smooth muscle (VSM) cells that express the bFGF gene and contain bioactive bFGF (Gospodarowicz *et al.,* 1988). A similar observation was made in the case of pericytes (unpublished observations). On the basis of sensitive and specific bioassays for bFGF and aFGF, it was concluded that, although bioactive aFGF is present in VSM cells, it accounts for only 5% of the cellular FGF, whereas 95% of the VSM FGF activity is accounted for by bFGF (Gospodarowicz, 1990). This contrasts with an earlier report by Winkles *et al.* (1987) which inferred that most, if not all, of the bioactivity present in VSM cells could be accounted for by aFGF. However, that conclusion was reached on the basis of radioimmunoassays and radioreceptor assays which did not distinguish between the basic and acidic forms of FGF. Therefore, as in capillary endothelial cells, which do not express the aFGF gene, bFGF seems to be the main autocrine growth factor of VSM cells.

D. Angiogenic Activity of FGF *in Vivo*

The formation of new blood vessels (angiogenesis) is required for a wide range of developmentally regulated processes that occur in the embryo, as well as for the remodeling of tissue in the neonate or the adult. It is also a key feature in pathological situations such as in the development of dormant solid tumors, when capillary invasion is a prerequisite for their further growth (Folkman and Cotran, 1976). A crucial step in the sequence of events that leads to the angiogenic response is the invasion of the perivascular ECM by sprouting capillary endothelial cells. The process includes increased endothelial cell migration, proliferation, and production of enzymes capable of modifying the ECM. Recently, it has become clear that, among the growth factors presently identified, bFGF and aFGF could be the angiogenic factors that control capillary endothelial cell proliferation during organogenesis and tumor progression (Folkman and Cotran, 1976).

bFGF is a potent angiogenic factor when tested by *in vivo* assays as different as the rabbit cornea, the chick chorioallantoic membrane, and the hamster cheek pouch assays (Gospodarowicz *et al.*, 1978c, 1987). aFGF, although less potent than the basic form, has also been shown to be angiogenic in the chorioallantoic membrane and the rabbit cornea assays (Thomas *et al.*, 1985). The presence of bFGF as the predominant mitogen in the corpus luteum (Gospodarowicz *et al.*, 1985), adrenal gland (Gospodarowicz *et al.*, 1986e), kidney (Baird *et al.*, 1985c), and retina (Baird *et al.*, 1985b) correlates extremely well with the strong angiogenic properties of these organs (Gospodarowicz *et al.*, 1986a, 1987).

1. Kidney

The case of the kidney, in which bFGF has been identified as the mitogen that accounts for the full mitogenic as well as angiogenic potential of crude extracts (Baird *et al.*, 1985c), is perhaps one of the most interesting because it suggests that the appearance of bFGF could be developmentally regulated. Embryonic kidneys strongly stimulate angiogenesis (Ekblom *et al.*, 1982; Sariola *et al.*, 1983), and the formation of kidney capillaries is developmentally regulated. Kidney differentiation is driven by interactions between cells of a different developmental history. The epithelial ureter bud induces differentiation of the mesenchyme, and this in turn leads to stimulation of blood vessels. The mesenchyme can be induced to differentiate in culture, and the mesenchymes thus induced stimulate neovascularization on the chorioalloantoic membrane (Ekblom *et al.*, 1982; Sariola *et al.*, 1983). These results suggest that the blood vessels of the embryonic kidney are of exogenous origin (Sariola *et al.*, 1984). Recently, Risau and Ekblom (1986) have described the presence of angiogenesis factors in embryonic kidney which, by their behavior on heparin–Sepharose affinity columns, could be related to bFGF and aFGF. Since the invasion by capillaries of embryonic kidneys is both temporally and spatially associated with the formation of peritubular mesenchymal aggregates, it is possible that the expression of FGF within these epithelial structures could be controlled by factors from the epithelial ureter bud that induce differentiation of the mesenchyme (Grobstein, 1956). This in turn would lead to a stimulation of blood vessel invasion (Sariola *et al.*, 1983; Preminger *et al.*, 1980).

2. Ovary

Another case in which the angiogenic activity of bFGF could be relevant is ovarian tissue. The activities that are required for follicular development and selection include angiogenesis, the release of PA, and the proliferation of granulosa cells (Ny *et al.*, 1985; Hsueh *et al.*, 1984). Each of these biological activities is also regulated by FGF (Gospodarowicz *et al.*, 1977b, 1985; Montesano *et al.*, 1986). The abilities of granulosa cells to express the bFGF gene and to produce bioactive bFGF suggest that this factor could act as an autocrine regulator of their growth (Neufeld *et al.*, 1987b) and differentiation.

Extremely rapid and radical vascular changes take place in the capillary wreath surrounding the follicle at the time of ovulation. The previously avascular granulosa cell layers are invaded by numerous, rapidly proliferating capillaries (Bassett, 1943). Rabbit luteinizing granulosa and luteal cells produce a diffusible substance that triggers the early vascular changes that occur during development of the corpus luteum and elicits a strong angiogenic response on the part of the host (Gospodarowicz and Thakral, 1978). bFGF, which is present in granulosa cells (Neufeld *et al.*, 1987b), accounts for the full mitogenic potential of corpus luteum crude extract (Gospodarowicz *et al.*, 1985) and is mitogenic for corpus luteum-derived capillary endothelial cells (Gospodarowicz *et al.*, 1986c). Therefore, bFGF could be responsible for the angiogenic activity observed in the developing corpus luteum. Here again, TGF-β could play a significant role in modulating the angiogenic activity of FGF, because it is a potent inhibitor of bFGF-stimulated vascular endothelial cell proliferation (Fràter-Schröder *et al.*, 1986; Baird and Durkin, 1986) and blocks FGF-induced angiogenesis in cultured cells (Muller *et al.*, 1987).

3. Tumors

FGF can also be implicated in the angiogenic infiltration of solid tumors (Folkman and Klagsbrun, 1987). An account of the various cell types on which bFGF acts suggests that this growth factor is an important agent in tumor progression. By increasing capillary endothelial cell proliferation, bFGF could be responsible for the increased vascular supply which delivers O_2 and nutrients and removes waste products from actively growing tumors. bFGF could also act on the tumor cell itself. By increasing the secreted levels of various proteases, bFGF could facilitate the metastatic process and tumor invasion. For example, the expression of cathepsin L (also called major excreted protein), which is regulated by FGF (Nilsen-Hamilton *et al.*, 1981), is correlated with the metastatic potential of tumor cells (Denhardt *et al.*, 1987). More discussion of cathepsin L and other proteases and their participation in cellular invasion can be found in Chapters 7 and 8 of this volume. As well as enabling cellular invasion in the development and metastasis of tumor cells, bFGF could also act as a mitogen for tumor cells (Gospodarowicz *et al.*, 1987), as it does for embryo-derived cells.

4. Angiogenic Factors Other Than FGF

The existence of angiogenic factors other than FGF that could complement the action of FGF is suggested by two types of evidence. First, FGF lacks a recognizable hydrophobic signal sequence that governs secretion (Abraham *et al.*, 1986a,b; Jaye *et al.*, 1986) and thus it is not clear whether FGF is secreted, and if so, how. However, it is expected that an angiogenic factor should be a diffusible secreted substance that induces new capillary formation from a microcirculatory bed. Second, FGF is produced by endothelial cells themselves (Schweigerer *et al.*, 1987b, 1988). If FGF is normally present in and around endothelial cells and yet the cells remain quiescent, then other factors must come into play to trigger angiogenesis. Such factors have recently been isolated and characterized by our group (Plouet et al., 1989; Gospodarowicz *et al.*, 1989; Tischer *et al.*, 1989).

X. The Extracellular Matrix

It was first reported in 1980 that for cells sensitive to this mitogen the bFGF requirement could be satisfied by an ECM produced by bovine corneal endothelial cells (Gospodarowicz and Tauber, 1980). Cells maintained on this ECM substrate proliferated at an optimal rate and also exhibited their proper phenotype (Gospodarowicz *et al.*, 1982). The nature of the ECM factors involved and their relationship to bFGF were then unknown. Early studies showed that such factors were unrelated to serum, plasma-derived growth factors (PDGFs), and purified ECM components such as fibronectin, laminin, and various collagen types. The effect of ECM was also not due to adsorbed bFGF that had been released by cell lysis during ECM denudation (Greenburg and Gospodarowicz; 1982; Gospodarowicz *et al.*, 1982).

The putative ECM components responsible for mimicking the effect of bFGF have recently been reported as being bFGF–heparan sulfate proteoglycan complexes that are an integral part of the ECM produced by either vascular or corneal endothelial cells. Indirect evidence for the integration of bFGF into an insoluble substrate such as the ECM can be derived from the observation that media that have been conditioned by cell types such as capillary or corneal endothelial cells, which have been shown to produce bFGF (Schweigerer *et al.*, 1987b, 1988; Vlodavsky *et al.*, 1987a,b) have no significant impact on proliferation of the same cells (Schweigerer *et al.*, 1987b, 1988). In contrast, seeding those cells on their own denuded ECM will induce them to rapidly proliferate and to express their correct phenotype once confluent (Gospodarowicz and Tauber, 1980). This suggests that bFGF, in contrast to other conventional growth factors such as TGF-α, TGF-β, EGF, and PDGF, is not released in a soluble form. In recent studies Vlodavsky *et al.* (1987a,b) have shown that the ECM from corneal endothelial cells contains a growth factor which, on the bases of its immunoreactivity and heparin affinity, seems to be closely related to bFGF.

Comparing the differential cellular release of PDGF versus FGF, Vlodavsky *et al.* (1987b) reported that endothelial cells synthesize multiple growth factors and regulate the storage and release of these growth factors differently. While PDGF-like growth factors are released into the medium, bFGF-like growth factors are incorporated into the ECM (Vlodavsky *et al.*, 1987a). It has also been reported that endothelial cell-derived heparan sulfate binds bFGF and protects it from proteolytic degradation (Saksela *et al.*, 1988). Recent studies (Globus *et al.*, 1989) using neutralizing antibodies directed against bFGF provided evidence that bFGF in the ECM was solely responsible for its mitogenic activity on mesoderm-derived cells. Through its integration into the ECM produced by these cells, FGF could act as a local growth regulator and induce the regeneration of these tissues following wounding. Hydrolysis of the ECM could result in the liberation of heparan sulfate–FGF complexes that would then be biologically active (Gospodarowicz *et al.*, 1986a,b).

In this context, it is interesting to note that, during morphogenesis, the areas of greatest mitotic activity are located where hydrolysis of the ECM occurs (Bernfield *et al.*, 1984). Similarly, in the case of the embryonic kidney, angiogenesis correlates with hydrolysis of the kidney mesenchymal stroma (Eckblom *et al.*, 1981). In the adult phase of development, heparan sulfate glycosaminoglycans are present in an insoluble form in the ECM and can be released from it by the enzyme heparinase. This is an inducible enzyme that is produced by platelets when they attach to the subendothelium and by macrophages once they are activated (Yahalom *et al.*, 1984). Local release of heparinase by activated platelets or macrophages could lead to the solubilization of biologically active heparan sulfate–FGF complexes that could then participate in various developmental and repair processes, such as wound healing. The localization of FGF in the ECM, where it can be considered an integral part of that structure and where it is protected from both proteolytic degradation and inactivation, is consistent with its early role as an embryonic inducer. Indeed, as pointed out by Hay (1981), embryonic induction is defined as a developmentally significant interaction between closely associated but dissimilarly derived tissue masses. As revealed by studies using isolated tissues, the "mechanism" of embryonic induction involves the ECM, the components of which could bind morphogenetic factors that promote or stabilize differentiation of embryonic tissues.

XI. Wound Healing

bFGF has been detected in macrophages (Baird *et al.*, 1985a), and following its release from damaged cells it could play a crucial role in wound healing processes. In contrast with other growth factors such as PDGF or TGF-β, bFGF stimulates the proliferation of all of the cell types involved in the wound healing process when assayed *in vivo* and with cells in culture. These include capillary endothelial cells, vascular smooth muscle, fibroblasts, and other cell types such as chondrocytes and myoblasts that are involved in the healing of wounds in specialized tissues. *In vivo,* bFGF increases the formation of granulation tissue (Buntrock *et al.*, 1982a,b, 1984). This is associated with stimulation of the synthetic functions of fibroblasts and myofibroblasts (Buntrock *et al.*, 1982b). Similar observations were reported by Davidson *et al.* (1985, 1988), who used polyvinyl alcohol sponges that were implanted subcutaneously into rats and then injected with bFGF. Recombinant bFGF also accelerates normal rat wound healing (McGee *et al.*, 1988) and stimulates the rate of reepithelialization when the epidermis (Fourtanier *et al.*, 1986) is detached from dermis and removed after blister induction. aFGF also accelerates corneal wound healing (Fredj-Reygrobelet *et al.*, 1987). These effects of FGF on keratinocyte proliferation *in vivo* are consistent with recent studies demonstrating that bFGF is a potent mitogen for keratinocytes cultured *in vitro* (Gospodarowicz *et al.*, 1977a; Gospodarowicz *et al.* 1990; O'Keefe *et al.*, 1988; Ristow and Messmer, 1988).

XII. Carcinogenic Transformation

The concept of autocrine stimulation of cell proliferation postulates that a normal diploid cell can gain growth autonomy by acquiring the ability to produce, secrete, and respond to a given growth factor (Todaro *et al.*, 1977; Sporn and Todaro, 1980). Verification of the autocrine hypothesis, in the case of FGF, requires the demonstration that expression of an introduced FGF gene in nontumorigenic cells results in or contributes to the malignant transformation of those cells.

This hypothesis has been tested using the normal genes for bFGF or aFGF. Using BHK-21 cells, a cell type that does not express the bFGF gene, Neufeld *et al.* (1988) have reported that transfection with plasmids carrying the human bFGF coding sequence under the control of the simian virus 40 (SV40) viral enhancer and human metallothionein II promoter results in autonomous cell growth and in the expression of a transformed phenotype. Similar results were reported by Jaye *et al.* (1988), who transfected 3T3 NR-6 cells with a plasmid carrying the human aFGF gene under the control of the SV40 viral early promoter region. They found that the transfected cells grew as transformed cells and, when injected into nude mice, formed small, nonprogressive tumors.

Because FGF does not have a signal secretory sequence, Rogelj *et al.* (1988) have assessed the transforming potential of a chimeric FGF gene composed of the coding immunoglobulin G signal peptide fused with the coding sequence for the bFGF gene and under the control of the SV40 viral early promoter region. NIH 3T3 cells transfected with such vectors became transformed and were highly tumorigenic when injected into nude mice. Similar results were reported by Blam *et al.* (1988), who used a chimeric FGF gene composed of the coding sequence for the growth hormone secretion signal peptide fused with the coding sequence for the bFGF gene. It seems, then, that the introduction of a secretion signal peptide sequence in front of the bFGF gene greatly increases its oncogenic potential. In the search for a possible direct role of bFGF in tumors, it will therefore be of interest to determine whether gene rearrangements that link the bFGF coding sequence to a signal peptide occur in human malignancies. It is of interest to note that the FGF-like oncogenes that have been isolated do possess recognizable signal sequences (Delli-Bovi *et al.*, 1987; Zhan *et al.*, 1988).

XIII. Conclusions

Although a number of growth factors have recently been isolated and characterized, their roles *in vivo,* as well as their physiological relevance, are still largely conjectural. In most cases (e.g., TGF-β, TGF-α, EGF, and PDGF) identification of their biological roles rests on the correlation between their mRNA expression in various tissues at various stages of development, rather than on a direct causality between growth factor expression and morphogenetic events. Until recently, only nerve growth factor, of all growth factors characterized to date, had a well-established physiological role, which is its ability to control the development of part of the peripheral and central nervous systems (Levi-Montalcini and Angeletti, 1968). Recent studies, conducted primarily at early embryonic stages (discussed in Sections III and IV), have helped to establish a physiological role for FGF. Thus, the importance of FGF in the ontogeny of development and the pathology of mesenchymal tissues can no longer be ignored. The recent molecular characterization of FGF, as well as the cloning and mapping of its genes, has led to the general consensus that most, and perhaps all, of the numerous heparin-binding growth factors that have been described (Table II) represent the products of two genes: bFGF and aFGF. The further demonstrations that both bFGF and aFGF have a high degree of structural identity and bind to the same receptor have led to the

Table II Synonyms under Which aFGF and bFGF Are Recorded in the Literature

	aFGF		bFGF
1	Embryonic kidney-derived angiogenesis factor I	1	Leukemia growth factor
2	Astroglial growth factor I	2	Macrophage growth factor
3	Endothelial cell growth factor	3	Embryonic kidney-derived angiogenesis factor 2
4	Retina-derived growth factor	4	Prostatic growth factor
5	Heparin-binding growth factor class I	5	Astroglial growth factor 2
6	Endothelial growth factor	6	Endothelial growth factor
7	Eye-derived growth factor II	7	Tumor angiogenesis factor
8	Prostatropin	8	Hepatoma growth factor
9	Glial maturation factor	9	Chondrosarcoma growth factor
		10	Cartilage-derived growth factor I
		11	Eye-derived growth factor I
		12	Heparin-binding growth factors class II
		13	Myogenic growth factor
		14	Human placenta purified factor
		15	Uterine-derived growth factor
		16	Embryonic carcinoma-derived growth factor
		17	Human pituitary growth factor
		18	Pituitary-derived chondrocyte growth factor
		19	Adipocyte growth factor
		20	Prostatic osteoblastic factor
		21	Mammary tumor-derived growth factor
		22	Glial growth factor[a]
		23	Brain-derived neurotropic factor[a]

[a] These growth factors have not yet been structurally characterized, but their biological properties and method of isolation are very similar or identical to those of bFGF.

conclusion that they have identical biological roles, although they differ in their specific activity (Gospodarowicz *et al.,* 1986a, 1987).

Probably one of the most important questions to be resolved is that of the role of FGF *in vivo*. The high degree of structural conservation of bFGF between species as different as mammals, birds, and amphibians, as well as its presence in all vertebrates studied to date, including pisceans, indicates that FGF could have a primordial role *in vivo*. This is what seems to be indicated by the studies by Slack and colleagues (Slack *et al.,* 1987; Slack and Isaacs, 1989), which have shown that bFGF can act as a primordial morphogen at one of the earliest embryonic stages of the amphibian by inducing the transformation of cells that were destined to be ectodermal into mesenchymal cells. This is consistent with the results of studies of the effects of bFGF on cultured cells, which have shown that FGF is a mitogen for all mesenchymal cells studied and that it can also act as a morphogen. The hypothesis that FGF has a significant role as a morphogen *in vivo* is also indicated by the observation that bFGF supports limb regeneration in lower vertebrates (Gospodarowicz and Mescher, 1981).

One of the most popularized aspects of the *in vivo* biology of FGF is based on its angiogenic activity. bFGF induces the appearance of blood islands in the early embryo. This activity and the effects of bFGF on the proliferation of capillary endothelial cells in culture and *in vivo,* as well as its presence in organs known to have potential angiogenic activity, provide a common denominator for the widespread angiogenic activity of FGF (Gospodarowicz *et al.,* 1986a). One would, however, have an extremely limited view of its potential targets *in vivo,* if one were to limit oneself to the angiogenic properties of FGF. Indeed, from muscle to bone, from cartilage to nervous tissue, FGF has proven to be an agent that plays an important role in vertebrate development.

References

Abraham, J. A., Whang, J. L., Tumolo, A., Mergia, A., Friedman, J., Gospodarowicz, D., and Fiddes, J. C. (1986a). *EMBO J.* **5,** 2523–2528.

Abraham, J. A., Mergia, A., Whang, J. L., Tumolo, A., Friedman, J., Hjerrild, K. A., Gospodarowicz, D., and Fiddes, J. C. (1986b). *Science* **233,** 545–548.

Abraham, J. A., Whang, L., Tumolo, A., Mergia, A., and Fiddes, J. C. (1987). "Molecular Biology of Homo Sapiens," Vol. 51, pp. 657–668. Cold Spring Harbor Laboratory, Cold Spring Harbor, New York.

Adashi, E. Y., and Resnick, C. E. (1986). *Endocrinology (Baltimore)* **119,** 1879–1882.

Adashi, E. Y., Resnick, C. E., Croft, C. S., May, J. V., and Gospodarowicz, D. (1988). *Mol. Cell. Endocrinol.* **55,** 7–14.

Anderson, K. J., Dam, D., Lee, S., and Cotman, C. W. (1988). *Nature (London)* **332,** 360–361.

Baird, A., and Durkin, T. (1986). *Biochem. Biophys. Res. Commun.* **138,** 476–482.
Baird, A., and Hsueh, J. W. (1986). *Regul. Pept.* **16,** 243–250.
Baird, A., Mormede, P., and Böhlen, P. (1985a). *Biochem. Biophys. Res. Commun.* **126,** 358–364.
Baird, A., Esch, F., Gospodarowicz, D., and Guillemin, R. (1985b). *Biochemistry* **24,** 7855–7860.
Baird, A., Esch, F., Ling, N., and Gospodarowicz, D. (1985c). *Regul. Pept.* **12,** 201–213.
Bassett, D. L. (1943). *Am. J. Anat.* **73,** 251–291.
Beers, W. H., Strickland, S., and Reich, E. (1979). *Cell (Cambridge, Mass.)* **6,** 387–394.
Bernfield, M., Banerjee, S. D., Koda, J. E., and Rapraeger, A. C. (1984). *In* "The Role of Extracellular Matrix in Development" (R. L. Trelstand, ed.), pp. 545–572. Liss, New York.
Birdwell, C. R., Gospodarowicz, D., and Nicolson, G. (1978). *Proc. Natl. Acad. Sci. U.S.A.* **75,** 3272–3277.
Blam, S., Mitchell, R., Tischer, E., Rubin, J. S., Silva, M., Silver, S., Fiddes, J. C., Abraham, J. A., and Aaronson, S. A. (1988). *Oncogene* **3,** 129–136.
Born, J., Geithe, H. P., Teidemann, H., Tiedemann, H. P., and Kocher-Becker, U. (1972). *Hoppe-Seyler's Z. Physiol. Chem.* **353,** 1075–1084.
Brockes, J. P. (1984). *Science* **225,** 1280–1287.
Brockes, J. P. (1987). *Methods Enzymol.* **147,** 217–225.
Brockes, J. P., and Kintner, C. R. (1986). *Cell (Cambridge, Mass.)* **45,** 301–306.
Buntrock, P., Jentzsch, K. D., and Heder, G. (1982a). *Exp. Pathol.* **21,** 46–53.
Buntrock, P., Jentzsch., K. D., and Heder, G. (1982b). *Exp. Pathol.* **21,** 62–67.
Buntrock, P., Buntrock, M., Marx, I., Kranz, D., Jentzch, K. D., and Heder, G. (1984). *Exp. Pathol.* **26,** 247–254.
Canalis, E., Centrella, M., and McCarthy, T. (1988). *J. Clin. Invest.* **81,** 1572–1577.
Carlone, R. L., and Foret, J. E. (1979). *J. Exp. Zool.* **210,** 245–252.
Carlone, R. L., Ganagarajah, M., and Rathbone, M. P. (1981). *Exp. Cell Res.* **132,** 15–21.
Choo, A. F., Logan, D. M., and Rathbone, M. P. (1981). *Exp. Neurol.* **73,** 558–570.
Claude, P., Parada, I. M., Gordon, K. A., D'Amore, P. A., and Wagner, J. A. (1988). *Neuron* **1,** 783–790.
Clegg, C. H., Linkhart, T. A., Olwin, B. B., and Hauschka, S. D. (1987). *J. Cell Biol.* **105,** 949–956.
Cohen, D. C., and Gospodarowicz, D. (1985). *J. Cell. Physiol.* **124,** 96–106.
Cohen, D. C., Massoglia, S. L., and Gospodarowicz, D. (1982a). *J. Biol. Chem.* **257,** 9429–9437.
Cohen, D. C., Massoglia, S. L., and Gospodarowicz, D. (1982b). *J. Biol. Chem.* **257,** 11106–11112.
Davidson, J., Klagsbrun, M., Hill, K., Buckley, A., Sullivan, R., Brewer, P., and Woodward, S. (1985). *J. Cell Biol.* **100,** 1219–1227.
Davidson, J., Buckley, A., Woodward, S., McGee, G., and Demetriou, A. (1988). "Growth Factors and Other Aspects of Wound Healing," pp. 63–75. Liss, New York.
De Lapeyrière, D., Marics, I., Adelaidem, J., Raybaud, F., Courlier, F., Rosnet, O., Benharrach, D., Mattei, M. G., and Birnbaum, D. (1989). *J. Cell. Biochem.* **13B,** 153.
Delli-Bovi, P., Curatola, A. M., Kern, F. G., Greco, A., Ittman, M., and Basilico, C. (1987). *Cell (Cambridge, Mass.)* **50,** 729–737.
Denhardt, D. T., Greenburg, A. H., Eagan, S. E., Hamilton, R. T., and Wright, J. A. (1987). *Oncogene* **2,** 55–59.
Dickson, C., and Peters, G. (1987). Nature *(London)* **326,** 833.
Dickson, C., Smith, R., Brookes, S., and Peters, G. (1984). *Cell (Cambridge, Mass.)* **37,** 529–536.

Dresden, M. H. (1969). *Dev. Biol.* **19,** 311–320.
Eccleston, P. A., and Silberberg, D. H. (1985). *Brain Res.* **353,** 315–318.
Eccleston, P. A., Kristjan, A., Jessen, R., and Mirsky, R. (1987). *Dev. Biol.* **127,** 409–418.
Ekblom, P., Lehtonen, E., Saxen, L., and Timpl, R. (1981). *J. Cell Biol.* **89,** 276–283.
Ekblom, P., Sariola, H., Karkinen-Jaaskelainen, M., and Saxen, L. (1982). *Cell differ.* **11,** 35–39.
Esch, F., Ueno, N., Baird, A., Hill, F., Denoroy, L., Ling, N., Gospodarowicz, D., and Guillemin, R. (1985a). *Biochem. Biophys. Res. Commun.* **133,** 554–562.
Esch, F., Baird, A., Ling, N., Ueno, N., Kill, F., Denoroy, L., Klepper, R., Gospodarowicz, D., Böhlen, P., and Guillemin, R. (1985b). *Proc. Natl. Acad. Sci. U.S.A.* **82,** 6507–6511.
Evans, H. (1909). *Anat. Rec.* **3,** 498–518.
Ferrara, N., Schweigerer, L., Neufeld, G., Mitchell, R., and Gospodarowicz, D. (1987). *Proc. Natl. Acad. Sci. U.S.A.* **84,** 5773–5777.
Ferrara, N., Ousley, F., and Gospodarowicz, D. (1988). *Brain Res.* **462,** 223–232.
Ferrari, G., Minozzi, M. C., Toffano, G., Leon, A., and Skaper, S. D. (1989). *Dev. Biol.* **133,** 140–147.
Flaumenhaft, R., Hoscatelli, D., Saksela, O., Rifkin, D. B. (1989). *J. Cell Physiol.* **140,** 75–81.
Florkiewicz, R. Z., and Sommer, A. (1989). *Proc. Natl. Acad. Sci. U.S.A.* **86,** 3978–3981.
Folkman, J. (1986). *Cancer Res.* **46,** 467–473.
Folkman, J., and Cotran, R. S. (1976). *Int. Rev. Exp. Pathol.* **16,** 207–248.
Folkman, J., and Klagsbrun, M. (1987). *Science* **235,** 442–447.
Fourtanier, A., Courty, J., Muller, E., Courtois, Y., Prunieras, M., and Barritault, D. (1986). *Invest. Dermatol.* **87,** 76–80.
Fràter-Schröder, M., Muller, G., Birchmeier, W., and Böhlen, P. (1986). *Biochem. Biophys. Res. Commun.* **137,** 295–302.
Fràter-Schröder, M., Risau, W., Hallmann, R., Gautschi, P., and Böhlen, P. (1987). *Proc. Natl. Acad. Sci. U.S.A.* **84,** 5277–5281.
Fredj-Reygrobelet, D., Plouet, J., Delayre, T., Baudouin, C., Bourret, F., and Lapalus, D. (1987). *Curr. Eye Res.* **6,** 1205–1209.
Friesel, R., Burgess, W. H., Mehlman, T., and Maciag, T. (1986). *J. Biol. Chem.* **261,** 7581–7584.
Friesel, R., Komoriya, A., and Maciag, T. (1987). *J. Cell Biol.* **104,** 689–696.
Gautschi-Sova, P., Muller, T., and Böhlen, P. (1986). *Biochem. Biophys. Res. Commun.* **140,** 874–880.
Gensburger, C., Labourdette, G., and Sensenbrenner, M. (1987). *FEBS Lett.* **217,** 1–5.
Gillespie, L. L., Paterno, G. D., Slack, J. H. W. (1989). *Development* **106,** 203–208.
Globus, R., Patterson-Buckendahl, P., and Gospodarowicz, D. (1988). *Endocrinology (Baltimore)* **123,** 98–105.
Globus, R., Plouet, J., and Gospodarowicz, D. (1989). *Endocrinology (Baltimore)* **124,** 1539–1547.
Gospodarowicz, D. (1976). *Prog. Clin. Biol. Res.* **9,** 1–19.
Gospodarowicz, D. (1987). *Methods Enzymol.* **147,** 106–119.
Gospodarowicz, D. (1990). *UCLA Symp. Mol. Cell. Biol., New Ser.* **114** (in press).
Gospodarowicz, D., and Bialecki, H. (1978). *Endocrinology (Baltimore)* **103,** 854–865.
Gospodarowicz, D., and Cheng, J. (1986). *J. Cell. Physiol.* **128,** 475–484.
Gospodarowicz, D., Plouet, J., and Malerstein, B., (1990). *J. Cell Physiol.* (in press).
Gospodarowicz, D., and Mescher, A. L. (1977). *J. Cell. Physiol.* **93,** 117–127.
Gospodarowicz, D., and Mescher, A. L. (1981). *Adv. Neurol.* **29,** 149–171.

Gospodarowicz, D., and Tauber, J.-P. (1980). *Endocr. Rev.* **1,** 201–227.
Gospodarowicz, D., and Thakral, K. K. (1978). *Proc. Natl. Acad. Sci. U.S.A.* **75,** 847–851.
Gospodarowicz, D., Rudland, P., Lindstrom, J., and Benirschke, K. (1975). *Adv. Metab. Disord.* **8,** 302–335.
Gospodarowicz, D., Moran, J., Braun, D., and Birdwell, C. R. (1976a). *Proc. Natl. Acad. Sci. U.S.A.* **73,** 4120–4124.
Gospodarowicz, D., Weseman, J., Moran, J., and Lindstrom, J. (1976b). *J. Cell Biol.* **70,** 395–405.
Gospodarowicz, D., Mescher, A. L., Brown, K., and Birdwell, C. R. (1977a). *Exp. Eye Res.* **25,** 631–649.
Gospodarowicz, D., Ill, C. R., and Birdwell, C. R. (1977b). *Endocrinology (Baltimore)* **100,** 1108–1120.
Gospodarowicz, D., Brown, K. D., Birdwell, C. R., and Zetter, B. R. (1978a). *J. Cell Biol.* **77,** 774–788.
Gospodarowicz, D., Greenburg, G., Bialecki, H., and Zetter, B. R. (1978b). *In Vitro* **14,** 85–118.
Gospodarowicz, D., Mescher, A. L., and Moran, J. S. (1978c). *Symp. Soc. Dev. Biol.* **35,** 33–61.
Gospodarowicz, D., Bialecki, H., and Thakral, T. K. (1979a). *Exp. Eye Res.* **28,** 501–514.
Gospodarowicz, D., Vlodavsky, I., Greenburg, G., and Johnson, L. K. (1979b). *Cold Spring Harbor Conf. Cell Proliferation* **6,** 561–592.
Gospodarowicz, D., Cohen, D. C., and Fujii, D. K. (1982). *Cold Spring Harbor Conf. Cell Proliferation* **9,** 95–124.
Gospodarowicz, D., Gonzalez, R., and Fujii, D. K. (1983). *J. Cell Physiol.* **114,** 191–202.
Gospodarowicz, D., Cheng, J., Lui, G. M., Baird, A., Esch, F., and Böhlen, P. (1985). *Endocrinology (Baltimore)* **117,** 2383–2391.
Gospodarowicz, D., Neufeld, G., and Schweigerer, L. (1986a). *Mol. Cell. Endocrinol.* **46,** 187–204.
Gospodarowicz, D., Neufeld, G., and Schweigerer, L. (1986b). *Cell Differ.* **19,** 1–17.
Gospodarowicz, D., Massoglia, S., Cheng, J., and Fujii, D. K. (1986c). *J. Cell. Physiol.* **127,** 121–136.
Gospodarowicz, D., Massoglia, S., Cheng, J., and Fujii, D. K. (1986d). *Exp. Eye Res.* **43,** 459–476.
Gospodarowicz, D., Baird, A., Cheng, J., Lui, G. M., Esch, F., and Böhlen, P. (1986e). *Endocrinology (Baltimore)* **118,** 82–90.
Gospodarowicz, D., Ferrara, N., Schweigerer, L., and Neufeld, G. (1987). *Endocr. Rev.* **8,** 95–114.
Gospodarowicz, D., Ferrara, N., Haaparanta, T., and Neufeld, G (1988). *Eur. J. Cell Biol.* **46,** 144–151.
Gospodarowicz, D., Schilling, J., Abraham, J. (1989). *Proc. Natl. Acad. Sci. U.S.A.* **80,** 7311–7315.
Gougeon, A. (1982). *In* "Follicular Maturation and Ovulation" (R. Rolland, E. V. Van Hall, S. G. Hillier, K. P. McNatty, and J. Schoemaker, eds.), pp. 155–163. Elsevier, Amsterdam.
Goustin, A. S., Leof, E. B., Shipley, G. D., and Moses, H. L (1986). *Cancer Res.* **46,** 1015–1029.
Greenburg, G., and Gospodarowicz, D. (1982). *Exp. Cell Res.* **140,** 1–14.
Greenburg, G., Vlodavsky, I., Foidart, J.-M., and Gospodarowicz, D. (1980). *J. Cell. Physiol.* **103,** 333–347.
Grobstein, C. (1956). *Exp. Cell Res.* **10,** 424–440.

Gutmann, E. (1976). *Annu. Rev. Physiol.* **38,** 177–216.

Hann, S. R., King M. W., Bentley, D. L., Anderson, C. W., and Eisenman, R. N. (1988). *Cell (Cambridge, Mass.)* **52,** 185–195.

Hatten, M. E., Lynch, M., Rydel, R. E., Sanchez, J., Joseph-Silverstein, J., Moscatelli, D., and Rifkin, D. B. (1988). *Dev. Biol.* **15,** 280–289.

Hauschka, P. V., Mavrakos, A. E., Iafrati, M. D., Doleman, S. E., and Klagsbrun, M. (1986). *J. Biol. Chem.* **261,** 12665–12674.

Hay, E. D. (1974). *In* "Cellular Basis of Regeneration" (J. W. Lash and J. R. Whitaker, eds.), pp. 404–228. Sinauer, Stamford, Connecticut.

Hay, E. D. (1981). *In* "Cell Biology of the Extracellular Matrix" (E. D. Hay, ed.), pp. 379–409. Plenum, New York.

Hsueh, A. J. W., Adashi, E. Y., Jones, P. B. C., and Welsh, T. H. (1984). *Endocr. Rev.* **5,** 76–127.

Jakobovits, A., Shackleford, G. M., Varmus, H. E., and Martin, G. R. (1986). *Proc. Natl. Acad. Sci. U.S.A.* **83,** 7806–7810.

Janet, T., Grothe, C., Pettmann, B., Unsicker, K., and Sensenbrenner, M. (1988). *J. Neurosci. Res.* **19,** 195–201.

Jaye, M., Howk, R., Burgess, W., Ricca, G. A., Chiu, I. M., Ravera, M. W., O'Brien, S. J., Modi, W. S., Maciag, T., and Drohan, W. N. (1986). *Science* **233,** 541–545.

Jaye, M., Lyall, R. M., Mudd, R., Schlessinger, J., and Sarver, N. (1988). *EMBO J.* **7,** 963–969.

Jennings, T., Jones, R. D., and Lipton, A. (1979). *J. Cell. Physiol.* **100,** 273–278.

Jentzch, K. D., Wellmitz, G., Heder, G., Petzold, P., Buntrock, P., and Oehme, P. A. (1980). *Acta. Biol. Med. Ger.* **39,** 967–971.

Johnson, H. M., and Torres, A. (1985). *J. Immunol.* **134,** 2824–2828.

Kato, Y., and Gospodarowicz, D. (1985a). *J. Cell Biol.* **100,** 477–485.

Kalcheim, C. (1989). *Dev. Biol.* **134,** 1–10.

Kato, Y., and Gospodarowicz, D. (1985b). *J. Cell Biol.* **100,** 486–495.

Kimelman, D., and Kirschner, M. (1987). *Cell (Cambridge, Mass.)* **51,** 869–877.

Kimelman, D., Abraham, J. A., Haaparanta, T., Palisi, T. M., and Kirschner, M. (1988). *Science* **242,** 1053–1056.

Lathrop, B., Olson, E., and Glaser, L. (1985a). *J. Cell Biol.* **100,** 1540–1547.

Lathrop, B., Thomas, K., and Glaser, L. (1985b). *J. Cell Biol.* **101,** 2194–2198.

Leonard, D. G. B., Ziff, E. B., and Greene, L. A. (1987). *Mol. Cell. Biol.* **7,** 3156–3167.

Levi-Montalcini, R., and Angeletti, P. U. (1968). *Physiol. Rev.* **48,** 534–569.

Lobb, R., Sasse, J., Sullivan, R., Shing, Y., D'Amore, P., Jacobs, J., and Klagsbrun, M. (1986). *J. Biol. Chem.* **261,** 1924–1928.

McGee, G., Davidson, J. M., Buckley, A., Sommer, A., Woodward, S. C., Aquino, A. M., Barbour, R., and Demetriou, A. A. (1988). *J. Surg. Res.* **45,** 145–153.

Marchok, A. C., and Herrmann, H. (1967). *Dev. Biol.* **15,** 129–155.

Mergia, A., Tischer, E., Graves, D., Tumolo, A., Miller, J., Gospodarowicz, D., Abraham, J. A., Shipley, G., and Fiddes, J. C. (1989). *Biochem. Biophys. Res. Comm.* **164,** 1121–1129.

Mescher, A. L., and Gospodarowicz, D. (1979). *J. Exp. Zool.* **207,** 497–503.

Mescher, A. L., and Loh, J. J. (1981). *J. Exp. Zool.* **216,** 235–245.

Mondschein, J. S., and Schomberg, D. W. (1981). *Science* **211,** 1179–1180.

Montesano, R., Vassalli, J. D., Baird, A., Guillemin, R., and Orci, L. (1986). *Proc. Natl. Acad. Sci. U.S.A.* **83,** 7297–7301.

Morrison, R. S., DeVeillis, J., Lee, Y. L., Bradshaw, R. A., and Eng, L. F. (1985). *J. Neurosci. Res.* **14,** 167–176.

Morrison, R. S., Sharma, A., DeVeillis, J., and Bradshaw, R. A. (1986). *Proc. Natl. Acad. Sci. U.S.A.* **83,** 7537–7541.

Moscatelli, D., Presta, M., Joseph-Silverstein, J., and Rifkin, D. B. (1986). *J. Cell. Physiol.* **129,** 273–276.

Moscatelli, D., Joseph-Silverstein, J., Manejias, R., and Rifkin, D. B. (1987). *Proc. Natl. Acad. Sci. U.S.A.* **84,** 5778–5782.

Muller, G., Behrens, J., Nussbaumer, U., Böhlen, P., and Birchmeier w. (1987). *Proc. Natl. Acad. Sci. U.S.A.* **84,** 5600–5604.

Munaim, S. I., Klagsbrun, M., and Toole, B. P. (1988). *Proc. Natl. Acad. Sci. U.S.A.* **85,** 8091–8093.

Neufeld, G., and Gospodarowicz, D. (1986). *J. Biol. Chem.* **261,** 5631–5637.

Neufeld, G., Gospodarowicz, D., Dodge, L., and Fujii, D. K. (1987a). *J. Cell. Physiol.* **131,** 131–140.

Neufeld, G., Ferrara, N., Schweigerer, L., Mitchell, R., and Gospodarowicz, D. (1987b). *Endocrinology (Baltimore)* **121,** 597–603.

Neufeld, G., Mitchell, R., Ponte, P., and Gospodarowicz, D. (1988). *J. Cell Biol.* **186,** 1385–1396.

Nieuwkoop, P. D. (1969). *Wilhelm Roux' Arch. Entwicklungs. mech. Org.* **162,** 341–373.

Nilsen-Hamilton, M., Hamilton, R. T., Allen, W. R., and Massoglia, S. L. (1981). *Biochem. Biophys. Res. Commun.* **101,** 411–417.

Ny, T., Bjersing, L., Hsueh, A. J. W., and Loskutoff, D. J (1985). *Endocrinology (Baltimore)* **116,** 1666–1668.

O'Keefe, E. M., Chiu, M. L., and Payne, R. E. (1988). *J. Invest. Dermatol.* **90,** 767–769.

Olwin, B. B., and Hauschka, S. D. (1986). *Biochemistry* **25,** 3487–3492.

Otto, D., Unsicker, K., and Grothe, C. (1987). *Neurosci. Lett.* **83,** 156–160.

Paterno, G. D., Gillespie, L. L., Dixon, M. S., Slack, Y. M. W., and Heath, J. K. (1989). *Development* **106,** 79–83.

Pettmann, B., Weibel, M., Sensenbrenner, M., and Labourdette, G. (1985). *FEBS Lett.* **189,** 102–108.

Pettmann, B., Labourdette, G., Weibel, M., and Sensenbrenner, M. (1986). *Neurosci. Lett.* **68,** 175–180.

Plouet, J., Schilling, J., and Gospodarowicz, D. (1989). *EMBO J.* **8,** 3801–3806.

Powell, J. A. (1969). *J. Exp. Zool.* **170,** 125–148.

Prats, H., Kaghad, M., Prats, A. C., Klagsbrun, M., Lelias, J. M., Liauzum, P., Chalon, P., Tauber, J. P., Amalric, F., Smith, J. A., and Caput, D. (1989). *Proc. Natl. Acad. Sci. U.S.A.* **86,** 1836–1840.

Preminger, G. M., Koch, W. E., Fried, F. A., and Mandell, J. (1980). *Am. J. Anat.* **159,** 17–24.

Ratner, N., Hong, D., Lieberman, M. A., Bunge, R. P., and Glaser, L. (1988). *Proc. Natl. Acad. Sci. U.S.A.* **85,** 6992–6996.

Risau, W. (1986). *Proc. Natl. Acad. Sci. U.S.A.* **83,** 3855–3859.

Risau, W., and Ekblom, P. (1986). *J. Cell Biol.* **103,** 1101–1107.

Ristow, H. J., and Messmer, T. O. (1988). *J. Cell. Physiol.* **137,** 277–284.

Roberts, A. B., Sporn, M. B., Assoian, R. K., Smith, J. M., Roche, N. S., Wakefield, L. M., Heine, U. I., Liotta, L. A., Falanga, V., Kehrl, J. H., and Fauci, A. S. (1986). *Proc. Natl. Acad. Sci. U.S.A.* **83,** 4167–4171.

Rodan, S. B., Wesolowski, G., Thomas, K., and Rodan, G. A. (1987). *Endocrinology (Baltimore)* **121,** 1917–1923.

Rogelj, S., Weinberg, R. A., Fanning, P., and Klagsbrun, M. (1988). *Nature (London)* **331,** 173–175.

Rosa, F., Roberts, A. B., Danielpour, D., Dart, L. L., Sporn, M. B., and Dawid, B. (1988). *Science* **239,** 783–785.

Ruiz i Altaba, A., and Melton, D. A. (1989a). *Development* **106,** 173–183.

Ruiz i Altaba, A., and Melton, D. A. (1989b). *Nature (London)* **341,** 33–38.
Sakaguchi, M., Kajio, T., Kawahara, K., and Kato, K. (1988). *FEBS Lett.* **233,** 163–166.
Saksela, O., Moscatelli, D., and Rifkin, D. B. (1987). *J. Cell Biol.* **105,** 957–963.
Saksela, O., Moscatelli, D., Sommer, A., and Rifkin, D. B. (1988). *J. Cell Biol.* **107,** 743–751.
Sariola, H., Ekblom, P., Lehtonen, E., and Saxen, L. (1983). *Dev. Biol.* **96,** 427–435.
Sariola, H., Timpl, R., von der Mark, K., Mayne, R., Fitch, M., Linsenmayer, T., and Ekblom, P. (1984). *Dev. Biol.* **101,** 86–96.
Sato, Y., and Rifkin, D. B. (1988). *J. Cell Biol. 107,* 1199–1205.
Savion, N., and Gospodarowicz, D. (1980). *Endocrinology (Baltimore)* **107,** 1798–1807.
Schnitzer-Polokoff, R., von Gunten, C., Logel, J., Torget, R., and Sinensky, M. (1982). *J. Biol. Chem.* **257,** 472–476.
Schweigerer, L., Malerstein, B., and Gospodarowicz, D. (1987a). *Biochem. Biophys. Res. Commun.* **143,** 997–1004.
Schweigerer, L., Neufeld, G., Friedman, J., Abraham, J. A., Fiddes, J. C., and Gospodarowicz, D. (1987b). *Nature (London)* **325,** 257–259.
Schweigerer, L., Ferrara, N., Neufeld, G., and Gospodarowicz, D. (1988). *Exp. Eye Res.* **46,** 71–80.
Seed, J., and Hauschka, S. D. (1988). *Dev. Biol.* **128,** 40–49.
Seed, J., Olwin, B. B., and Hauschka, S. D. (1988). *Dev. Biol.* **128,** 50–57.
Seivers, J., Harrismann, B., Unsicker, K., and Berry, M. (1987). *Neurosci. Lett.* **76,** 157–159.
Sinensky, M., and Logel, J. (1985). *Proc. Natl. Acad. Sci. U.S.A.* **82,** 3257–3261.
Singer, M. (1954). *J. Exp. Zool.* **126,** 419–471.
Singer, M. (1974). *Ann. N.Y. Acad. Sci.* **228,** 308–322.
Singer, M., and Craven, L. (1948). *J. Exp. Zool.* **108,** 279–308.
Skinner, M. K., Keski-Oja, J., Osteen, K. G., and Moses, H. L. (1986). *Endocrinology (Baltimore)* **121,** 786–792.
Slack, J. M. W. (1983). "From Egg to Embryo: Determinative Events in Early Development." Cambridge Univ. Press, London.
Slack, J. M. W., and Isaacs, H. V. (1989). *Development* **105,** 147–153.
Slack, J. M. W., Darlington, B., Heath, J., and Godsave, S. (1987). *Nature (London)* **326,** 197–200.
Slack, J. M. W., Isaacs, H. V., and Darlington, B. G. (1988). *Development* **103,** 581–590.
Smith, J. C. (1987). *Development* **99,** 3–14.
Smith, J. C., Dale, L., and Slack, J. M. W. (1985). *J. Embryol. Exp. Morphol.* **89,** (Suppl.), 317–331.
Smith, J. C., Yagoob, M., and Symes, K. (1988). *Development* **103,** 591–600.
Sommer, A., Rifkin, D. B. (1988). *J. Cell Physiol.* **138,** 215–220.
Sporn, M. B., and Todaro, G. (1980). *N. Engl. J. Med.* **303,** 878–880.
Sporn, M. B., Roberts, A. B., Wakefield, L. M., and Assoian, R. K. (1986). *Science* **233,** 532–534.
Sporn, M. B., Roberts, A. B., Lalage, M., Wakefield, M., and DeCrombrugghe, B. (1987). *J. Cell Biol.* **105,** 1039–1045.
Stein, R., Orit, S., and Anderson, D. J. (1988). *Dev. Biol.* **127,** 316–325.
Stemple, D. L., Mahanthrappa, N. J., and Anderson, D. J. (1988). *Neuron* **1,** 517–525.
Taira, M., Yoshida, T., Miyagawa, K., Sakamoto, H., Terada, M., and Sugimura, T. (1987). *Proc. Natl. Acad. Sci. U.S.A.* **84,** 2980–2984.
Tauber, J.-P., Cheng, J., and Gospodarowicz, D. (1980). *J. Clin. Invest.* **66,** 696–708.
Tauber, J.-P., Cheng, J., Massoglia, S., and Gospodarowicz, D. (1981). *In Vitro* **17,** 519–530.

Thalacker, F. W., and Nilsen-Hamilton, M. (1987). *J. Biol. Chem.* **262,** 2283–2290.

Thelander, L., and Reichard, P. (1979). *Annu. Rev. Biochem.* **48,** 133–153.

Thomas, K. A., Rios-Candelore, M., Gimenez-Gallego, G., DiSalvo, J., Bennett, C., Rodkey, J., and Fitzpatrick, S. (1985). *Proc. Natl. Acad. Sci. U.S.A.* **82,** 6409–6413.

Tiedemann, H. (1982). *In* "Biochemistry of Differentiation and Morphogenesis" (L. Jaenicke, ed.), Colloq. Ges. Biol. Chem., Vol. 33, pp. 275–287. Springer-Verlag, Berlin.

Tischer, E., Gospodarowicz, D., Mitchell, R., Silva, M., Schilling, J., Lau, K., Crisp, T., Fiddes, J. C., and Abraham, J., (1989). *Science* (in press).

Todaro, G. J., DeLarco, J. E., Nissley, S. P., and Rechler, M. M. (1977). *Nature (London)* **267,** 526–528.

Todd, J. T. (1823). *Q. J. Microsc. Sci. Lit. Arts* **16,** 84–96.

Togari, A., Baker, D., Dickens, G., and Guroff, G. (1983). *Biochem. Biophys. Res. Commun.* **114,** 1189–1193.

Togari, A., Dickens, G., Huzuya, H., and Guroff, G. (1985). *J. Neurosci.* **5,** 307–316.

Tseng, S. C. G., Savion, N., Stern, R., and Gospodarowicz, D. (1982). *Eur. J. Biochem.* **122,** 355–360.

Ucer, U., Bartsch, H., Scheurich, P., and Pfizenmaier, K. (1985). *Int. J. Cancer* **36,** 103–108.

Unsicker, K., Reichert-Preisbsch, J., Schmidt, R., Pettmann, B., Labourdette, G., and Sensenbrenner, M. (1987). *Proc. Natl. Acad. Sci. U.S.A.* **84,** 5459–5463.

Vlodavsky, I., and Gospodarowicz, D. (1979). *J. Supramol. Struct.* **12,** 73–114.

Vlodavsky, I., Johnson, L. K., Greenburg, G., and Gospodarowicz, D. (1979). *J. Cell Biol.* **83,** 468–486.

Vlodavsky, I., Fridman, R., Sullivan, R., Sasse, J., and Klagsbrun, M. (1987a). *J. Cell. Physiol.* **131,** 402–408.

Vlodavsky, I., Folkman, J., Sullivan, R., Fridman, R., Ishai-Michaeli, R., Sasse, J., and Klagsbrun, M. (1987b). *Proc. Natl. Acad. Sci. U.S.A.* **84,** 2292–2296.

Wagner, J. A., and D'Amore, P. (1986). *J. Cell Biol.* **103,** 1363–1367.

Wahl, S. M., Hunt, D. A., Wakefield, L. M., McCartney-Francis, N., Wahl, L. M., Roberts, A. B., and Sporn, M. B. (1987). *Proc. Natl. Acad. Sci. U.S.A.* **84,** 5788–5792.

Walicke, P., Cowan, W. M., Ueno, N., Baird, A., and Guillemin, R. (1986). *Proc. Natl. Acad. Sci. U.S.A.* **83,** 3012–3016.

Weeks, D. L., and Melton, D. A. (1987). *Cell (Cambridge, Mass.)* **51,** 861–867.

Westall, F. C., Rubin, R., and Gospodarowicz, D. (1983). *Life Sci.* **33,** 2425–2429.

Wice, B., Milbrandt, J., and Glaser, L. (1987). *J. Biol. Chem.* **262,** 1810–1817.

Wilkinson, D. G., Peters, G., Dickson, C., and McMahon, A. P. (1988). *EMBO J.* **7,** 691–695.

Winkles, J. A., Friesel, R., Burgess, W. H., Howk, R., Mehlman, T., Weinstein, R., and Maciag, T. (1987). *Proc. Natl. Acad. Sci. U.S.A.* **84,** 7124–7128.

Yahalom, J., Eldor, A., Fuks, Z., and Vlodavsky, I. (1984). *J. Clin. Invest.* **74,** 1842–1849.

Zhan, X., Bates, B., Hu, X., and Goldfarb, M. (1988). *Mol. Cell. Biol.* **8,** 3487–3495.

4

Transforming Growth Factor-β and Its Actions on Cellular Growth and Differentiation

Marit Nilsen-Hamilton
Molecular, Cellular and Developmental Biology Program
Department of Biochemistry and Biophysics
Iowa State University
Ames, Iowa 50011

Current Topics in Developmental Biology, Vol. 24

I. Transforming Growth Factor-β and Its Many Forms and Diverse Functions

The proteins that are now commonly called transforming growth factor-β (TGF-β) were discovered several times over the past decade. Each independent discovery also identified a different function for this protein, and therefore it has several names that reflect its different functions. As well as TGF-β, these names include the BSC-1 growth inhibitor, cartilage-inducing factors A and B, and polyergin.

A. The TGF-β Family in Vertebrates and Invertebrates

The mammalian TGF-β family consists of three related proteins, TGF-β1, TGF-β2, and TGF-β3. The genes and cDNAs for all three TGF-βs have been cloned and sequenced (Derynck *et al.*, 1985, 1986; de Martin *et al.*, 1987; Duke *et al.*, 1988; Hanks *et al.*, 1988; Sharples *et al.*, 1987; ten Dijke *et al.*, 1988; Jakowlew *et al.*, 1988). The identity between the mature forms of these three protein sequences is 70– 80%. Cartilage-inducing factor A is a type 1 TGF-β (Seyedin *et al.*, 1986), whereas the BSC-1 growth inhibitor (Tucker *et al.*, 1984b; Hanks *et al.*, 1988) and cartilage-inducing factor B (Seyedin *et al.*, 1987) are type 2 TGF-βs.

There is a remarkable degree of identity among the mature TGF-β sequences of different mammalian species. For example, the sequences of mature TGF-β1 from human, porcine, simian, and bovine sources are identical and differ by only one amino acid residue from those of murine TGF-β1. The 112-amino acid mature forms of the TGF-βs are produced from larger precursors of approximately 390 amino acids.

Other mammalian proteins that are related to TGF-β include activin (Ling *et al.*, 1986), inhibin (Mason *et al.*, 1985; Ling *et al.*, 1986; Vale *et al.*, 1986), Müllerian inhibitory substance (MIS) (Cate *et al.*, 1986), bone morphogenetic proteins (Wozney *et al.*, 1988), and T cell suppressor factor (de Martin *et al.*, 1987; Wrann *et al.*, 1987). The homology among these related genes is limited to their carboxy-terminal sequences that encode the mature growth factors. All of these related proteins are expressed as longer precursors and are terminated by the sequence Cys–X–Cys–X (Padgett *et al.*, 1987).

Genes related to mammalian TGF-β are also found in nonmammalian systems. Proteins encoded by the *Vg1* gene in *Xenopus laevis* (Weeks and Melton, 1987) and decapentaplegic (DPP-C) (Padgett *et al.*, 1987) in *Drosophila melanogaster* are homologous to mammalian TGF-β. These two genes are discussed in more detail in Chapters 9 and 10 of this volume.

B. Overlapping Functions of the Mammalian TGF-βs

As well as having a significant sequence homology, TGF-β1 and TGF-β2 are also functionally equivalent in mammalian systems. It was postulated that these two TGF-βs might have separate functions on the basis of two observations: that they are madc in different ratios by different cell types (Roberts *et al.*, 1988) and that there are three receptor proteins with different relative affinities for the two TGF-βs. Despite these arguments, only occasional functional differences have been observed between TGF-β1 and TGF-β2 (Ohta *et al.*, 1987; Rosa *et al.*, 1988; Ottmann and Pelus, 1988). Although the TGF-β3 protein has not yet been purified, it is likely that TGF-β3 has activities similar to those of TGF-β1 and TGF-β2.

Although the reason for the multiple forms of TGF-βs is not understood, it is not unusual to find two closely related and functionally equivalent growth factors. Other known functionally equivalent pairs of growth factors are basic and acidic fibroblast growth factor (FGF), epidermal growth factor (EGF), TGF-α, and the platelet-derived growth factor (PDGF) A and B chains (Roberts *et al.*, 1988). As they are for TGF-β, the two members of each of these growth factor pairs are independently expressed in a tissue-specific manner (see Chapters 1 and 3 of this volume). Some distinction in activity of members of the pairs has been found in nonmammalian systems. For example, although the mammalian EGF receptor (EGF-R) does not seem to distinguish between EGF and TGF-α, the avian receptor can distinguish between them (Lax *et al.*, 1988). Similarly, the *Drosophila* EGF protease distinguishes between EGF and TGF-α (Garcia *et al.*, 1987). TGF-β1 and TGF-β2 are distinguished in the amphibian system, in which only TGF-β2 induces mesoderm formation from ectoderm (Rosa *et al.*, 1988). It is likely that the expression of the various forms of TGF-β will be found to be segregated in the developing animal and that each type of TGF-β will perform a different, but related, functions *in vivo*.

C. Multiple Functions for TGF-βs in Development

The activities of which the TGF-βs are capable include (1) inhibition of anchorage-dependent growth of cells in monolayer culture, (2) stimulation of anchorage-independent growth of cells in soft agar, (3) stimulation of cartilage growth, (4) inhibition of differentiation of some cells, (5) stimulation of differentiation of other cells, and (6) stimulation of cell migration. Different cell types can respond to the same TGF-β protein with completely different—even opposite—responses. Each of these effects of TGF-β is discussed in this chapter.

It is not known how the TGF-β molecule can have so many different activities. However, it is clear that TGF-β is quite different in its action from growth factors such as FGF and EGF and that the ability of TGF-β to regulate cell proliferation may be secondary to other actions. Because TGF-β is so different in its action from other growth factors, it is unfortunate that the name "transforming growth factor" has been applied to this protein. The label "growth factor" implies a proliferation factor to most readers. To resolve the problem of nomenclature, the name "polyergin" was proposed as an alternate to "TGF-β" (Hanks *et al.*, 1988). Although this name has not yet been adopted by the scientific community, it more appropriately describes the multiple functions of TGF-β and perhaps this or a similar name will be adopted in the future to describe the multifunctional protein that we now call TGF-β.

The effects of TGF-β on cell proliferation and differentiation are probably achieved in several ways. In some cases TGF-β stimulates proliferation by stimulating the production of PDGF (Leof *et al.*, 1986). In other cases the action of TGF-β probably involves regulation of the expression of secreted proteases and their inhibitors and the proteins of the extracellular matrix (ECM) and their receptors.

The multifunctional nature of TGF-β suggests that it could play a very important role in embryogenesis; there is evidence that this supposition is correct. Members of the TGF-β family and their mRNAs are found in developing mammalian, *Xenopus*, and *Drosophila* embryos, where they are believed to act in concert with other "proliferative" growth factors and differentiation factors to regulate cellular proliferation, differentiation, and migration. Specific functions and the developmental expression of the TGF-βs in mammals are discussed in more detail in Sections IV–VI and in Chapter 8 of this volume. Reviews of the roles of TGF-β-related proteins in amphibian and invertebrate development can be found in Chapters 9 and 10, of this volume, respectively. For other discussions of the actions of TGF-β as they relate to mammalian development, the reader is referred to several recent reviews (Sporn *et al.*, 1987; Massagué, 1987; Roberts *et al.*, 1988; Rizzino, 1988; Nilsen-Hamilton, 1989).

The focus of this chapter is on the roles of TGF-β and related family members in mammalian development. From a synthesis of the results of molecular, cellular, and developmental studies on the action and distribution of the TGF-β family, the probable molecular bases for many of the effects of TGF-β are discussed. Two important aspects of the molecular mechanism of TGF-β action have been identified. The first observation is the ability of TGF-β to regulate genes encoding proteins that influence the composition or amount of the ECM or that control interaction of ECM proteins with the cells. The second important discovery is that TGF-β regulates the expression of the *sis* protooncogene that encodes the PDGF B chain. Combined with cell- and tissue-specific responses, the ability of

TGF-β to regulate genes that influence the ECM and a gene that encodes a growth factor could be the molecular basis for the many and varied actions of TGF-β.

II. Synthesis and Properties of TGF-β

A. Latent TGF-β–Precursor Complex

The mature TGF-β1 protein is found in human platelets as a disulfide-linked homodimer of about 25 kDa that is associated with a disulfide-linked dimer of the amino terminus of its precursor (Miyazono *et al.*, 1988; Wakefield *et al.*, 1988; Okada *et al.*, 1989). The dimeric amino-terminal portion of the precursor is noncovalently associated with the mature TGF-β and also seems to be covalently associated, through disulfide bonds, with another protein of 125–160 kDa, which is a dimer of two 70-kDa polypeptides. This latter protein has been called a TGF-β-binding protein and is not related to TGF-β either immunologically (Wakefield *et al.*, 1988) or in sequence (Miyazono *et al.*, 1988). It is also not related to other known growth factor-binding proteins (Wakefield *et al.*, 1988). The TGF-β-binding protein is glycosylated, and the results of gel filtration studies suggest that it might exist in solution in higher-molecular-weight aggregates. The carbohydrate on the TGF-β precursor is necessary for the interaction of TGF-β with the complex (Miyazono and Heldin, 1989). A similar high-molecular-weight complex of TGF-β was reported in rat platelets. The apparent molecular mass of the combined associated proteins in this complex was reported as 440 kDa, which is twice the size of that reported for the human TGF-β complex (Nakamura *et al.*, 1986).

The functions of the proteins associated with TGF-β are not understood. However, the observation that their sequences are conserved between species suggests that these TGF-β-associated proteins have functions of their own (Wakefield *et al.*, 1988). Thus, TGF-β exists in a complex of proteins, all of which are highly conserved and are likely to have biological functions. It will be of great interest to know whether the biological functions of these proteins are related, and if so, how.

The latent TGF-β complex is released by platelets when they are stimulated to degranulate by thrombin (Wakefield *et al.*, 1988). A latent form of TGF-β is also found in many tissues (Roberts *et al.*, 1982) and released by many cells in culture (Lawrence *et al.*, 1984). In its latent form TGF-β1 may be buried within the complex because it is not recognized by anti-TGF-β1 antibody. Howver, the TGF-β complex can be dissociated in extremes of pH or in the presence of sodium dodecyl sulfate and 8 *M* urea which releases active TGF-β (Lawrence *et al.*, 1985; Pircher *et al.*, 1986).

Some of the complex can also be dissociated at more moderate acidic pHs, such as might be found *in vivo* (Lyons *et al.*, 1988). The complex is proposed to be a delivery system for TGF-β (Wakefield *et al.*, 1988). The latent TGF-β may be activated in acid environments and by proteolytic action, as occurs during blood clotting. During wound healing or fetal development, TGF-β may also be activated by proteases released into the wound area by cells that have been stimulated to proliferate by growth factors such as PDGF, FGF, and EGF. Both serine and thiol proteases are released in response to stimulation by these growth factors (see Chapters 7 and 8 of this volume). Plasmin and cathepsin D can generate active TGF-β from about 30% of the latent form that is secreted by NRK cells in culture (Lyons *et al.*, 1988).

The inclusion of TGF-β in an inactive complex is likely to be a very important determinant of the distribution of TGF-β activity, because it ensures that TGF-β activity is only generated in the appropriate environment, which is in the presence of the appropriate proteases and/or low pH. This knowledge should also evoke a note of caution regarding the interpretation of observed tissue distributions of the expression of genes encoding TGF-β and the TGF-β receptor (TGF-βR). Thus, the observation that a cell that is capable of responding to TGF-β also produces the growth factor is not sufficient evidence to support the hypothesis that these cells are undergoing autocrine regulation by TGF-β. For example, there are cell lines that are inhibited in their proliferation by TGF-β but that secrete the inactive complex and proliferate in its presence (Wakefield *et al.*, 1987). Similarly, in analyzing the developmental significance of TGF-β expression, it will not be sufficient to have determined the location and the time period of TGF-β synthesis. Rather, it will also be necessary to determine the ratios of active and inactive TGF-β.

B. Inactive TGF-β Complex with α_2-Macroglobulin

As well as being found in an inactive complex in platelets, TGF-β is also found in serum as an inactive complex with α_2-macroglobulin, in which the TGF-β can be recognized by anti-TGF-β1 antiserum (Huang *et al.*, 1988; O'Connor-McCourt and Wakefield, 1987). Thus, this complex is unlike the TGF-β complex found in platelets in which TGF-β is not recognized by its antiserum. Although [^{125}I]TGF-β can bind to α_2-macroglobulin in a noncovalent manner such that it dissociates at low pH, TGF-β is found covalently linked to α_2-macroglobulin in serum (O'Connor-McCourt and Wakefield, 1987). From these observations it has been suggested that the TGF-β in the plasma that is bound to α_2-macroglobulin is destined for destruction and that complexation with α_2-macroglobulin provides a means of scavenging active free TGF-β that is released by platelets at sites of injury (O'Connor-McCourt and Wakefield, 1987).

Although the mature protein does not appear to be glycosylated, the TGF-β precursor that is secreted by Chinese hamster ovary cells is N-glycosylated at Asn-82, Asn-136, and Asn-176 (Purchio *et al.*, 1988). The carbohydrate on the TGF-β precursor is necessary for maintaining the association of TGF-β with a complex of precursor peptide and TGF-β-binding protein (Miyazono and Heldin, 1989). Another possible function of the glycosylation may be to protect the protein from degradation. The high-mannose carbohydrates are also the means by which the liver and the pancreas remove plasma proteins from circulation.

C. Glycosylated TGF-β Precursor with Mannose-6-Phosphate

The glycosylated precursor of TGF-β that was produced by Chinese hamster ovary cells transfected with a TGF-β expression vector also contained mannose-6-phosphate (M6P) in the carbohydrates linked to Asn-82 and Asn-136 (Brunner *et al.*, 1988). M6P is a marker which is used to sort lysosomal proteins intracellularly and which is also used as a signal for their retrieval after they have been secreted. The large, cation-independent M6P receptor (M6P-R) is also the receptor for insulinlike growth factor (IGF)-II (Morgan *et al.*, 1987; MacDonald *et al.*, 1988), to which it binds through a different site than the one that recognizes the phosphorylated sugar. It has been suggested that the M6P-R may be important in transduction of the TGF-β signal (Purchio *et al.*, 1988). However, it has not yet been shown that the TGF-β complex released *in vivo* is phosphorylated on mannose. Alkaline phosphatase found in plasma is likely to remove the phosphate. For example, mitogen-regulated protein [(MRP), also called proliferin (PLF)] (Nilsen-Hamilton *et al.*, 1980) that is produced by transfected Chinese hamster ovary cells contains phosphorylated mannose and binds the M6P-R (Lee and Nathans, 1988), as does the MRP/PLF found in placental extracts (unpublished observations). However, the MRP/PLF found in the plasma does not bind to the M6P-R (unpublished observations). There is evidence that MRP/PLF is sorted along similar pathways to lysosomal proteins and that the newly synthesized protein is degraded in the lysosomes (Nilsen-Hamilton *et al.*, 1988; see also Chapter 7 of this volume). Thus, it is possible that the phosphorylated sugars on the TGF-β precursor are important for the intracellular sorting of the TGF-β precursor, rather than for its function after it is released.

Although the meaning of these findings is not yet clear, it is of interest that TGF-β has several structural similarities with proteolytic enzymes: It is secreted in a precursor form with a high-mannose carbohydrate moiety that is marked with M6P, and it associates very tightly with a protease inhibitor. TGF-β also regulates the expression of genes encoding proteases and their inhibitors. Also, it is interesting that BMP-1, which is not a member of the TGF-β family but has a similar activity to the TGF-β-like BMP-2A and BMP-2B, is homologous with a crayfish protease (Wozney *et al.*, 1988). Perhaps there is an ancestral association of TGF-β and a protease or a protein that interacts with proteases to modulate their activity.

III. Receptors for TGF-β

A. Cell Distribution

Most cell types display receptors for TGF-β on their cell surfaces (Tucker *et al.*, 1984a; Massagué and Like, 1985), with the exception of retinoblastoma cells (Kimchi *et al.*, 1988) and undifferentiated embryonal carcinoma (EC) cells (Rizzino, 1987). For retinoblastoma cells the lack of TGF-βRs has been suggested as a means by which the transformed cells are able to escape the negative proliferative signal provided by TGF-β to normal retinal cells (Kimchi *et al.*, 1988). A similar argument could apply to undifferentiated embryonic cell types, because TGF-β is expressed in the early embryo (Rappolee *et al.*, 1988). Although they are absent from cultured EC cells, the number of high-affinity TGF-βRs in two EC cell lines (PC-13 and F9) increases when the cells are induced to differentiate by treatment with retinoids (Rizzino, 1987).

In a variety of tumor cells, there was an inverse correlation between the amount of TGF-β binding and their ability to form colonies in soft agar (Tucker *et al.*, 1984a). However, further investigation with TGF-β1 demonstrated that there was also an inverse correlation between the number of TGF-βRs and their affinity for TGF-β1. The consequence of this is that, even though the number of receptors differed, all of the cell lines tested bound approximately the same amount of TGF-β at low concentrations of TGF-β (Wakefield *et al.*, 1987). TGF-βRs are also present on fetal cells in culture (Kimchi *et al.*, 1988). Thus, it appears that most cells in the adult and in the developing fetus have the ability to respond to TGF-β.

B. Binding Properties and Down-Regulation

Binding of TGF-β to its receptor is saturable with an affinity of $3–9 \times 10^{-11}$ M (Tucker *et al.*, 1984a; Frolik *et al.*, 1984; Massagué and Like,

1985). At 37°C the receptor is down-regulated to about 50% of its normal level in some cells (Frolik *et al.*, 1984; Wakefield *et al.*, 1987), but not in others (Massagué, 1985a; Wakefield *et al.*, 1987). Even in those cells in which down-regulation of the TGF-βR did occur, it was not extensive (Wakefield *et al.*, 1987). After binding its receptor, TGF-β is degraded by lysosomal proteases (Frolik *et al.*, 1984). This result indicates TGF-β and its receptor are taken into the cells by a mechanism that involves endocytic vesicles. However, whereas a major fraction of the internalized EGF-R is degraded, the same fate does not seem to await the TGF-βR. The absence of extensive down-regulation of the TGF-βR might be the result of rapid recycling of the TGF-βR back to the cell surface. Another explanation for this apparent escape by the TGF-βR from degradation in the lysosomes could reside in the multiplicity of TGF-βRs (discussed in Section III,D). Some receptors may serve as a cell surface sink for TGF-β and not be internalized, whereas other receptors might be internalized with the growth factor and down-regulated.

C. Mechanism of Signal Transduction

The mechanism by which the TGF-β signal is transduced is not known. However, none of the TGF-βRs seem to be tyrosine protein kinases (Fanger *et al.*, 1986). There is evidence that a G protein, perhaps G_i, is involved in transducing the TGF-β signal. This evidence is that pertussis toxin inhibits stimulation of AKR-2B murine fibroblast proliferation by TGF-β (Murthy *et al.*, 1988), whereas it does not inhibit EGF-stimulated proliferation. TGF-β is believed to stimulate DNA synthesis in AKR-2B cells by inducing expression of the *sis* protooncogene (Leof *et al.*, 1986), but the effect of pertussis toxin on the cells' response to PDGF was not tested in this study. However, these investigators also demonstrated the interesting observation that the affinity for TGF-β of the TGF-βR(s) in membranes from AKR-2B cells was decreased approximately sixfold in the presence of Gpp(NH)p, the nonhydrolyzable analog of GTP. These results suggest that TGF-β might regulate cellular function through a receptor linked to a G protein that is similar to G_i. Whereas the cholera toxin substrate, G_s, is involved in generating many positive hormonal signals, including increased proliferation. The pertussis toxin substrate, G_i, often mediates negative hormonal signals (Ross, 1988). It has recently been demonstrated that the negative proliferative effect of TGF-β is also mediated through a pertussis toxin-sensitive step (Howe *et al.*, 1990).

To explain how the cellular responses to TGF-β can be so varied and sometimes in opposition, one might propose that the mechanism of action of this growth factor involves several different signal transduction pathways. These signal transduction pathways might interact differently in different cells, with variable outcomes. Alternately, the balance of the consequences of the signal transduction pathways might determine the overall cellular response. If the latter is so, then there are two basic means by which different cellular responses can be generated. Positive and negative signals could be transmitted simultaneously from the TGF-βR. In this case the ability of the cell to respond to each signal, which is a function of its intracellular biochemical status, would determine the overall cellular response. Alternatively, there may be two different types of receptors for TGF-β—one that conveys a negative signal, and the other, a positive signal. If this were true, then the cells would determine the type of signal that they can receive from TGF-β by exposing the appropriate TGF-βR on their surfaces.

D. Multiple Types of TGF-β Receptors

Three macromolecules on the surface of cells in culture have been identified as TGF-βRs because of their high affinity for TGF-β. These receptors were identified by affinity-labeling the surface of cultured cells with [^{125}I]TGF-β and are designated types I, II, and III (Cheifetz *et al.*, 1986; reviewed by Massagué *et al.*, 1987). Type I TGF-βRs (TGF-βRIs) appeared after electrophoresis as 65-kDa, affinity-labeled proteins and were found in all animal cells tested. Type II TGF-βRs (TGF-βRIIs) yielded 85- to 110-kDa, affinity-labeled proteins. Types I and II receptors have similar and higher affinities for TGF-β1 than for TGF-β2 (Cheifetz *et al.*, 1987), but can be distinguished by their tryptic peptide maps (Cheifetz *et al.*, 1986). Type III receptors (TGF-βRIIIs) have equal affinities for TGF-β1 and TGF-β2, yield 250- to 350-kDA, affinity-labeled products, are found on most cell types, but are absent from rat skeletal muscle myoblasts (Cheifetz *et al.*, 1986).

E. Type I Receptor

Although these three TGF-β-binding molecules are all referred to as receptors for TGF-β, a true receptor function has only been demonstrated for TGF-βRI. In these studies mutants resistant to inhibition of proliferation by TGF-β were selected from the mink lung epithelial cell line (CC164) by growing the cells in the presence of TGF-β (Boyd and Massagué, 1989). These mutants lacked TGF-βRI, whereas clones sensitive to inhibition by TGF-β that were collected from the same population expressed TGF-βRI.

F. Type III Receptor

TGF-βRIIIs have high affinity for TGF-β1 and TGF-β2, and their occupancy correlates with the ability of these TGF-βs to inhibit cell proliferation (Cheifetz *et al.*, 1987). This receptor has been solubilized in an active form, and its physical properties have been examined (Massagué, 1985a). TGF-βRIII is a disulfide-linked, glycosylated dimer. Each subunit is about 330 kDa and binds to wheat germ agglutinin (Massagué, 1985a; Fanger *et al.*, 1986). Unlike the EGF-R, the TGF-βRIII neither aggregates nor becomes phosphorylated upon binding TGF-β (Fanger *et al.*, 1986). The TGF-βRIII is a proteoglycan that contains chains of heparan sulfate and chondroitin sulfate and a core protein of 110–140 kDa (Segarini and Seyedin, 1988; Cheifetz *et al.*, 1988a). Enzymatic removal of the glycosaminoglycan (GAG) chains of the TGF-βRIII does not alter its affinity for TGF-β, nor does it release the receptor from the cell surface (Segarini and Seyedin, 1988; Cheifetz *et al.*, 1988a). The proteoglycan nature of TGF-β RIII indicates that it can interact with other components of the ECM. TGF-βRIII is the first polypeptide growth factor receptor that has been found to be a proteoglycan. This finding is of interest not only because of its uniqueness, but also because one of the major functions of TGF-β is to regulate the expression of adhesion proteins and GAGs of the ECM (see Section IV,A,1 and Chapters 7 and 8 of this volume).

The results of investigations of the domain structure of TGF-βRIII have been interpreted to mean that the receptor has a large external GAG-linked domain; a carboxy-terminal, membrane-inserted domain; and little, if any, cytoplasmic domain. The TGF-β binding site on TGF-β RIII is associated with the extracellular domain of the protein core of this proteoglycan. Trypsin treatment of membrane-bound-TGF-βRIII that has been affinity-labeled with [^{125}I]TGF-β releases the GAG-containing domain and leaves 72-, 63-, and 60-kDa membrane-associated fragments cross-linked with TGF-β (Cheifetz *et al.*, 1988a). The 60-kDa domain is released into the medium, whereas the 63- and 72-kDa fragments remain associated with the cell. These results suggest that the GAG portion of TGF-βRIII is located farthest from the cell surface, that most of its remaining core polypeptide is exposed extracellularly, and that the receptor is associated with the membrane by way of a short, 3-kDa terminal segment. This length of membrane-associated terminal polypeptide is probably sufficient to penetrate the lipid bilayer of the cell surface membrane, but would not provide for a substantial intracellular domain, as is found on the EGF-R (see Chapter 1 of this volume). Although TGF-βRIII may not transduce a signal from TGF-β, it does seem to be important for TGF-β action because it is the only one of the three receptors whose relative affinities for TGF-β1 and TGF-β2 correlate with the EC_{50}'s at which these two species stimulate the expression of ECM proteins, such as fibronectin, proteoglycans, and the fibronectin receptor (Ignotz and Massagué, 1987; Bassols and Massagué, 1988; Cheifetz *et al.*, 1987, 1988b). Despite the correlation between the response curve to TGF-β and the binding curve for TGF-β RIII, studies show that the loss of TGF-β function in TGF-β-resistant mutants of mink lung epithelial cells is correlated with loss of TGF-βRI (53 kDa) rather than TGF-βRIII (Boyd and Massagué, 1989). Unlike TGF-βRIII, TGF-βRI has a higher affinity for TGF-β1 than for TGF-β2 (Cheifetz *et al.*, 1988b).

To reconcile the results of the studies of relative affinities of the TGF-βRs for TGF-β1 and TGF-β2, which implicate TGF-βRIII as the true TGF-βR, and the results of studies of CC164 cell mutants, which suggest that the TGF-βRI is responsible for mediating signal transduction from TGF-β, it has been proposed that TGF-βRIII interacts with TGF-βRI in signal transduction (Boyd and Massagué, 1989). Thus, the affinity of the combined types I and III receptors could be determined by the affinity of the TGF-βRIII. This proposal is supported by the observation that TGF-β1 and TGF-β2 are equally potent in cells that display both TGF-βRI and TGF-βRIII, whereas TGF-β1 is much more potent than TGF-β2 in cells that only display TGF-βRI. However, the existence of cells that respond to TGF-β but that have only TGF-βRI demonstrates that TGF-βRIII does not have to be present for the cells to respond to TGF-β.

The proteoglycan nature of TGF-βRIII suggests several interesting possibilities for its function in development. The TGF-βRIII might act as a reservoir for TGF-β near the cell surface. The high affinity of this proteoglycan for TGF-β may allow it to hold stores of TGF-β in particular tissue locations during development. Similarly, heparin, another proteoglycan, probably acts as a reservoir for FGF (Roberts *et al.*, 1988; see also Chapter 3 of this volume). Alternatively, Cheifetz *et al.* (1988a) have suggested that, as well as mediating the signal that regulates expression of the ECM components, the TGF-βRIII could itself participate in cell–matrix or cell–cell interactions. Knowledge of the precise nature of this TGF-β-binding proteoglycan and its spatial and temporal distributions in the developing embryo may add significantly to our understanding of the role of TGF-β in regulating developmental processes.

IV. Effects of TGF-β at the Molecular Level

A. Regulation of Genes Encoding Proteins That Contribute to the Extracellular Matrix

A major function of TGF-β is to regulate the expression of genes whose products contribute to building the ECM. These genes include those encoding protein components of the ECM, membrane proteins that interact with the ECM, enzymes that modify the ECM, and inhibitors of those enzymes. The effects of TGF-β on the expression of these genes can be dissociated from its effects on cell proliferation (Centrella *et al.*, 1987; Chiang and Nilsen-Hamilton, 1986; Thalacker and Nilsen-Hamilton, 1987)

Cellular movements, proliferation, and differentiation are all influenced by the composition and quantity of the ECM (Hynes, 1981; Enat *et al.*, 1984; see also Rizzino, 1988; Dufour *et al.*, 1988; and Chapters 7 and 8 of this volume). Thus, by both qualitatively and quantitatively altering the expression of extracellular ECM proteins and their receptors, TGF-β could regulate many developmental events. Other aspects of the involvement of the ECM, such as cell adhesion proteins and secreted proteases and their inhibitors in development, are discussed in this section and in Chapters 7 and 8 of this volume.

1. Protein and Carbohydrate Components of the ECM

TGF-β stimulates the production of collagen and fibronectin (Ignotz and Massagué, 1987; Ignotz *et al.*, 1987; Fine and Goldstein, 1987; Centrella *et al.*, 1987; Rossi *et al.*, 1988), thrombospondin (Penttinen *et al.*, 1988), osteopontin (Noda *et al.*, 1988), proteoglycans (Chen *et al.*, 1987; Morales and Roberts, 1988; Bassols and Massagué, 1988), and glycosaminoglycans (Hiraki *et al.*, 1988; Redini *et al.*, 1988) and their incorporation into the ECM by mesenchymal and epithelial cells in culture. It also increases the expression of the integrins which are the cell surface receptors through which ECM proteins such as fibronectin and collagen interact with the cell (Ignotz and Massagué, 1987; Roberts *et al.*, 1988; Heino *et al.*, 1989). Although, in the vast majority of cases, TGF-β increases the expression of proteins and other constituents of the ECM, it occasionally inhibits the expression of ECM constituents (Noda and Rodan, 1987; Kelly and Rizzino, 1989). These and other effects of TGF-β on the expression of proteins that make up the ECM are described in Chapters 7 and 8 of this volume.

2. Proteases

Genes encoding proteases and protease inhibitors that effect turnover of the ECM are highly regulated by TGF-β and by other growth factors. Most often, the ultimate effect of TGF-β is to conserve the ECM. For example, TGF-β decreases the expression of genes encoding proteases that degrade the protein components of the ECM. The proteases regulated in this way by TGF-β include plasminogen activator (Laiho *et al.*, 1986b; Saksella *et al.*, 1987), cathepsin L [also known as major excreted protein (MEP)] (Chiang and Nilsen-Hamilton, 1986; see also Chapter 7 of this volume), transin (also known as stromolysin) (Matrisian *et al.*, 1985, 1986; Machida *et al.*, 1988; see also Chapter 8 of this volume), and collagenase (Edwards *et al.*, 1987). Although decreased protease expression is the general response to TGF-β, adult human skin fibroblasts cell respond by increasing their expression of plasminogen activator (Laiho *et al.*, 1986b). It is not clear whether this increase in plasminogen activator activity is a direct effect of TGF-β or a secondary effect of the induction of the c-*sis* protooncogene (with subsequent production of the B chain of PDGF) by TGF-β (see Section IV,B,1).

3. Protease Inhibitors

One of the most prominent and widespread of the cellular responses to TGF-β is an increased expression of genes encoding protease inhibitors; this includes the gene for the inhibitor of plasminogen activator [(PAI-1), also known as IIP48] (Nilsen-Hamilton and Holley, 1983; Laiho *et al.*, 1986a; Thalacker and Nilsen-Hamilton, 1987; Lund *et al.*, 1987) and the gene encoding the tissue inhibitor of metalloproteases (Edwards *et al.*, 1987; see also Chapter 8 of this volume), which is a collagenase inhibitor.

B. Regulation of Genes That Encode Growth and Differentiation Regulators

One important group of genes regulated by TGF-β is the group that encodes growth factors and proteins known to regulate cell differentiation. In conjunction with its regulation of genes encoding proteins that modify the ECM, this ability of TGF-β to regulate the expression of growth and differentiation factors is likely to be the main reason for the many different effects of TGF-β on cell proliferation and differentiation.

1. Oncogenes

Oncogenes were defined by their ability to alter cellular proliferative characteristics. The increased expression of certain protooncogenes is associated with increased proliferation. Thus, TGF-β might regulate cell proliferation and differentiation by regulating the expression of genes that regulate DNA synthesis. TGF-β regulates the expression of several oncogenes. The most prominent among them is c-*sis* (Leof *et al.*, 1986; Daniel *et al.*, 1987). The ability of AKR-2B cells to synthesize the c-*sis* protein, which is the B chain of PDGF, is believed to be the basis for the positive proliferative response of these cells to TGF-β. Just as the cellular response to TGF-β can vary from one cell type to another, there is no consistent change in protooncogene expression in response to TGF-β when several different cell lines are compared. For example, TGF-β inhibits c-*myc* expression in human colon carcinoma cells (Mulder *et al.*, 1988), BALB/MK murine keratinocytes (Coffey *et al.*, 1988), EGF-induced c-*myc* expression in endothelial cells (Takehara *et al.*, 1987), and human mammary carcinoma MDA-468 cells (Fernandez-Pol *et al.*, 1987), but does not alter the c-*myc* mRNA level in B lymphocytes (Smeland *et al.*, 1987). In contrast, TGF-β increases expression of c-*fos* mRNA in EL2 rat fibroblasts and NIH 3T3 cells (Liboi *et al.*, 1988), but does not alter c-*fos* expression in endothelial cells (Takehara *et al.*, 1987).

2. Genes Encoding Growth Factors

As well as inducing the expression of c-*sis*, which encodes the PDGF B chain, TGF-β also induces the expression of the A chain of PDGF in some cells (Makela *et al.*, 1987), stimulates expression of interleukin (IL)-1 in murine monocytes (Wahl *et al.*, 1987), and inhibits expression of the tumor necrosis factors TNF-α (cachectin) and TNF-β (lymphotoxin) and IFN-γ by human adherent blood monocytes and murine peritoneal macrophages (Espevik *et al.*, 1987). By affecting the expression of these genes, TGF-β can indirectly alter cellular proliferation and differentiation.

TGF-β also regulates the expression of its own gene. In normal and transformed murine and human cell lines that were mainly of fibroblast origin, TGF-β was found to increase the expression of its own mRNA by a factor of about 6 (van Obberghen-Schilling *et al.*, 1988). EGF and PDGF also induce TGF-β mRNA. The effect of EGF on TGF-β mRNA levels was synergistic with that of TGF-β in NRK cells. This latter observation suggests again that the mechanisms of action of EGF and TGF-β differ. The ability to induce the expression of its own gene means that TGF-β could amplify its own signal in regulating specific developmental events.

TGF-β also stimulates expression of its own gene while simultaneously inhibiting proliferation of the rat jejunal crypt cell line, IEC-6 (Barnard *et al.*, 1989). When freshly isolated rat enterocytes were sequentially eluted from the crypt villus, it was found that the level of expression of the TGF-β gene increased as the cells moved away from the crypt. Thus, the more terminally differentiated, nonproliferating cells of the villus tip expressed the highest level of TGF-β. These results prompted the proposal that TGF-β may form an autocrine axis that regulates the ordered progression from the rapidly proliferating cells of the crypt to the highly differentiated, nonproliferating cells of the villus tip (Barnard *et al.*, 1989). Similar axes of TGF-β expression may also regulate the ordered developmental progression of other rapidly renewing epithalial tissues, such as skin. This concept of an autocrine axis may also be important in establishing axes of developing tissues. That TGF-β is involved in the establishment of such axes is suggested by the fact that the *Drosophila* homolog of TGF-β, DPP-C, is a homeotic locus that is primarily concerned with establishment of segmentation and the developmental axis of the organism.

3. Mitogen-Regulated Protein (Proliferin)

The level of expression of MRP/PLF and its mRNA (Chiang and Nilsen-Hamilton, 1986; Chiang *et al.*, 1990) by 3T3 cells in culture is decreased by TGF-β. MRP/PLF is expressed by the trophoblastic giant cells of the placenta in midgestation and is secreted into the maternal and fetal fluids (Jang *et al.*, 1987; Nilsen-Hamilton *et al.*, 1988; Lee *et al.*, 1988). Although the function of MRP/PLF is not yet known, one form of this protein inhibits muscle-specific gene expression when expressed in myoblast cell lines (Wilder and Linzer, 1989). The regulation of MRP/PLF production by growth factors and its appearance in murine development is discussed in Chapter 7 of this volume.

C. Effects of TGF-β on the Action of Other Growth Factors

As well as regulating the expression of genes that encode growth factors, TGF-β also alters cellular responses to some growth factors. For example, it opposes the action of growth factors such as EGF, PDGF, and FGF on many cells in monolayer culture (Holley *et al.*, 1978, 1980; Roberts *et al.*, 1985). These actions of TGF-β could occur because TGF-β (1) prevents signal transduction by the stimulating growth factor, (2) initiates a series of changes that prevent any cellular response and so negates the actions of stimulatory growth factors, or (3) initiates a series of events that result in an opposite effect, but do not negate the cellular responses to the stimulatory growth factors.

One way that TGF-β could prevent the action of stimulatory growth factors is to cause down-regulation of the receptor for the growth factor. TGF-β alters the affinity and the number of EGF-Rs on the surface of NRK cells (Assoian, 1985; Massagué, 1985b). However, the inhibitory effect of TGF-β on the number of receptors is transient (Assoian, 1985). Thus, it is unlikely that down-regulation of the EGF-R is the means by which TGF-β effects a permanent inhibition of DNA synthesis.

To distinguish between the proposals that TGF-β acts to oppose versus to negate the actions of other growth factors, as stated in proposals 2 and 3 above, it is necessary to identify functional changes that occur specifically in response to either TGF-β or the "opposing" growth factor, but not in response to both factors. Thus, DNA synthesis and proliferation are not adequate indicators of the separate actions of TGF-β and other growth factors. Independent indicators of the actions of EGF and TGF-β can be found in BSC-1 African green monkey kidney epithelial cells which respond to EGF by synthesizing and secreting three proteins of 30, 59, and 62 kDa. These same cells respond to TGF-β by synthesizing and secreting PAI-1 (Nilsen-Hamilton and Holley, 1983). Whereas EGF stimulates DNA synthesis in BSC-1 cells, TGF-β inhibits DNA synthesis. Because different proteins are expressed by these cells in response to TGF-β and EGF, we were able to ask whether the cellular responses to TGF-β and EGF oppose each other through independent cellular pathways or whether TGF-β negates the cellular responses to EGF. The result (Fig. 1) shows clearly that TGF-β and EGF initiate two separate, noninteracting cellular regulatory pathways that regulate the expression of these proteins. The time course for the induction of these secreted proteins precedes the increase in DNA synthesis induced by EGF. In other studies of the effect of TGF-β on renal proximal tubule cells, it was found that the early responses to insulin are also not inhibited by TGF-β, even though insulin-induced DNA synthesis is inhibited in the same cells (Fine *et al.,* 1985). The results of both of these studies suggest that, when TGF-β inhibits EGF or insulin-stimulated DNA synthesis, it does not negate the cellular responses to EGF or insulin. Instead, the products of the cellular response to TGF-β oppose the actions of EGF or insulin on DNA synthesis.

Whereas the independent actions of TGF-β and EGF oppose each other in their effects on DNA synthesis on many cells that grow in monolayer culture, the actions of both of these growth factors support colony formation of certain cells in suspension culture. One characteristic of TGF-β is that it interacts synergistically with one of several growth factors (including PDGF, EGF, and FGF) to stimulate colony formation of NRK cells (see Section V,A,1). These are all growth factors that stimulate entry into, or progression through, the cell cycle. A synergistic interaction suggests that the two interacting growth factors affect the same event but by different mechanisms. Thus, the frequent observation of a synergistic interaction between TGF-β and these other growth factors suggests that TGF-β does not stimulate proliferation by the same mechanism as EGF, FGF, or PDGF.

One interesting example of how TGF-β and EGF/TGF-α interact synergistically to stimulate cellular changes is in the effect of these two growth factors on membrane ruffling (Myrdal *et al.,* 1986). TGF-β stimulates the secretion by NRK cells of a factor that prolonged the membrane ruffling response of these cells to TGF-α. The factor prevented the normal shut-off of membrane ruffling that occurs soon after a stimulus from TGF-α.

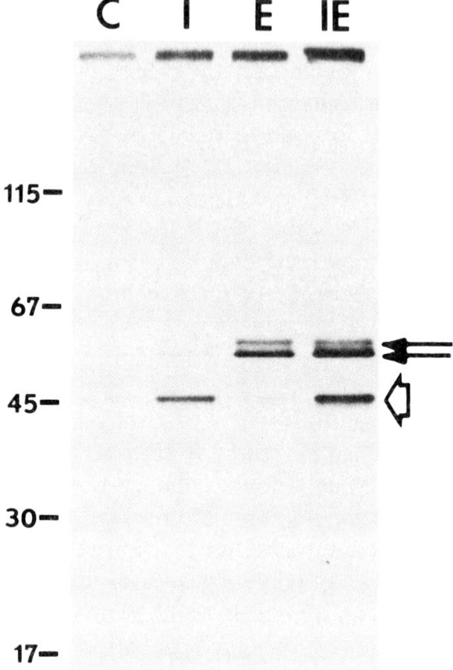

Fig. 1 Interaction between EGF and TGF-β in regulating the expression of proteins secreted by BSC-1, African green monkey kidney cells. BSC-1 cells were treated for 5.5 hours with EGF, TGF-β2 (BSC-1 growth inhibitor), or a combination of EGF and TGF-β2. The cells were then labeled with [^{35}S]methionine for 4 hours. The treatments were: C, no addition; I, 10 ng/ml of BSC-1 growth inhibitor (monkey TGF-β2); E, 40 ng/ml of EGF; IE, TGF-β2 with EGF. A fluorogram is shown, with the positions of the EGF-induced proteins indicated by the arrows and the position of the inhibitor of plasminogen activator (PAI-1) indicated by the arrowhead. The numbers indicate molecular weights $\times 10^{-3}$. (From Nilsen-Hamilton and Holley, 1983; reprinted with permission.)

V. Effects of TGF-β at the Cellular Level

Among growth factors, TGF-β is unique in the number and variety of its effects on cellular differentiation and proliferation. What is known of the molecular bases of these effects of TGF-β is discussed in Section IV and can be summarized as involving the regulation of two sets of genes: (1) genes encoding secreted proteins that contribute to the rate of accumulation or to the composition of the ECM and (2) genes encoding growth factors and perhaps differentiation factors.

A. Effects of TGF-β on Cellular Proliferation

TGF-β can either stimulate or inhibit cell proliferation, depending on the cell type and its environment. The importance of the cellular environment in determining the response to TGF-β is underscored by the observation that the same cell type can be inhibited from proliferating when grown in monolayer cultures, but stimulated to proliferate in suspension cultures (Assoian and Sporn, 1986; Madri *et al.*, 1988).

1. Anchorage-Independent Proliferation

The ability of cells that are normally anchorage dependent to proliferate in the absence of a solid substratum (e.g., suspended in soft agar or methyl cellulose) is a good indicator of the ability of those cells to proliferate and form a tumor in immune-deficient mice (Shin *et al.*, 1975). Thus, it was by using this assay as a measure of the transformed status of cell lines that one of the activities of TGF-β was discovered (DeLarco and Todaro, 1978). Because of the demonstrated ability of TGF-β to stimulate cells to grow in soft agar, it was named a transforming growth factor. However, the early preparations of TGFs (called sarcoma growth factor) actually contained two active proteins—TGF-β and TGF-α (Roberts *et al.*, 1982). TGF-α is a "proliferative" growth factor that acts through the EGF-R to stimulate the initiation of DNA synthesis. TGF-β and TGF-α act synergistically to stimulate anchorage-independent proliferation of NRK cells (Anzano *et al.*, 1982). TGF-α probably performs the function of stimulating DNA synthesis and proliferation because it can be replaced in this assay by other proliferative growth factors, such as EGF, PDGF, or FGF (Roberts *et al.*, 1982, 1985; van Zoelen *et al.*, 1986). IGF-II is another growth factor that is necessary for growth of rodent fibroblasts in suspension (Massagué *et al.*, 1985). TGF-β also acts synergistically with insulin to stimulate Swiss 3T3 cell proliferation (Brown and Holley, 1987).

One explanation of the ability of TGF-β to stimulate anchorage-independent proliferation might be that it induces c-*sis* and therefore PDGF, as it does when the cells are growing attached to plastic (Leof *et al.*, 1986). However, this does not seem to be sufficient to explain the action of TGF-β on cells in suspension culture, because PDGF acts synergistically with TGF-β to stimulate anchorage-independent growth (van Zoelen *et al.*, 1986). If TGF-β were to act by stimulating the production of

PDGF, then the addition of PDGF to the assay would have no effect on colony growth or would have an additive, rather than synergistic, effect at subsaturating levels of TGF-β.

The most likely action of TGF-β that would complement the proliferative response of the cells to PDGF and other growth factors is its ability to regulate gene expression to achieve an accumulation of the ECM (see Section IV,A). This activity of TGF-β is particularly important for cells that are normally anchorage dependent but that grow in suspension. When they are unable to find an appropriate attachment site while in suspension culture, anchorage-dependent cells must attach to each other and may require quite an extensive network of ECM proteins in order to form a compact colony. By inducing genes that encode protease inhibitors and repressing the expression of genes encoding proteases, TGF-β decreases the extracellular expression of proteolytic activity and thereby acts as an ECM-sparing agent. The decreased proteolytic activity and increased expression of genes encoding ECM proteins that are also orchestrated by TGF-β result in the accumulation of ECM. This allows the cells to proliferate in colonies by providing them with the necessary substratum. This ECM-sparing activity may be the crucial activity by which TGF-β acts synergistically with proliferative growth factors such as EGF, TGF-α, and PDGF to stimulate colony formation in soft agar.

That the ECM-sparing effect of TGF-β is important for the growth of cells in soft agar is indicated by the observations that the addition of fibronectin (Ignotz and Massagué, 1986) to the soft agar medium results in increased colony growth. Also, the addition of a peptide that competes with fibronectin for binding to integrin, its cell surface receptor, decreases colony growth (Ignotz and Massagué, 1986). Thus, the real significance of the observation that TGF-β increases colony growth in soft agar to understanding developmental processes may be the fact that TGF-β regulates the production and turnover of components of the ECM.

Not all cells respond to TGF-β with increased anchorage-independent proliferation. TGF-β inhibits the proliferation of many human tumor cells in both monolayer and suspension cultures (Roberts *et al.*, 1985). This inhibitory effect of TGF-β on the proliferation of tumor cells may be related to the ability of TGF-β to stimulate the differentiation of many cell types (see Section V,B).

Because most cells possess TGF-βRs and different cell types produce different ECM proteins, a local increase in the concentration of TGF-β in the developing embryo could produce a profound change in both the composition and the amount of the ECM. The resulting changes could alter proliferation, differentiation, and directed cell migration.

2. Anchorage-Dependent Proliferation

TGF-β inhibits the anchorage-dependent proliferation of many cells in monolayer culture. Decreased proliferation is the most wide-reaching cellular response to TGF-β. Cell types that are inhibited in their proliferation by TGF-β include endothelial cells (Baird and Durkin, 1986; Fràter-Schröder *et al.*, 1986; Heimark *et al.*, 1986), T lymphocytes (Kehrl *et al.*, 1986a), hepatocytes (Carr *et al.*, 1986; Nakamura *et al.*, 1985), keratinocytes (Ristow, 1986; Shipley *et al.*, 1986; Reiss and Sartorelli, 1987; Coffey *et al.*, 1988), intestinal epithelial cells (Kurokowa *et al.*, 1987; Lee *et al.*, 1987), renal proximal tubular cells (Fine *et al.*, 1985), mammary epithelial cells (Knabbe *et al.*, 1987; Silberstein and Daniel, 1987), various tumor cells (Roberts *et al.*, 1985; Pfeilschifter *et al.*, 1987; Ranchalis *et al.*, 1987; Koyasu *et al.*, 1988), and some fibroblasts (Wrana *et al.*, 1986; Kamijo *et al.*, 1989). The growth-inhibitory effect of TGF-β was first demonstrated by Holley *et al.* (1978, 1980) when they identified and purified a protein that inhibited proliferation and was secreted by BSC-1 African green monkey cells. The BSC-1 growth inhibitor was later shown to be a TGF-β2 (Hanks *et al.*, 1988).

Inhibition of proliferation and morphogenesis in response to TGF-β can also be observed *in vivo*. TGF-β inhibits proliferation in the developing mouse mammary gland (Silberstein and Daniel, 1987) and induces a transient inhibition of proliferation in regenerating liver (Russell *et al.*, 1988). Braun *et al.* (1988) showed that the level of TGF-β mRNA increases during liver regeneration and reaches a peak of expression after the initial wave of hepatocyte mitosis. They proposed that the induction of TGF-β might be part of a negative feedback loop to prevent any further liver growth. TGF-β may also be a hormonally regulated negative autocrine growth regulator for mammary cells. This is suggested by the observation that secretion of active TGF-β, which inhibits mammary epithelial cell proliferation, is induced eight- to 27-fold in cultured mammary carcinoma cells by antiestrogens (Knabbe *et al.*, 1987). Thus, *in vivo* one function of the growth-inhibitory effect of TGF-β that is also observed *in vitro* may be to limit the proliferative response of a tissue.

The ability of TGF-β to inhibit proliferation could be a consequence of its ability to alter the expression of genes encoding proteases and protease inhibitors. Proliferation of many cells is stimulated by proteases (Sefton and Rubin, 1970; Chen and Buchanan, 1975; Moonan *et al.*, 1985; Bar-Shavit *et al.*, 1986; reviewed by Scher, 1987), and the ability of proteases to stimulate proliferation is a function of their proteolytic activity (Glenn *et al.*, 1980). Proteases could stimulate cell proliferation by activating latent growth factors. Cells may dampen the mitogenic effect of proteases by secreting protease inhibitors (Low *et al.*, 1982). Thus, TGF-β could inhibit the proliferation of certain cells in monolayer culture through its ability to decrease the overall proteolytic activity in the medium or the activity of particular proteases.

Although TGF-β inhibits cellular proliferation in most cells when they are grown in monolayer culture (Moses *et al.*, 1987), it stimulates DNA synthesis and proliferation of osteoblasts (Centrella *et al.*, 1986; Globus *et al.*, 1988), mouse embryo AKR-2B cells (Shipley *et al.*, 1985; Leof *et al.*, 1986), and EL2 rat fibroblasts (Libio *et al.*, 1988) in monolayer culture. In almost every case in which TGF-β stimulates proliferation, it has been demonstrated that it acts though another growth factor, by either enhancing the effect of FGF (Globus *et al.*, 1988) or inducing the synthesis of PDGF (Leof *et al.*, 1986). If TGF-β did not induce c-*sis* in AKR-2B cells, it is likely that these cells would respond to TGF-β like most cells, with inhibition of DNA synthesis. This is evident because the increased rate of initiation of DNA synthesis in response to TGF-β in AKR-2B cells is preceded by a period of inhibition of DNA synthesis. The delayed stimulation of DNA synthesis by TGF-β occurs after sufficient PDGF is induced to act as the immediate autocrine stimulator of AKR-2B cell proliferation (Leof *et al.*, 1986). The observation that TGF-β stimulates cell proliferation by inducing c-*sis* may explain why TGF-β generally stimulates proliferation in cells of mesenchymal origin. PDGF-Rs are usually only expressed on cells of mesenchymal origin (Heldin *et al.*, 1981; Glenn *et al.*, 1982) and the PDGF produced by TGF-β-stimulated cells can only act as an autocrine growth factor for those cells that also express the PDGF-R. This suggests that, in the embryo and the developing fetus, selective proliferative responses to TGF-β may be determined by local expression of the PDGF-R.

In summary, the ability of TGF-β to both stimulate and inhibit cellular proliferation might be understood in view of its ability to simultaneously induce c-*sis* and to regulate genes encoding proteases and protease inhibitors. The effect of TGF-β on cellular proliferation might derive from the balance of positive (c-*sis* expression) and negative (decreased proteolysis) signals for DNA synthesis. If the cells do not express the PDGF-R, then the negative signal would prevail. If the PDGF signal can be received by the cell, then the balance of strengths of the negative and positive signals would determine the proliferative response of the cell to TGF-β (Fig. 2). If the strengths of the two signals were equal, then there would be no change in proliferation, but other cellular changes initiated by the two signal pathways could alter the differentiation state of the cell.

The mechanistic dissociation of the proliferative and ECM-sparing effects of TGF-β provides the means by which TGF-β can play a major role in the formation of the ECM and basement membranes, without inhibiting

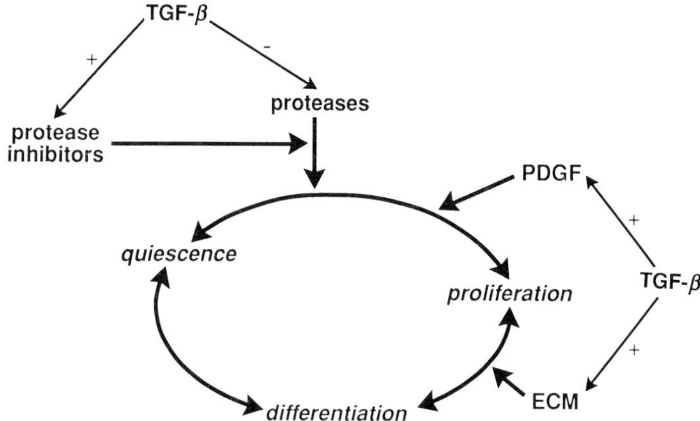

Fig. 2 The varied actions of TGF-β on cellular proliferation and differentiation. By altering the levels of several secreted proteins that affect proliferation and differentiation in different ways, TGF-β might act as a stimulator or an inhibitor of cellular growth or differentiation, depending on the strengths of the cellular responses to each extracellular signal.

cell proliferation, in the early embryo and during organogenesis. The ECM-sparing effect of TGF-β is expected to be important during periods in development when specific membranes are deposited to delineate the organs, or during the development of tissues, such as cartilage and bone, in which a large amount of ECM must accumulate.

For the formation of new tissues during fetal development, TGF-β and a proliferative growth factor (e.g., PDGF, EGF, or FGF) might coordinate their actions so that the proliferative growth factor would stimulate cell multiplication and TGF-β would stimulate the accumulation of the ECM. As well, TGF-β could increase tissue growth during development by acting synergistically with one of these growth factors to stimulate cell proliferation and/or by inducing PDGF synthesis.

Whether cells respond to TGF-β with increased or decreased proliferation will depend on their relative sensitivities to the action of extracellular proteases, the PDGF produced in response to TGF-β, and the other growth factors in the environment. A cell's response to TGF-β and other growth factors is, in turn, determined by its intracellular biochemical state, the receptors expressed on its surface, and the regulatory molecules (including the ECM) in its environment. Thus, to summarize the model for TGF-β action in development (Fig. 2), it is proposed that TGF-β regulates the expression of two important sets of genes: One set of TGF-β-regulated genes encodes growth factors and differentiation factors, and another set of TGF-β-regulated genes encodes proteins that in one way or another impact on the ECM. Depending on the cell's biochemical condition and its environment, it will respond to TGF-β with increased or decreased proliferation or differentiation.

B. Effects of TGF-β on Cellular Differentiation

The flexibility of the cellular response to TGF-β allows this molecule a large range of possibilities for regulating cellular growth and differentiation in development. Such a range is evident in the variety of responses that have already been reported for cells treated with TGF-β. For example, TGF-β inhibits the differentiation of adipocytes (Ignotz and Massagué, 1985) and keratinocytes (Reiss and Sartorelli, 1987; Ristow, 1986) without altering the growth rates of the affected cells, and it inhibits both proliferation and differentiation of skeletal and smooth muscle cells (Florini *et al.*, 1986; Olson *et al.*, 1986; Assoian and Sporn, 1986; Massagué *et al.*, 1986). By contrast, TGF-β stimulates differentiation of human bronchial epithelial cells (Masui *et al.*, 1986) and intestinal crypt epithelial cells (Kurokowa *et al.*, 1987; Lee *et al.*, 1987) concomitant with inhibiting their proliferation.

Another action of TGF-β on cells in culture that may be related to its action *in vivo* is its ability to allow hypertrophy while inhibiting hyperplasia. This effect has been observed in renal proximal tubular epithelial cells (Fine *et al.*, 1985) and in vascular smooth muscle cells (Owens *et al.*, 1988). Hypertrophy accompanied by DNA endoreplication is commonly found in mammalian cells *in vivo*. Although much of this activity occurs during postnatal life, there are some instances in which hypertrophy is a normal part of embryonic development; a notable example of this is the trophoblastic giant cell in the rodent, which is the product of massive hypertrophy and DNA endoreplication. The giant cell, which is the functional equivalent of the human syncytiotrophoblast, is the source of several placental hormones. It is not understood whether this altered cellular condition helps the giant cell in its function, and if so, how; however, it is possible that the giant cell got that way because of the action of TGF-β.

1. Bone and Cartilage

TGF-β clearly plays a special role in the growth and development of bone and cartilage by stimulating the proliferation and differentiation of osteoblasts and chondrocytes. One of the major sites of TGF-β synthesis and localization in the fetus is the developing bone and cartilage (Heine *et al.*, 1987; Lehnert and Akhurst, 1988; see also Chapter 8 of this volume).

Fetal rat calvaria secrete TGF-β into the culture medium (Centrella and Canalis, 1985; Centrella *et al.*, 1986). The hypothesis that this secreted

TGF-β is part of an autocrine loop to stimulate osteoblast proliferation is supported by the results of one study, in which DNA synthesis in cultures of fetal rat calvaria was stimulated by TGF-β (Centrella *et al.*, 1986), which also stimulated proliferation of osteoblasts in culture (Robey *et al.*, 1987). However, in other studies TGF-β inhibited DNA synthesis in murine MC3T3E1 osteoblastlike cells (Noda and Rodan, 1986) and rat osteoblastic osteosarcoma cells (Pfeilschifter *et al.*, 1987; Noda and Rodan, 1987). These seemingly contradictory results might be explained by the results of another study, in which it was demonstrated that, although TGF-β alone did not stimulate DNA synthesis in osteoblast-like cells that migrated out of cultured rat calvaria, it potentiated the stimulatory effect of FGF on osteoblast proliferation (Globus *et al.*, 1988). The ability of TGF-β to enhance osteoblast proliferation is noteworthy because the highest concentrations of TGF-β in the body, other than that in platelets, are found in bone (Seyedin *et al.*, 1985), and one of the major sites of TGF-β expression in the fetus is the developing fetal bone (Seyedin *et al.*, 1986; Heine *et al.*, 1987).

Some studies have shown that TGF-β stimulates osteoblastic differentiation of osteosarcoma cells (Pfeilschifter *et al.*, 1987; Noda and Rodan, 1987) and osteoblasts from fetal rat calvaria (Centrella *et al.*, 1987), whereas others demonstrated inhibition of differentiation of murine osteoblast-like cells (Noda and Rodan, 1986) and no effect on differentiation of fetal rat osteoblasts (Robey *et al.*, 1987). TGF-β also induces chondrogenesis by embryonic rat mesenchymal cells (Ellingsworth *et al.*, 1986; Seyedin *et al.*, 1987).

During formation of bone tissue, latent TGF-β is secreted and incorporated into the bone matrix. This TGF-β may be important for later bone remodeling events and may be released from the matrix during bone resorption by activated osteoclasts (Oreffo *et al.*, 1989). Factors that stimulate bone resorption (e.g., interleukin 1, 1,25-dihydroxy-vitamin D_3, and parathyroid hormone) also increase TGF-β production by cultures of rat fetal calvaria. Calcitonin, an inhibitor of bone resorption, decreases TGF-β production by these cells (Pfeilschifter and Mundy, 1987). The TGF-β released in the resorbing bone would inhibit osteoclast formation (Chenu *et al.*, 1988) and stimulate proliferation of osteoblasts in collaboration with bFGF (Globus *et al.*, 1988). Basic FGF is also an ECM-associated growth factor that might be released by the action of osteoclasts (see Chapter 3 of this volume). Bone-derived latent TGF-β is activated by osteoclasts (Oreffo *et al.*, 1989). This provides for what is probably a negative feedback regulatory loop for osteoclast activation. A more detailed discussion of the role of TGF-β in bone development can be found in Chapter 8 of this volume. Figure 2 in Chapter 8 presents a model for the interactions involving TGF-β that are proposed to occur between osteoclasts and osteoblasts during bone growth and remodeling.

2. Angiogenesis

Another important aspect of fetal development is vascularization, which depends on the generation of angiogenic factors. TGF-β is a strong angiogenic factor *in vivo* (Madri *et al.,* 1988); however, it inhibits the proliferation of cultured endothelial cells from human renal microvasculature, bovine aortas, and fetal bovine heart (Fràter-Schröder *et al.*, 1986; Heimark *et al.*, 1986; Müller *et al.*, 1987; Madri *et al.*, 1988). The inhibitory effect of TGF-β was temporary (Heimark *et al.,* 1986) and reversed after removal of TGF-β, but could not be overcome with high concentrations of FGF (Fràter-Schröder *et al.,* 1986). The addition of fibronectin to the culture medium of microvascular endothelial cells also inhibited their proliferation (Madri *et al.,* 1988). This result suggests that TGF-β might inhibit endothelial cell proliferation through its extracellular matrix-sparing action. Other effects of TGF-β on endothelial cells grown in monolayer culture are the inhibition of adhesiveness for blood neutrophils (Gamble and Vadas, 1988), a decreased number of high-affinity binding sites for EGF, a decreased ability to respond to EGF with the induction of a set of "competence" genes (e.g., c-*myc,* JE, and KC), but no change in the level of EGF-induced c-*fos* (Takehara *et al.,* 1987).

Despite the observed inhibitory effects of TGF-β on cultured cells, it stimulates endothelial cells to express c-*sis* (Daniel *et al.,* 1987), which encodes PDGF, a potent mitogen for these cells (Zetter and Antoniades, 1979). One report described a transient growth-inhibitory effect of TGF-β on endothelial cell proliferation (Heimark *et al.,* 1986). Perhaps the later reversion of the inhibition was due to the production of PDGF. The ability of TGF-β to induce c-*sis* may be the means by which it stimulates angiogenesis *in vivo*.

The reason for the discrepancy between the results of studies of the effect of TGF-β on proliferation of endothelial cells in culture and on angiogenesis *in vivo* seems to be the different three-dimensional organizations of the cells relative to the ECM. Thus, the effect of TGF-β on endothelial cellular proliferation is quite different when microvascular endothelial cells are allowed to grow in three-dimensional collagen gels: Proliferation is not inhibited and the cells are stimulated to form complex, branching, tubelike structures that resemble capillaries (Madri *et al.,* 1988).

3. Hematopoietic Cells and the Immune System

TGF-β has profound and wide-reaching effects on the cells of the immune system. It inhibits proliferation of B lymphocytes (Kehrl *et al.,* 1986a,b; Rook *et al.,* 1986; Smeland *et al.,* 1987), IL-2-induced T lymphocytes

(Kehrl *et al.*, 1985), and IL-1-induced thymocytes (Ristow, 1986; Wahl *et al.*, 1988) and maturation of B lymphocytes (Lee *et al.*, 1987). TGF-β also suppresses the generation of interferon-induced (but not IL-1-induced) natural killer (T) cell cytolytic activity (Rook *et al.*, 1986), cytotoxic T lymphocytes (Ranges *et al.*, 1987), and lymphokine-activated human killer cell precursors (Kasid *et al.*, 1988). Specific evidence of maturation and differentiation that are prevented by TGF-β includes induction of the IL-2 receptor and IL-2-dependent generation of immunoglobulin G by B cells (Kehrl *et al.*, 1986a). TGF-β also inhibits the expression of class II histocompatibility antigens on human melanoma HS294T cells, with concomitant decreases in the amount of class II human leukocyte antigen (HLA)-DR mRNA transcripts (Czarniecki *et al.*, 1988).

Not all effects of TGF-β on hematopoietic cells are inhibitory. For example, it induces IL-1 production by human peripheral blood monocytes and stimulates their directed migration (Varga *et al.*, 1987). Macrophages and T cells possess receptors with a higher affinity for TGF-β (1–10 p*M*) than do fibroblasts (Rook *et al.*, 1986; Varga *et al.*, 1987), and their chemotaxis is stimulated by picogram-per-milliliter levels of TGF-β. By contrast, IL-1 production is stimulated by about 1 ng/ml of TGF-β (Varga *et al.*, 1987).

When tested at various times after its activation, it was found that TGF-β inhibits the proliferative B lymphocyte response, which involves a transition from the G_0/G_1 phase to the S phase of the cell cycle (Smeland *et al.*, 1987). However, in the same cells TGF-β did not inhibit events such as increased Ca^{2+} flux, induction of c-*myc* mRNA and the 4F2 activation antigen, and cellular enlargement that may be involved in activation of the lymphocytes (Smeland *et al.*, 1987). In contrast, TGF-β deactivated macrophages and reduced their rate of H_2O_2 output by about 86% after 2 days (Tsunawaki *et al.*, 1988).

TGF-β may act in some hematopoietic cells in an autocrine mode. For example, lymphokine-activated killer cell precursors constitutively express TGF-β and TGF-βRs, and the TGF-β mRNA level increases three- to fivefold in response to IL-2 (Kasid *et al.*, 1988). Macrophages (Assoian *et al.*, 1987) and human T lymphocytes (Kehrl *et al.*, 1986b) also produce increased amounts of TGF-β after their activation. Both lymphokine-activated killer cells and activated macrophages secrete TGF-β.

Consistent with these many effects of TGF-β on functions of hematopoietic cells is the observation that a high level of TGF-β is found in the bone marrow and in hematopoietic precursors of the fetal liver (Ellingsworth *et al.*, 1986). Although, for most cells, there is no distinction in effectiveness between TGF-β1 and TGF-β2, TGF-β1 was 100 times more effective than TGF-β2 in inhibiting proliferation of hematopoietic progenitor cells in response to IL-3 or granulocyte–macrophage colony-stimulating factor (GM-CSF) (Ohta *et al.*, 1987; Ottmann and Pelus, 1988). TGF-β also inhibited M-CSF (CSF-1)-stimulated colony formation by bone marrow cells (Ohta *et al.*, 1987; Strassmann *et al.*, 1988; Ottmann and Pelus, 1988) and by a c-*myc* partially transformed CSF-1-dependent macrophage cell line (Strassman *et al.*, 1988). However, TGF-β1 (but not TGF-β2) enhanced by about 50% the proliferation of GM colony-forming progenitor cells that grew in response to IL-3, G-CSF, and GM-CSF (Ottmann and Pelus, 1988).

4. Steroidogenic Cells

TGF-β regulates the differentiation of several steroidogenic cell types, such as the ovarian granulosa cell and the adrenocortical cell. The effects of TGF-β are of two types: (1) to regulate the levels of steroidogenic enzymes and (2) to regulate the number of cell surface receptors for proteins that regulate steroidogenesis. For example, in ovarian granulosa cells, TGF-β stimulates follicle-stimulating hormone (FSH)-stimulated (but not basal) estrogen and progesterone syntheses by ovarian granulosa cells (Knecht *et al.*, 1987; Dodson and Schomberg, 1987; Ying *et al.*, 1986b). TGF-β also augmented the stimulatory effect of FSH on the exposure of luteinizing hormone receptors (Feng *et al.*, 1986; Knecht *et al.*, 1987). TGF-β had a small (25% increase) stimulatory effect on EGF-stimulated proliferation of porcine granulosa cells when they were cultured in low concentrations of platelet-poor plasma (0.1–0.25%) cells, but inhibited EGF-stimulated proliferation in the presence of higher concentrations (0.5–2.5%) of platelet-poor plasma (May *et al.*, 1988). The conditional stimulation of granulosa cell proliferation by TGF-β observed by May *et al.* (1988) may be related to the observation by Dorrington *et al.* (1988) that TGF-β-stimulated DNA synthesis in rat granulosa cells is augmented by FSH.

Another function of TGF-β in the ovary may be to stimulate meiotic maturation of oocytes and thus to regulate oocyte selection and maturation during follicular development (Feng *et al.*, 1988). The source of TGF-β for regulating ovarian development *in vivo* is probably the thecal cells, which secrete TGF-β in culture (Skinner *et al.*, 1987).

TGF-β regulates steroidogenesis in the testes, as well as in the ovary, by inhibiting human chorionic gonadotropin (hcG)-stimulated testosterone production by Leydig cells (Avallet *et al.*, 1987; Lin *et al.*, 1987) and stimulating the conversion of exogenous progesterone to testosterone (Avallet *et al.*, 1987).

TGF-β also inhibits adrenocorticotropic hormone (ACTH)-stimulated cortisol production by bovine adrenocortical cells without altering proliferation or the ACTH-induced cAMP increase (Hotta and Baird, 1986). The effect of TGF-β on steroidogenesis has been variably ascribed to a decrease in the amount of 17 α-hydroxylase activity (Feige *et al.*, 1987) and decreased low-density lipoprotein uptake (Hotta and Baird, 1987). TGF-β also inhibited angiotensin II-stimulated cortisol production by the same mechanism and decreased angiotensin II receptor levels (Feige *et al.*, 1987). This effect is specific for TGF-β compared with inhibin and activin (see Section VII,B for more discussion of the latter two TGF-related hormones).

C. Cell Migration

Directed movements of selected cells within the embryo are essential in early mammalian development. TGF-β could be responsible for producing at least two types of secreted stimuli to direct the movement of cells through the embryo. The first is the secretion of a "track" of a particular composition of ECM by cells in the specified path. The prominence of genes encoding proteins responsible for ECM deposition and maintenance among the genes regulated by TGF-β suggest that TGF-β could play an important role in the development of these directional tracks. In this regard it will be of great interest to determine whether various forms of TGF-β cause the production of ECMs of different composition, thus producing different types of migration tracks.

The second means by which TGF-β might regulate specific cell migration during development is through a property that it shares with many other growth factors. This is the ability to stimulate chemotaxis of human fibroblasts (Postlethwaite *et al.*, 1987) and monocytes (Varga *et al.*, 1987) in culture. Thus, TGF-β stimulates the production of two potential migration signals: It might induce the synthesis of a track in the ECM, and it is itself a soluble chemotactic factor.

VI. TGF-β *in Vivo*

A. Wound Healing

Another rich source of TGF-β in the adult is the platelet fraction of blood (Assoian *et al.*, 1983). In the mouse embryo the fetal liver megakaryocytes are locations of abundant TGF-β mRNA (Lehnert and Akhurst, 1988). This concentration of TGF-β in platelets may be related to its ability to accelerate cellular functions needed during wound healing. Intradermal treatment of rats with TGF-β results in fibrosis *in vivo* (Roberts *et al.*, 1986). TGF-β also causes increased accumulation of total protein, collagen, and DNA in wound chambers implanted *in vivo*. (Sporn *et al.*, 1983) and accelerates the rate of healing of excisional wounds in rats (Mustoe *et al.*, 1987). These effects of TGF-B *in vivo* are consistent with the ECM-sparing effects of TGF-β observed in cultured cells. Similarly, TGF-β is expected to parallel effects on developmental events that involve cellular proliferation and tissue expansion.

By far the largest response of most cells to TGF-β is the expression of protease inhibitors (Nilsen-Hamilton and Holley, 1983; Laiho *et al.*, 1986a; Thalacker and Nilsen-Hamilton, 1987; Lund *et al.*, 1987; Edwards *et al.*, 1987; see also Chapter 8 of this volume). The protease inhibitors are believed to be produced to limit the destruction wrought by the proteases induced by growth factors such as EGF, FGF, and PDGF. Although the growth factor-induced proteases perform useful functions, such as degrading the ECM and allowing cellular migration or providing space for the daughter cells, their destruction of the ECM must be limited to maintain the integrity of the developing embryo. TGF-β may be the major embryonic factor that limits the destructive effects of these growth factor-induced proteases in developing tissues. For more discussion of the concept that localized expression of TGF-β may provide localized protection from protease action, see Chapter 8 of this volume.

B. Mammalian Development

TGF-β can be found in mouse embryos (Proper *et al.*, 1982; Twardzik *et al.*, 1982) and term human placentas (Frolik *et al.*, 1984). Consistent with the knowledge that it is a cartilage-inducing factor and also regulates osteoclast and osteoblast functions (see Section V,B,1), TGF-β is found concentrated in the centers of developing bone and cartilage in the 6-month bovine fetus (Ellingsworth *et al.*, 1986) and in fetal human bone (Sandberg *et al.*, 1988). TGF-β and its mRNA are concentrated in fetal cartilage and bone in 11- to 18-day mouse embryos (Heine *et al.*, 1987; Lehnert and Akhurst, 1988). The specific localization of TGF-β in cartilage and bone depended on the day of development. For example, at day 11, the somites in the caudal part of the axial skeleton were uniformly stained with anti-TGF-β. However, after the somites had differentiated (between days 11 and 13) the TGF-β was found only in the schlerodome and dermatome (Heine *et al.*, 1987). For more discussion of TGF-β and fetal bone development, see Chapter 8 of this volume.

The fetal liver, which contains the developing hematopoietic system, is another fetal location of high concentration of TGF-β and its mRNA (Ellingsworth *et al.*, 1986; Lehnert and Akhurst, 1988; Wilcox and Derynck, 1988). The TGF-β protein was found to be absent from the hepatocytes of bovine fetal liver and was located in the hematopoietic stem cells (Ellingsworth *et al.*, 1986). TGF-β mRNA was also located in the hematopoietic cells of the blood islands and capillaries (Wilcox and Derynck, 1988). Also, TGF-β mRNA is induced in regenerating adult liver, but is absent from the hepatocytes (Braun *et al.*, 1988). These results are consistent with observations of the high TGF-β content of platelets and megakaryocytes, and also of the many effects of TGF-β on hematopoietic cellular growth and differentiation (see Section V,B,3).

Another prominent location of TGF-β in the fetus is in regions in which there is a lot of angiogenic activity (Heine *et al.*, 1987). This is also consistent with the effects of TGF-β on endothelial cellular proliferation and migration (see Section V,B,2).

TGF-β mRNA predominated in certain developing organs, such as the oral cavity, otic vesicle, fetal heart, submandibular gland, pharyngeal pouch, and kidneys (Wilcox and Derynck, 1988; Lehnert and Akhurst, 1988). Antiserum to TGF-β recognized the protein in tissues in which development is known to involve epithelial–mesenchymal interactions: the hair follicles and tooth buds (see Chapter 2 of this volume). *In situ* hybridization for TGF-β mRNA showed that wherever TGF-β protein was found in the mesenchyme, TGF-β mRNA was found in the adjacent epithelium (Lehnert and Akhurst, 1988). Thus, it appears that TGF-β might act as a paracrine factor which is produced by epithelial cells and regulates growth and differentiation in adjacent mesenchymal cells. The same TGF-β could be a paracrine regulator of epithelial cell function (Lehnert and Akhurst, 1988).

As well as regulating events in organogenesis, TGF-β may have a regulatory role in the early embryo (see also Chapter 9 of this volume). TGF-β protein and its mRNA were detected, along with the mRNAs for TGF-α and PDGF, in mouse preimplantation blastocysts. Although there were maternal transcripts of TGF-α and PDGF before fertilization, TGF-β1 transcripts only appeared after fertilization (Rappolee *et al.*, 1988).

VII. The TGF-β Family in Development

A. Müllerian Inhibitory Substance

Although the existence of MIS was predicted in 1916 (Lillie, 1916), the molecule was not purified until the late 1970s and was then found to contain two 70- 74-kDa glycoprotein subunits in covalent association through disulfide bonds (Josso *et al.*, 1981). MIS is expressed during early gonadal development in the male and causes regression of the Müllerian duct, which, in the female, would normally develop into the vagina, uterus, and fallopian tubes (Picon, 1979). Regression of the Müllerian ducts occurs early in development, before the delineation of the seminiferous tubules. When human and bovine genomic and cDNA clones for MIS were isolated and sequenced, the MIS gene was found to encode a 58-kDa protein that contained a carboxy-terminal region having extensive sequence homology with that of mature TGF-β (Cate *et al.*, 1986). The sequence of this TGF-β-like region shows complete conservation of its six cysteines, which indicates that the secondary structures of these two proteins are likely to be similar. It is interesting to note in this context that MIS inhibits cell proliferation, as does TGF-β. As well as causing regression of the Müllerian ducts in the embryo, MIS inhibits the proliferation of a large number of ovarian and endometrial tumors, both as cultured cells (Donahoe *et al.*, 1979; Fuller *et al.*, 1982, 1985) and in nude mice (Donahoe *et al.*, 1981).

B. Inhibin and Activin

Inhibin was first identified as an activity which could be extracted from follicular fluid that specifically inhibited the secretion of FSH (but not luteinizing hormone) by pituitary gonadotrophs (McCullagh, 1932; Bronson and Channing, 1978; Marder *et al.*, 1977). It also acts directly on granulosa cells to inhibit FSH-stimulated estrogen synthesis (Ying *et al.*, 1986b). This activity is in direct opposition to the effect of TGF-β on granulosa cell steroid synthesis (Ying *et al.*, 1986b). Inhibin was purified and found to be a heterodimeric glycoprotein hormone with its subunits linked through disulfide bonds (Mason *et al.*, 1985; reviewed by Meunier *et al.*, 1988). One type of inhibin α subunit and two types of β subunit (A and B) associate in various combinations. The β subunit is related in sequence to TGF-β (Mason *et al.*, 1985; Ling *et al.*, 1986; Vale *et al.*, 1986).

The inhibin α and β chains are expressed in many adult tissues, including the ovarian follicle, brain, bone marrow, testes, adrenal gland, kidney, and spinal cord (Mason *et al.*, 1986; Forage *et al.*, 1986; Meunier *et al.*, 1988). Inhibin is also expressed in the human placenta (Mayo *et al.*, 1986). The inhibin α chain was found to be localized specifically in the cytotrophoblasts of the human placenta by using an immunocytochemical stain (Merchenthaler *et al.*, 1987).

Inhibin secretion by the ovary (granulosa cells) and the testes (Sertoli cells) is stimulated by FSH (Ying *et al.*, 1987; Bicsak *et al.*, 1987) in a manner that is potentiated by estrogen and androstenedione (Ying *et al.*, 1987). EGF inhibits the expression of inhibin by granulosa cells (Zhiwen *et al.*, 1987). It is not known what regulates the expression of inhibin in the placenta, but TGF-α is synthesized by the decidua (Han *et al.*, 1987), and androstenedione and testosterone are believed to be synthesized by the placenta (Soares and Talamantes, 1983; Matt *et al.*, 1986). These could regulate inhibin secretion by the placenta.

As well as the α–β inhibin dimer, the β subunit also forms a homodimer that has different effects from those induced by inhibin. For example, both homodimers and heterodimers of the β subunits stimulate FSH release by isolated pituitary cells in culture and thereby oppose the action of inhibin (Ling *et al.*, 1986). Similarly TGF-β stimulates FSH production by pituitary cells in culture (Ying *et al.*, 1986a). The β chain homodimer of inhibin has been named activin (Ling *et al.*, 1986), or FSH-releasing protein (Vale *et al.*, 1986). It is the same molecule as the erythropoietic factor that was isolated from a human leukemia cell line (Eto *et al.*, 1987). Although inhibin, activin, and TGF-β all regulate granulosa cell differentiation, TGF-β is the only member of the family that has been found to regulate steroidogenesis by adrenocortical cells; neither activin nor inhibin has this activity (Hotta and Baird, 1987).

VIII. Summary and Conclusions

TGF-β stimulates the anchorage-dependent proliferation of some cells and inhibits the proliferation of others. Although the ability of TGF-β to affect different cell types in opposite ways is puzzling, it may not reflect fundamental differences in the initial cellular responses to TGF-β. Instead, the different types of cellular responses may be because TGF-β initiates a number of changes in all responsive cells, some of which may lead to proliferation and others, to proliferative arrest. Depending on the individual responses of specific cell types and on the environment of the cells, the balance of the effects of these changes could lead to cellular proliferation or inhibition of proliferation. This hypothesis is discussed in more detail below, with specific reference to the effects of TGF-β on the expression of genes encoding proteases, protease inhibitors, ECM components, and growth and differentiation factors.

TGF-β also promotes the anchorage-independent growth of some cells in soft agar, but inhibits the anchorage-independent proliferation of some tumor cells. In stimulating proliferation TGF-β often acts synergistically with EGF, FGF, TGF-α, or PDGF. The observed increase in soft agar growth in response to TGF-β could be explained by a model which proposes that TGF-β stimulates the accumulation of the ECM, which supports the action of the growth factors (e.g., EGF, TGF-α, PDGF, and FGF) that directly stimulate cellular proliferation. The ability of TGF-β to inhibit the proliferation of some cells in soft agar again reminds us that the mechanism of action of this growth factor is not readily described by a single model.

Although its proven ability to regulate the expression of genes that encode proteins that constitute or modify the ECM ensures TGF-β a role in ECM remodeling, the complexity of the multiple cellular responses to this growth factor suggest that there is another aspect of the function of this growth factor. Perhaps the observations that TGF-β stimulates the production of FSH and PDGF are the tip of the iceberg. If TGF-β regulates a subset of genes that encode growth factors and their receptors, then this could help to explain the many and varied cellular responses to TGF-β. By regulating genes encoding other hormones and growth factors, TGF-β might be a "master morphogen" during development and orchestrate the local elaboration of growth factors and hormones by individual cell types.

References

Anzano, M. A., Roberts, A. B., Meyers, C. A., Komoriya, A., Lamb, L. C., Smith, J. M., and Sporn, M. B. (1982). *Cancer Res.* **42,** 4776–4778.

Assoian, R. K. (1985). *J. Biol. Chem.* **260,** 9613–9617.

Assoian, R. K., and Sporn, M. B. (1986). *J. Cell Biol.* **102,** 1217–1223.

Assoian, R. K., Komoriya, A., Meyers, C. A., Miller, D. M., and Sporn, M. B. (1983). *J. Biol. Chem.* **258,** 7155–7160.

Assoian, R. K., Fleurdelys, B. E., Stevenson, H. C., Miller, P. J., Madtes, D. K., Raines, E. W., Ross, R., and Sporn, M. B. (1987). *Proc. Natl. Acad. Sci. U.S.A.* **84,** 6020–6024.

Avallet, O., Vigier, M., Perrard-Sapori, M. H., and Saez, J. M. (1987). *Biochem. Biophys. Res. Commun.* **146,** 575–581.

Baird, A., and Durkin, T. (1986). *Biochem. Biophys. Res. Commun.* **138,** 476–482.

Barnard, J. A., Beauchamp, R. D., Coffey, R. J., and Moses, H. L. (1989). *Proc. Natl. Acad. Sci. U.S.A.* **86,** 1578–1582.

Bar-Shavit, R., Kahn, A. J., Mann, K. G., and Wilner, G. D. (1986). *Proc. Natl. Acad. Sci. U.S.A.* **83,** 976–980.

Bassols, A., and Massagué, J. (1988). *J. Biol. Chem.* **263,** 3039–3045.

Bicsak, T. A., Vale, W., Vaughan, J., Tucker, E. M., Cappel, S., and Hsueh, A. J. W. (1987). *Mol. Cell. Endocrinol.* **49,** 211–217.

Boyd, F. T., and Massagué, J. (1989). *J. Biol. Chem.* **264,** 2272–2278.

Braun, L., Mead, J. E., Panzica, M., Mikumo, R., Bell, G. I., and Fausto, N. (1988). *EMBO J* **85,** 1539–1543.

Bronson, F. H., and Channing, C. P. (1978). *Endocrinology* (*Baltimore*) **103,** 1894.

Brown, K. D., and Holley, R. W. (1987). *Proc. Natl. Acad. Sci. U.S.A.* **84,** 3743–3747.

Brunner, A. M., Gentry, L. E., Cooper, J. A., and Purchio, A. F. (1988). *Mol. Cell. Biol.* **8,** 2229–2232.

Carr, B. I., Hayashi, I., Branum, E. L., and Moses, H. L. (1986). *Cancer Res.* **46,** 2330–2334.

Cate, R. L., Mattaliano, R. J., Hession, C., Tizard, R., Farber, N. M., Cheung, A., Ninfa, E. G., Frey, A. Z., Gash, D. J., Chow, E. P., Fisher, R. A., Bertonis, J. M., Torres, G., Wallner, B. P., Ramachandran, K. L., Ragin, R. C., Manganaro, T. F., MacLaughlin, D. T., and Donahoe, P. K. (1986). *Cell* (*Cambridge, Mass.*) **45,** 685–698.

Centrella, M., and Canalis, E. (1985). *Proc. Natl. Acad. Sci. U.S.A.* **82,** 7335–7339.

Centrella, M., Massagué, J., and Canalis, E. (1986). *Endocrinology (Baltimore)* **119,** 2306–2312.

Centrella, M., McCarthy, T. L., and Canalis, E. (1987). *J. Biol. Chem.* **262,** 2869–2874.

Cheifetz, S., Like B., and Massagué, J. (1986). *J. Biol. Chem.* **261,** 9972–9978.

Cheifetz, S., Weatherbee, J. A., Tsang, M. L.-S., Anderson, J. K., Mole, J. E., Lucas, R., and Massagué, J. (1987). *Cell (Cambridge, Mass.)* **48,** 409–415.

Cheifetz, S., Andres, J. L., and Massagué, J. (1988a). *J. Biol. Chem.* **263,** 16984–16991.

Cheifetz, S., Bassols, A., Stanley, K., Ohta, M., Greenberger, J., and Massagué, J. (1988b). *J. Biol. Chem.* **263,** 10783–10789.

Chen, J.-K., Hoshi, H., and McKeehan, W. L. (1987). *Proc. Natl. Acad. Sci. U.S.A.* **84,** 5287–5291.

Chen, L. B., and Buchanan, J. M. (1975). *Proc. Natl. Acad. Sci. U.S.A.* **72,** 131–135.

Chenu, C., Pfeilschifter, J., Mundy, G. R., and Roodman, G. D. (1988). *Proc. Natl. Acad. Sci.U.S.A.* **85,** 5683–5687.

Chiang, C.-P., and Nilsen-Hamilton, M. (1986). *J. Biol. Chem.* **261,** 10478–10481.

Chiang, C.-P., Hamilton, R. T., Parfett, C. L. J., and Nilsen-Hamilton, M. (1990). Submitted for publication.

Coffey, R. J., Jr., Bascom, C. C., Sipes, N. J., Graves-Deal, R., Weissman, B. E., and Moses, H. L. (1988). *Mol. Cell. Biol.* **8,** 3088–3093.

Czarniecki, C. W., Chiu, H. H., Wong, G. H. W., McCabe, S. M., and Palladino, M. A. (1988). *J. Immunol.* **140,** 4217–4223.

Daniel, T. O., Gibbs, V. C., Milfay, D. F., and Williams, L. T. (1987). *J. Biol. Chem.* **262,** 11893–11896.

DeLarco, J. E., and Todaro, G. J. (1978). *Proc. Natl. Acad. Sci. U.S.A.* **75,** 4001–4005.

de Martin, R., Haendler, B., Hofer-Warbinek, R., Gaugitsch, H., Wrann, M., Schlusenger, H., Seifert, J. M., Bodmer, S., Fontana, A., and Hofer, E. (1987). *EMBO J.* **6,** 3673–3677.

Derynck, R., Jarrett, J. A., Chen, E. Y., Eaton, D. H., Bell, J. R., Assoian, R. K., Roberts, A. B., Sporn, M. B., and Goeddel, D. V. (1985). *Nature (London)* **316,** 701–705.

Derynck, R., Jarrett, J. A., Chen, E. Y., and Goeddel, D. V. (1986). *J. Biol. Chem.* **261,** 4377–4379.

Dodson, W. C., and Schomberg, D. W. (1987). *Endocrinology (Baltimore)* **120,** 512–516.

Donahoe, P. K., Swann D. A., Hayashi, A., and Sullivan, M. D. (1979). *Science* **205,** 913–915.

Donahoe, P. K., Fuller, A. F., Jr., Sailly, R. E., Guy, S. B., and Budzik, G. P. (1981). *Ann. Surg.* **194,** 472–480.

Donahoe, P. K., Krane, I., Boyden, A. E., Kamagata, S., and Budzik, G. P. (1984). *J. Pediatr. Surg.* **19,** 863.

Dorrington, J., Chuma, A. V., and Bendell, J. J. (1988). *Endocrinology (Baltimore)* **123,** 353–359.

Dufour, S., Duband, J.-L., Kornblihtt, A. R., and Thiery, J. P. (1988). *Trends Genet.* **4,** 198–203.

Duke, P. T., Hansen, P., Iwata, K. K., Pieler, C., and Foulkes, J. G. (1988). *Proc. Natl. Acad. Sci. U.S.A.* **85,** 4715–4719.

Edwards, D. R., Murphy, G., Reynolds, J. J., Whitham, S. E., Docherty, A. J. P., Angel, P., and Heath, J. K. (1987). *EMBO J.* **6,** 1899–1904.

Ellingsworth, L. R., Brennan, J. E., Fok, K., Rosen, D. M., Bentz, H., Piez, K. A., and Seyedin, S. M. (1986). *J. Biol. Chem.* **261,** 12362–12367.

Enat, R., Jefferson, D. M., Ruiz-Opaya, N., Gatmaitan, A., Leinwand, L. A., and Reid, L. M. (1984). *Proc. Natl. Acad. Sci. U.S.A.* **81,** 1411–1415.

Espevik, T., Figari, I., Shalaby, M. R., Lackides, G. A., Lewis, G. D., Shepard, H. M., and Palladino, M. A. (1987). *J. Exp. Med.* **166,** 571–576.

Eto, Y., Tsuji, T., Takezawa, M., Takano, S., Yokigawa, Y., and Shibai, H. (1987). *Biochem. Biophys. Res. Commun.* **142,** 1095–1103.

Fanger, B. O., Wakefield, L. M., and Sporn, M. B. (1986). *Biochemistry* **25,** 3083–3091.

Feige, J.-J., Cochet, C., Rainey, W. E., Madani, C., and Chambaz, E. M. (1987). *J. Biol. Chem.* **262,** 13491–13495.

Feng, P., Catt, K. J., and Knecht, M. (1986). *J. Biol. Chem.* **261,** 14167–14170.

Feng, P., Catt, K. J., and Knecht, M. (1988). *Endocrinology (Baltimore)* **122,** 181–186.

Fernandez-Pol, J. A., Talkad, V. D., Klos, D. J., and Hamilton, P. D. (1987). *Biochem. Biophys. Res. Commun.* **144,** 1197–1205.

Fine, A., and Goldstein, R. H. (1987). *J. Biol. Chem.* **262,** 3897–3902.

Fine, L. G., Holley, R. W., Nasri, H., and Badie-Dezfooly, B. (1985). *Proc. Natl. Acad. Sci. U.S.A.* **82,** 6163–6166.

Florini, J. R., Roberts, A. B., Ewton, D. Z., Falen, S. L., Flanders, K. C., and Sporn, M. B. (1986). *J. Biol. Chem.* **261,** 16509–16513.

Forage, R. G., Ring, J. M., Brown, R. W., McInerny, B. V., Cobon, G. S., Gregson, R. P., Robertson, D. M., Morgand, F. J., Hearn, M. T. W., Findlay, J. K., Wettenhall, R. E. H., Burger, H. G., and Krester, D. M. (1986). *Proc. Natl. Acad. Sci. U.S.A.* **83,** 3091–3095.

Fràter-Schröder, M., Muller, G., Birchmeier, W., and Böhlen, P. (1986). *Biochem. Biophys. Res. Commun.* **137,** 295–302.

Frolik, C. A., Wakefield, L. M., Smith, D. M., and Sporn, M. B. (1984). *J. Biol. Chem.* **259,** 10995–11000.

Fuller, A. F., Jr., Guy, S. R., Budzik, G. P., and Donahoe, P. K. (1982). *J. Clin. Endocrinol. Metab.* **54,** 1051–1055.

Fuller, A. F., Jr., Krane, I. M., Budzik, G. P., and Donahoe, P. K. (1985). *Gynecol. Oncol.* **22,** 135–148.

Gamble, J. R., and Vadas, M. A. (1988). *Science* **242,** 97.

Garcia, J. V., Stoppelli, M. P., Thompson, K. L., Decker, S. J., and Rosner, M. R. (1987). *J. Cell Biol.* **105,** 449–456.

Glenn, K. C., Carney, D. H., Fenton, J. W., II, and Cunningham, D. D. (1980). *J. Biol. Chem.* **255,** 6609–6616.

Glenn, K., Bowen-Pope, D. F., and Ross, R. (1982). *J. Biol. Chem.* **257,** 5172–5176.

Globus, R. K., Patterson-Buckendahl, P., and Gospodarowicz, D. (1988). *Endocrinology (Baltimore)* **123,** 98–105.

Han, V. K. M., Hunter, E. S., III, Pratt, R. M., Zendegui, J. G., and Lee, D. C. (1987). *Mol. Cell. Biol.* **7,** 2335–2343.

Hanks, S. K., Armour, R., Baldwin, J. H., Maldonado, F., Spiess, J., and Holley, R. W. (1988). *Proc. Natl. Acad. Sci. U.S.A.* **85,** 79–82.

Heimark, R. L., Twardzik, D. R., and Schwartz, S. M. (1986). *Science* **233,** 1078–1080.

Heine, U. I., Munoz, E. F., Flanders, K. C., Ellingsworth, L. R., Lam, H.-Y. P., Thompson, N. L., Roberts, A. B., and Sporn, M. B. (1987). *J. Cell Biol.* **105,** 2861–2876.

Heldin, C.-H., Westermark, B., and Wasteson, A. (1981). *Proc. Natl. Acad. Sci. U.S.A.* **78,** 3664–3668.

Hiraki, Y., Inoue, H., Hirai, R., Kato, Y., and Suzuki, F. (1988). *Biochim. Biophys. Acta* **969,** 91–99.

Holley, R. W., Armour, R., and Baldwin, J. H. (1978). *Proc. Natl. Acad. Sci. U.S.A.* **75,** 1864–1866.

Holley, R. W., Böhlen, P., Fava, R., Baldwin, J. H., Kleeman, G., and Armour, R. (1980). *Proc. Natl. Acad. Sci. U.S.A.* **77,** 5989–5992.

Hotta, M., and Baird, A. (1986). *Proc. Natl. Acad. Sci. U.S.A.* **83,** 7795–7799.
Hotta, M., and Baird, A. (1987). *Endocrinology* (*Baltimore*) **121,** 150–159.
Howe, P., Cunningham, M., and Leof, E. (1990). *Biochem J.,* (in press).
Huang, S. S., O'Grady, P., and Huang, J. S. (1988). *J. Biol. Chem.* **263,** 1535–1541.
Hynes, R. O. (1981). *In* "Cell Biology of the Extracellular Matrix" (E. D. Hay, ed.), pp. 295–334. Plenum, New York.
Ignotz, R. A., and Massagué, J. (1985). *Proc Natl. Acad. Sci. U.S.A.* **82,** 8530–8534.
Ignotz, R. A., and Massagué, J. (1986). *J. Biol. Chem.* **261,** 4337–4345.
Ignotz, R. A., and Massagué, J. (1987). *Cell* (*Cambridge, Mass.*) **51,** 189–197.
Ignotz, R. A., and Endo, T., and Massagué, J. (1987). *J. Biol. Chem.* **262,** 6443–6446.
Jakowlew, S. B., Dillart, P. J., Kondaiah, P., Sporn, M. B., and Roberts, A. B. (1988). *Mol. Endocrinol.* **2,** 747–755.
Jang, Y. J., Mubaidin, A. M. D., and Nilsen-Hamilton, M. (1987). *J. Cell Biol.* **105,** 256a.
Josso, N., Picard, J. V., and Vigier, B. (1981). *C. R. Acad. Sci.* **293,** 447–450.
Kamijo, R., Takeda, K., Nagumo, M., and Konno, K. (1989). *Biochem. Biophys. Res. Commun.* **158,** 155–162.
Kasid, A., Bell, G. I., and Director, E. P. (1988). *J. Immunol.* **141,** 690–698.
Kehrl, J. H., Alvarex-Mon, M., and Fauci, A. S. (1985). *J. Clin. Res.* **33,** 610.
Kehrl, J. H., Roberts, A. B., Wakefield, L. M., Jakowlew, S., Sporn, M. B., and Fauci, A. S. (1986a). *J. Immunol.* **137,** 3855.
Kehrl, J. H., Wakefield, L. M., Roberts, A. B., Jakowlew, S., Alvarez-Mon, M., Derynck, R., Sporn, M. B., and Fauci, A. S. (1986b). *J. Exp. Med.* **163,** 1037–1050.
Kelly, D., and Rizzino, A. (1989). *Differentiation* (*Berlin*) **41,** 34–41.
Kimchi, A., Wang, X.-F., Weinberg, R. A., Cheifetz, S., and Massagué, J. (1988). *Science* **240,** 196–199.
Knabbe, C., Lippman, M. E., Wakefield, L. M., Flanders, K. C., Kasid, A., Derynck, R., and Dickson, R. B. (1987). *Cell* (*Cambridge, Mass.*) **48,** 417–428.
Knecht, M., Feng, M., and Catt, K. (1987). *Endocrinology* (*Baltimore*) **120,** 1243–1249.
Koyasu, S., Kadowaki, T., Nishida, E., Tobe, K., Abe, E., Kasuga, M., Sakai, H., and Yahara, I. (1988). *Exp. Cell Res.* **176,** 107–116.
Kurokowa, M., Lynch, K., and Podolsky, D. K. (1987). *Biochem. Biophys. Res. Commun.* **142,** 775–582.
Laiho, M., Saksela, O., Andreasen, P. A., and Keski-Oja, J. (1986a). *J. Cell Biol.* **103,** 2403–2410.
Laiho, M., Saksela, O., and Keski-Oja, J. (1986b). *Exp. Cell Res.* **164,** 399–407.
Lawrence, D. A., Pircher, R., Krycève-Martinerie, C., and Jullien, P. (1984). *J. Cell. Physiol.* **121,** 184–188.
Lawrence, D. A., Pircher, R., and Jullien, P. (1985). *Biochem. Biophys. Res. Commun.* **133,** 1026–1034.
Lax, I., Johnson, A., Howk, R., Sap. J., Bellot, F., Winkler, M., Ullrich, A., Veenstrom, B., Schlessinger, J., and Givol, D. (1988). *Mol. Cell. Biol.* **8,** 1970–1978.
Lee, G., Ellingsworth, L. R., Gillis, S., Wall, R., and Kincade, P. W. (1987). *J. Exp. Med.* **166,** 1290–1299.
Lee, S.-J., and Nathans, D. (1988). *J. Biol. Chem.* **263,** 3521–3527.
Lee, S.-J., Talamantes, F., Wilder, E., Linzer, D. I. H., and Nathans, D. (1988). *Endocrinology* (*Baltimore*) **122,** 1761–1768.
Lehnert, S. A., and Akhurst, R. J. (1988). *Development* **104,** 263–273.
Leof, E. B., Proper, J. A., Goustin, A. S., Shipley, G. D., DiCorleto, P. E., and Moses, H. L. (1986). *Proc. Natl. Acad. Sci. U.S.A.* **83,** 2453–2457.
Liboi, E., Di Francesco, P., Gallinari, P., Testa, U., Rossi, G. B., and Peschle, C. (1988). *Biochem. Biophys. Res. Commun.* **151,** 298–305.
Lillie, F. (1916). *Science* **43,** 611–613.

Lin, T., Blaisdell, J., and Haskell, J. F. (1987). *Biochem. Biophys. Res. Commun.* **146,** 387–394.

Ling, N., Ying, S.-Y., Ueno, N., Shimasaki, S., Esch, F., Hotta, M., and Guillemin, R. (1986). *Nature (London)* **321,** 779–782.

Low, D. A., Scott, R. W., Baker, J. B., and Cunningham, D. D. (1982). *Nature (London)* **298,** 476–478.

Lund, L. R., Riccio, A., Andreassen, P. A., Nielsen, L. S., Kristensen, P., Laiho, M., Saksels, O., Blasi, F., and Dane, K. (1987). *EMBO J.* **6,** 1281–1286.

Lyons, R. M., Keski-Oja, J., and Moses, H. L. (1988). *J. Cell Biol.* **106,** 1659–1665.

McCullagh, A. (1932). *Science* **76,** 19–20.

MacDonald, R. G., Pfeffer, S. R., Coussens, L., Tepper, M. A., Brocklebank, C. M., Mole, J. E., Anderson, J. K., Chen, E., Czech, M. P., and Ullrich, A. (1988). *Science* **239,** 1134–1137.

Machida, C. M., Muldoon, L. L., Rodland, K. D., and Magun, B. E. (1988). *Mol. Cell. Biol.* **8,** 2479–2483.

Madri, J. A., Pratt, B. M., and Tucker, A. M. (1988). *J. Cell Biol.* **106,** 1375–1384.

Makela, T. P., Alitalo, R., Paulsson, Y., Westermark, B., Heldin, C.-H., and Alitalo, K. (1987). *Mol. Cell. Biol.* **7,** 3656–3662.

Marder, M. L., Channing, C. P., and Schwartz, N. B. (1977). *Endocrinology (Baltimore)* **101,** 1639–1642.

Mason, A. J., Hayflick, J. S., Ling, N., Esch, F., Ueno, N., Ying, S.-H., Guillemin, R., Nia, N. H., and Seeburg, P. H. (1985). *Nature (London)* **318,** 659–663.

Mason, A. J., Niall, H. D., and Seeburg, P. H. (1986). *Biochem. Biophys. Res. Commun.* **135,** 957–964.

Massagué, J. (1985a). *J. Biol. Chem.* **260,** 7059–7066.

Massagué, J. (1985b). *J. Cell Biol.* **100,** 1508–1514.

Massagué, J. (1987). *Cell (Cambridge, Mass.)* **49,** 437–438.

Massagué, J., and Like, B. (1985). *J. Biol. Chem.* **260,** 2636–2645.

Massagué, J., Kelly, B., and Mottola, C. (1985). *J. Biol. Chem.* **260,** 4551–4554.

Massagué, J., Cheifetz, S., Endo, T., and Nadal-Ginard, B. (1986). *Proc. Natl. Acad. Sci. U.S.A.* **83,** 8206–8210.

Massagué, J., Cheifetz, S., Ignotz, R. A., and Boyd, F. T. (1987). *J. Cell. Physiol., Suppl.* **5,** 43–47.

Masui, T., Wakefield, L. M., Lechner, J. F., LaVeck, M. A., Sporn, M. B., and Harris, C. C. (1986). *Proc. Natl. Acad. Sci. U.S.A.* **83,** 2438–2442.

Matrisian, L. M., Glaichenhaus, N., Gesnel, M.-C., and Breathnach, R. (1985). *EMBO J.* **4,** 1435–1440.

Matrisian, L. M., Leroy, P., Ruhlmann, C., Gesnel, M.-C., and Breathnach, R. (1986). *Mol. Cell. Biol.* **6,** 1679–1686.

Matt, D. W., Gibney, J. A., Malamad, M., and MacDonald, G. J. (1986). *Biol. Reprod.* **34,** 587–593.

May, J. V., Frost, J. P., and Schomberg, D. W. (1988). *Endocrinology (Baltimore)* **123,** 168–179.

Mayo, K. E., Cerelli, G. M., Spiess, J., Rivier, J., Rosenfeld, M. G., Evans, R. M., and Vale, W. (1986). *Proc. Natl. Acad. Sci. U.S.A.* **83,** 5849–5853.

Merchenthaler, I., Culler, M. D., Petrusz, P., and Negro-Vilar, A. (1987). *Mol. Cell. Endocrinol.* **54,** 239–243.

Meunier, H., Rivier, C., Evans, R. M., and Vale, W. (1988). *Proc. Natl. Acad. Sci. U.S.A.* **85,** 247–251.

Miyazono, K., and Heldin, C.-H. (1989). *Nature (London)* **338,** 158–160.

Miyazono, K., Hellman, U., Wernstedt, C., and Heldin, C.-H. (1988). *J. Biol. Chem.* **263,** 6407–6415.

Moonan, G., Grau-Wagemans, M.-P., Selak, I., Lefebvre, P. P., Rogister, B., Vassilli, J. D., and Belin, D. (1985). *Dev. Brain Res.* **20,** 41–48.

Morales, T. I., and Roberts, A. B. (1988). *J. Biol. Chem.* **263,** 12828–12831.

Morgan, D. O., Edman, J. C., Standring, D. N., Fried, V. A., Smith, M. C., Roth, R. A., and Rutter, W. J. (1987). *Nature (London)* **329,** 301–307.

Moses, H. L., Coffey, R. J., Jr., Leof, E. B., Lyons, R. M., and Keski-Oja, J. (1987). *J. Cell. Physiol., Suppl.* **5,** 1–7.

Müller, K. M., Behrens, J., Nussbaumer, U., Böhlen, P., and Birchmeier, W. (1987). *Proc. Natl. Acad. Sci. U.S.A.* **84,** 5600–5604.

Mulder, K. M., Levine, A. E., Hernandez, X., McKnight, M. K., Brattain, D. E., and Brattain, M. G. (1988). *Biochem. Biophys. Res. Commun.* **150,** 711–716.

Murthy, U. S., Anzano, M. A., Stadel, J. M., and Greig, R. (1988). *Biochem. Biophys. Res. Commun.* **152,** 1228–1235.

Mustoe, T. A., Pierce, G. F., Thomason, A., Gramates, P., Sporn, M. B., and Deuel, T. F. (1987). *Science* **237,** 1333–1336.

Myrdal, S. E., Twardzik, D. R., and Auersperg, N. (1986). *J. Cell Biol.* **102,** 1230–1234.

Nakamura, T., Tomita, Y., Hirai, R., Yamaoka, K., Kaji, K., and Ichihara, A. (1985). *Biochem. Biophys. Res. Commun.* **133,** 1042–1050.

Nakamura, T., Kitazawa, T., and Ichihara, A. (1986). *Biochem. Biophys. Res. Commun.* **141,** 176–184.

Nilsen-Hamilton, M. (1989). *In* "Growth Factors in Early Development" (I. Y. Rosenblum and S. Heyner, eds.), CRC Press, Boca Raton, Florida. pp. 135–174.

Nilsen-Hamilton, M., and Holley, R. W. (1983). *Proc. Natl. Acad. Sci. U.S.A.* **80,** 5636–5640.

Nilsen-Hamilton, M., Shapiro, J. M., Massoglia S. L., and Hamilton, R. T. (1980). *Cell (Cambridge, Mass.)* **20,** 19–28.

Nilsen-Hamilton, M., Jang, Y.-J., Alvarez-Azaustre, E., and Hamilton, R. T. (1988). *Mol. Cell. Endocrinol.* **56,** 179–190.

Noda, M., and Rodan, G. A. (1986). *Biochem. Biophys. Res. Commun.* **140,** 56–65.

Noda, M., and Rodan, G. A. (1987). *J. Cell. Physiol.* **133,** 426–437.

Noda, M., Yoon, K., Prince, C. W., Butler, W. T., and Rodan, G. A. (1988). *J. Biol. Chem.* **263,** 13916–13921.

O'Connor-McCourt, M. D., and Wakefield, L. M. (1987). *J. Biol. Chem.* **262,** 14090–14099.

Ohta, M., Greenberger, J. S., Anklesaria, P., Bassols, A., and Massagué, J. (1987). *Nature (London)* **329,** 539–541.

Okada, F., Yamaguchi, K., Ichihara, A., and Nakamura, T. (1989). *FEBS Lett.* **242,** 240–244.

Olson, E. N., Sternberg, E., Hu, J. S., Spizz, G., and Wilcox, C. (1986). *J. Cell Biol.* **103,** 1799–1805.

Oreffo, R. O. C., Mundy, G. R., Seyedin, S. M., and Bonewald, L. F. (1989). *Biochem. Biophys. Res. Commun.* **158,** 817–823.

Ottmann, O. G., and Pelus, L. M. (1988). *J. Immunol.* **140,** 2661–2665.

Owens, G. K., Geisterfer, A. A. T., Yang, Y. W.-H., and Komorya, A. (1988). *J. Cell Biol.* **107,** 771–780.

Padgett, R. W., St. Johnston, R. D., and Gelbart, W. M. (1987). *Nature (London)* **325,** 81–84.

Penttinen, R. P,., Kobayashi, S., and Bornstein, P. (1988). *Proc. Natl. Acad. Sci. U.S.A.* **85,** 1105–1108.

Pfeilschifter, J., and Mundy, G. R. (1987). *Proc. Natl. Acad. Sci. U.S.A.* **84,** 2024–2028.

Pfeilschifter, J., D'Souza, S. M., and Mundy, G. R. (1987). *Endocrinology (Baltimore)* **121,** 212–218.

Picon, R. (1979). *Arch. Anat. Microsc. Morphol. Exp.* **58,** 1–19.
Pircher, R., Jullien, P., and Lawrence, D. A. (1986). *Biochem. Biophys. Res. Commun.* **136,** 30–37.
Postlethwaite, A. E., Keski-Oja, J., Moses, H. L., and Kang, A. H. (1987). *J. Exp. Med.* **165,** 251–256.
Proper, J. A., Bjornson, C. L., and Moses, H. L. (1982). *J. Cell. Physiol.* **110,** 169–174.
Purchio, A. F., Cooper, J. A., Brunner, A. M., Lioubin, M. N., Gentry, L. E., Kovacina, K. S., Roth, R. A., and Marquardt, H. (1988). *J. Biol. Chem.* **263,** 14211–14215.
Ranchalis, J. E., Gentry, L., Ogawa, Y., Seyedin, S. M., McPherson, J., Purchio, A., and Twardzik, D. R. (1987). *Biochem. Biophys. Res. Commun.* **148,** 783–789.
Ranges, G. E., Figari, I. S., Espevik, T., and Palladino, M. A., Jr. (1987). *J. Exp. Med.* **166,** 991–998.
Rappolee, D. A., Brenner, C. A., Schultz, R., Mark, D., and Werb, Z. (1988). *Science* **241,** 1823–1825.
Redini, F., Galera, P., Mauviel, A., Loyau, G., and Pujol, J.-P. (1988). *FEBS Lett.* **234,** 172–176.
Reiss, M., and Sartorelli, A. C. (1987). *Cancer Res.* **47,** 6705–6709.
Ristow, H.-J. (1986). *Proc. Natl. Acad. Sci. U.S.A.* **83,** 5531–5533.
Rizzino, A. (1987). *Cancer Res.* **47,** 4386–4390.
Rizzino, A. (1988). *Dev. Biol.* **130,** 411–422.
Roberts, A. B., Anzano, M. A., Lamb, L. C., Smith, J. M., Frolik, C. A., Marquardt, H., Todaro, G. J., and Sporn, M. B. (1982). *Nature (London)* **295,** 417–419.
Roberts, A. B., Anzano, M. A., Wakefield, L. M., Roche, N. S., Stern, D. F., and Sporn, M. B. (1985). *Proc. Natl. Acad. Sci. U.S.A.* **82,** 119–123.
Roberts, A. B., Sporn, M. B., Assoian, R. K., Smith, J. M., Roche, N. S., Wakefield, L. M., Heine, U. I., Liotta, L. A., Falanga, V., Kehrl, J. H., and Fauci, A. S. (1986). *Proc. Natl. Acad. Sci. U.S.A.* **83,** 4167–4171.
Roberts, C. J., Birkenmeier, T. M., McQuillan, J. J., Akiyama, S. K., Yamada, S. S., Chen, W.-T., Yamada, K. M., and McDonald, J. A. (1988). *J. Biol. Chem.* **263,** 4586–4592.
Robey, P. G., Young, M. F., Flanders, K. C., Roche, N. S., Kondaiah, P., Reddi, A. H., Termine, J. D., Sporn, M. B., and Roberts, A. B. (1987). *J. Cell Biol.* **105,** 457–463.
Rook, A. H., Kehrl, J. H., Wakefield, L. M., Roberts, A. B., Sporn, M. B., Burlington, D. B., Lane, H. C., and Fauci, A. S. (1986). *J. Immunol.* **136,** 3916–3920.
Rosa, F., Roberts, A. B., Danielpour, D., Dart, L. L., Sporn, M. B., and Dawid, I. B. (1988). *Science* **39,** 783–785.
Ross, E. M. (1988). *J. Chem. Educ.* **65,** 937–942.
Rossi, P., Karsenty, G., Roberts, A. B., Roche, N. S., Sporn, M. B., and de Crombrugghe, B. (1988). *Cell (Cambridge, Mass.)* **52,** 405–414.
Russell, W. E., Coffey, R. J., Jr., Ouellette, A. J., and Moses, H. L. (1988). *Proc. Natl. Acad. Sci. U.S.A.* **85,** 5126–5130.
Saksela, O., Moscatelli, D., and Rifkin, D. B. (1987). *J. Cell Biol.* **105,** 957–963.
Sandberg, M., Vurio, T., Hirrovan, H., Alitalo, K., and Vurio, E. (1988). *Development* **102,** 461–470.
Scher, W. (1987). *Lab. Invest.* **57,** 607–623.
Sefton, B., and Rubin, H. (1970). *Nature (London)* **227,** 843–845.
Segarini, P. R., and Seyedin, S. M. (1988). *J. Biol. Chem.* **263,** 8366–8370.
Seyedin, S. M., Thomas, T. C., Thompson, A. Y., Rosen, D. M., and Piez, K. A. (1985). *Proc. Natl. Acad. Sci. U.S.A.* **82,** 2267–2271.
Seyedin, S. M., Thompson, A. Y., Bentz, H., Rosen, D. M., McPherson, J. M., Conti, A., Siegel, N. R., Galluppi, G. R., and Piez, K. A. (1986). *J. Biol. Chem.* **261,** 5693–5695.

Seyedin, S. M., Segarini, P. R., Rosen, D. M., Thompson, A. Y., Bentz, H., and Graycar, J. (1987). *J. Biol. Chem.* **262,** 1946–1949.
Sharples, K., Plowman, G. D., Rose, T. M., Twardzik, D. R., and Purchio, A. F. (1987). *DNA* **6,** 239–244.
Shin, S.-I., Freedman, V. H., Risser, R., and Pollack, R. (1975). *Proc. Natl. Acad. Sci. U.S.A.* **72,** 4435–4439.
Shipley, G. D., Tucker, R. F., and Moses, H. L. (1985). *Proc. Natl. Acad. Sci. U.S.A.* **82,** 4147–4151.
Shipley, G. D., Pittelkow, M. R., Wille, J. J., Jr., Scott, R. E., and Moses, H. L. (1986). *Cancer Res.* **46,** 2068–2071.
Silberstein, G. B., and Daniel, C. W. (1987). *Science* **237,** 291–293.
Skinner, M. K., Keski-Oja, J., Osteen, K. G., and Moses, H. J. (1987). *Endocrinology (Baltimore)* **121,** 786–792.
Smeland, E. B., Blomhoff, H. K., Holte, H., Ruud, E., Beiske, K., Funderud, S., Godal, T., and Ohlsson, R. (1987). *Exp. Cell Res.* **171,** 213–222.
Soares, M. J., and Talamantes, F. (1983). *Endocrinology (Baltimore)* **113,** 1408–1412.
Sporn, M. B., Roberts, A. B., Shull, J. H., Smith, J. M., and Ward, J. M. (1983). *Science* **219,** 1329–1331.
Sporn, M. B., Roberts, A. B., Wakefield, L. M., and de Crombrugghe, B. (1987). *J. Cell Biol.* **105,** 1039–1045.
Strassmann, G., Cole, M. D., and Newman, W. (1988). *J. Immunol.* **140,** 2645–2651.
Takehara, K., LeRoy, E. C., and Grotendorst, G. R. (1987). *Cell (Cambridge, Mass.)* **49,** 415–422.
ten Dijke, P. T., Hansen, P., Iwata, K. K., Pieler, C., and Foulkes, J. G. (1988). *Proc. Natl. Acad. Sci. U.S.A.* **85,** 4715–4719.
Thalacker, F. W., and Nilsen-Hamilton, M. (1987). *J. Biol. Chem.* **262,** 2283–2290.
Tsunawaki, S., Sporn, M., Ding, A., and Nathan, C. (1988). *Nature (London)* **334,** 260–262.
Tucker, R. F., Branum, E. L., Shipley, G. D., Ryan, R. J., and Moses, H. L. (1984a). *Proc. Natl. Acad. Sci. U.S.A.* **81,** 6757–6761.
Tucker, R. F., Shipley, G. D., Moses, H. L., and Holley, R. W. (1984b). *Science* **226,** 705–707.
Twardzik, D. R., Ranchalis, J. E., and Todaro, G. J. (1982). *Cancer Res.* **42,** 590–593.
Vale, W., Rivier, J., Vaughan, J., McClintock, R., Corrigan, A., Woo, W., Karr, D., and Spiess, J. (1986). *Nature (London)* **321,** 776–779.
van Obberghen-Schilling, E., Roche, N. S., Flanders, K. C., Sporn, M. B., and Roberts, A. M. (1988). *J. Biol. Chem.* **263,** 7741–7746.
van Zoelen, E. J. J., van Oostwaard, T. M. J., and de Laat, S. W. (1986). *J. Biol. Chem.* **261,** 5003–5009.
Varga, J., Rosenbloom, J., and Jimenez, S. A. (1987). *Biochem. J.* **247,** 597–604.
Wahl, S. M., Hunt, D. A., Wakefield, L. M., McCartney-Francis, N., Wahl, L. M., Roberts, A. B., and Sporn, M. B. (1987). *Proc. Natl. Acad. Sci. U.S.A.* **83,** 5788–5792.
Wahl, S. M., Hunt, D. A., Wong, H. L., Dougherty, S., McCartney-Francis, N., Wahl, L., Ellingsworth, L., Schmidt, J. A., Hall, G., Roberts, A. B., and Sporn, M. B. (1988). *J. Immunol.* **140,** 3026–3032.
Wakefield, L. M., Smith, D. M. Masui, T., Harris, C. C., and Sporn, M. B. (1987). *J. Cell Biol.* **105,** 965–975.
Wakefield, L. M., Smith, D. M., Flanders, K. C., and Sporn, M. B. (1988). *J. Biol. Chem.* **263,** 7646–7654.
Weeks, D. L., and Melton, D. A. (1987). *Cell (Cambridge, Mass.)* **51,** 861–867.
Wilcox, J. N., and Derynck, R. (1988). *Mol. Cell. Biol.* **8,** 3415–3422.
Wilder, E. L., and Linzer, D. I. H. (1989). *Mol. Cell. Biol.* **9,** 430–441.

Wozney, J. M., Rosen, V., Celeste, A. J., Mitsock, L. M., Whitters, M. J., Kriz, R. W., Hewick, R. M., and Wang, E. A. (1988). *Science* **242,** 1528–1534.

Wrana, J. L., Sodeck, J., Ber, R. L., and Bellows, C. G. (1986). *Eur. J. Biochem.* **159,** 69–76.

Wrann, M., Bodmer, S., de Martin, R., Siepl, C. Hofer-Warbinek, R., Frei, K., Hofer, E., and Fontana, A. (1987). *EMBO J.* **6,** 1633–1636.

Ying, S.-Y., Becker, A., Baird, A., Ling, N., Ueno, N., Esch, F., and Guillemin, R. (1986a). *Biochem. Biophys. Res. Commun.* **135,** 950–956.

Ying, S.-Y., Becker, A., Ling, N., Ueno, N., and Guillemin, R. (1986b). *Biochem. Biophys. Res. Commun.* **136,** 969–975.

Ying, S.-Y., Czvik, J., Becker, A., Ling, N., Ueno, N., and Guillemin, R. (1987). *Proc. Natl. Acad. Sci. U.S.A.* **84,** 4631–4635.

Zetter, B. R., and Antoniades, H. N. (1979). *J. Supramol. Struct.* **11,** 361–370.

Zhiwen, Z., Herington, A. C., Carson, R. S., Findlay, J. K., and Burger, H. G. (1987). *Mol. Cell. Endocrinol.* **54,** 213–220.

5

The Insulin Family of Peptides in Early Mammalian Development

Susan Heyner and Martin Farber
Department of Obstetrics and Gynecology
Albert Einstein Medical Center
Philadelphia, Pennsylvania 19141

I. Y. Rosenblum
Pharmacology and Toxicology Section
Warner Lambert Company
Morris Plains, New Jersey 07950

I. Introduction

Development of the early mammalian embryo is governed primarily by the embryonic genome, although it requires a continuous supply of energy, growth factors, and hormones. In addition, there is a considerable body of evidence to suggest that maternal and embryonic endocrine influences are important in mammalian embryogenesis.

Rapid cellular proliferation that is characteristic of embryonic growth may be mediated by specific cell receptors that are expressed in early embryonic tissues. Among the various candidates for this role, recent

Current Topics in Developmental Biology, Vol. 24

attention has focused on the insulin family of peptides, including insulin and the insulinlike growth factors (IGFs), also known as somatomedins. Receptors for insulin and IGFs are expressed as early as the morula stage of preimplantation development (Mattson *et al.*, 1988), while receptors, as well as the corresponding ligands, have been identified in early postimplantation embryonic tissues (Beck *et al.*, 1987; Smith *et al.*, 1987). Although these reports imply that insulin and IGFs play roles in early embryonic development and growth, the precise biological activities of these peptides have yet to be clearly delineated. In this chapter we review evidence that preimplantation and early postimplantation embryos express receptors that bind IGFs and insulin. We also discuss the experimental evidence for autocrine production of these factors by the early embryo and speculate on the role that these peptides may play in mammalian development.

II. Structure and Function of IGFs and Insulin

IGF-I and IGF-II are single-chain peptide hormones that have a high degree of amino acid homology with each other and with proinsulin. Indeed, this family of polypeptides has a number of overlapping activities (Blundell and Humbel, 1980), due perhaps in part to the retained similarity in tertiary structure, the so-called "insulin fold" (Blundell *et al.*, 1978). Because of the structural similarities, each of these hormones can bind to its own specific cell surface receptor, and also with reduced affinity to the heterologous receptors. This ligand–receptor cross-reactivity accounts for the well-documented overlap of biological activities reported in numerous cell, tissue, and whole-animal models that have been used to investigate the effects of these hormones on metabolic processes.

Originally named "somatomedins," because of their potent growth-promoting activity in cartilage and skeletal tissues (Daughday *et al.*, 1972), the IGFs are now known to act on a variety of other cells and nonskeletal tissues. IGF-I is identical to somatomedin C (Klapper *et al.*, 1983), and IGF-II is the human homolog of another growth factor, multiplication-stimulating activity (MSA), that was purified first from rat liver cell cultures (Marquardt *et al.*, 1981). While the importance of the IGFs in the regulation of postnatal growth and development is firmly established, the role these peptides play during embryonic and fetal growth represents a relatively new area of investigation in developmental biology.

A. IGF-I

The classic source of IGF-I is the liver, where the peptide is produced in response to growth hormone. It is considered a primary growth regulator in peri- and postnatal life. More recent observations have shown that IGF-I activity, binding proteins, and receptors are expressed much earlier in development than was previously recognized. Indeed, in the chick embryo, expression of the IGF-I receptor predates insulin receptor expression and can be detected on whole embryos by day 2 (Bassas *et al.*, 1985).

B. IGF-II

In contrast to IGF-I, the physiological function of IGF-II is not known. It has been suggested that IGF-II acts primarily to stimulate undifferentiated cells, whereas IGF-I acts primarily following differentiation (Bhaumick and Bala, 1987). Although the expression of the peptide and its receptor has been demonstrated in various stages of embryonic and fetal growth (reviewed by de Pablo, 1989; Heyner *et al.*, 1989a), there is scant evidence that IGF-II promotes growth. For example, nude mice and rats with IGF-II-producing tumors and elevated levels of circulating IGF-II do not show an increase in body weight or tail length (Wilson *et al.*, 1987). Thus, results from more studies using embryonic systems are needed to clarify the role of this peptide.

C. Insulin

In humans insulin is a 6-kDa polypeptide hormone. The initial translation product of insulin mRNA is preproinsulin, which is a 109-amino acid, single-chain precursor, containing an amino-terminal signal peptide of 24 amino acids linked to proinsulin. Preproinsulin is synthesized in the rough endoplasmic reticulum of pancreatic β cells. Proteolytic cleavage in the Golgi complex converts proinsulin to insulin. The resultant molecule consists of two polypeptide chains, A and B, linked by two invariant disulfide bonds. Although insulin can exist as a monomer, dimer, or hexamer, the biologically active form of the hormone is thought to be the monomer (Blundell and Wood, 1975). Studies of the amino acid sequences of insulin from a number of vertebrates show that insulin has been highly conserved through evolution. Sequence data indicate that the disulfide bridges and the hydrophobic core of the monomer are invariant, which suggests that evolutionary pressures have acted to preserve the secondary and tertiary hormone structures.

Insulin has been viewed classically as a vertebrate hormone, synthesized and secreted by pancreatic β cells. Studies in a wide variety of *in vivo* and cell culture systems have established its vital endocrine role in glucoregulation and related metabolic pathways. *In vivo,* insulin is a primary regulator of rapid anabolic responses. Its physiological actions include the regulation of glucose uptake in muscle and fat cells, the regulation of glycogen synthesis in the liver, fat synthesis in adipocytes, and the stimulation of amino acid and ion uptake in muscle, and possibly other target cells (Rosen, 1987). In addition to these rapid metabolic actions, there is considerable evidence that physiological concentrations of insulin may regulate gene action. Some well-documented examples include the stimulatory effects of insulin on RNA and protein syntheses in muscle and liver cells and lipid synthesis in adipocytes. More recently, the use of a number of cultured cell lines has shown that insulin is capable of stimulating DNA synthesis and cellular growth and proliferation. These findings have provided support for long-standing speculation that insulin may be a more versatile hormone than was previously proposed and that, among its numerous functions, it may mediate such fundamental processes as oocyte maturation, embryonic growth, and fetal development.

III. Structure and Function of IGF and Insulin Receptors

A. Insulin and IGF-I Receptors

The biological effects of insulin and the IGFs are initiated by the interaction of the ligand with a specific cell surface receptor. The insulin receptor has been studied extensively and is very similar to the IGF-I receptor (Froesch *et al.*, 1985; Rechler and Nissley, 1985). Both receptors are integral transmembrane glycoproteins with intrinsic enzyme activity. The insulin receptor is a glycosylated tetramer made up of two α subunits that are linked by disulfide bonds to each other and to the two β subunits (Fig. 1). The β subunits traverse the plasma membrane and possess an insulin-dependent protein tyrosine kinase domain. The entire sequences of the human insulin receptor mRNA (Ullrich *et al.*, 1985; Ebina *et al.*, 1985) and the human IGF-I receptor mRNA (Ullrich *et al.*, 1986) have been deduced from overlapping cDNA clones. In both cases the mRNA codes for a single polypeptide precursor that is 1370 amino acids long. The precursors include a 27- to 30-residue signal peptide, followed by the α receptor subunit of about 700 amino acids (~80 kDa) and the β receptor subunit of about 625 amino acids (~70 kDa). The latter correspond to the mature 135-kDa (α) and 90-kDa (β) fully glycosylated subunits. Despite the structural similarities of the two receptors (Fig. 1), they are products of two different genes, located on separate chromosomes (Yang-Feng *et al.*, 1985). Thus, they are likely to be controlled by different regulatory signals and to have different functions during development.

Because of the structural similarity between the receptors, it is difficult

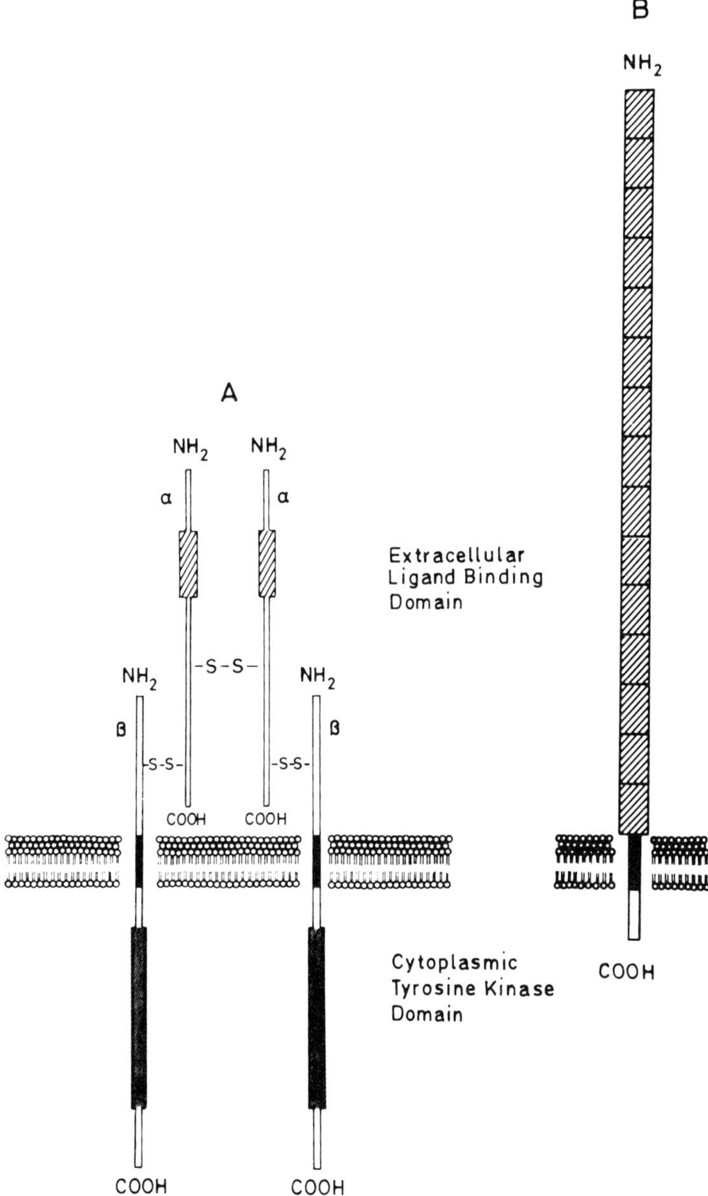

Fig. 1 The receptors that bind the insulin family of peptides. (A) The insulin and IGF-I receptors, which are indistinguishable on the basis of protein subunit structure. (B) The IGF-II receptor, which is structurally identical to the cation-independent mannose-6-phosphate receptor (see text for details).

to discriminate between them using serological reagents. However, they may be identified readily by the affinity with which they bind ligands. Insulin binds with high affinity to the insulin receptor, and also binds to the IGF-I receptor, but with an affinity approximately one one-hundredth that for its own receptor. Likewise, the IGF-I receptor is able to bind both IGF-I and insulin; however, it binds the homologous ligand with an affinity approximately 100 times higher (Rechler *et al.*, 1980).

Both receptors undergo rapid autophosphorylation in response to ligand binding. This reaction, which involves the stimulation of a receptor tyrosine kinase activity, appears to be essential for the ligand to produce a biological effect on the target cell (Kasuga *et al.*, 1983; Petruzzelli *et al.*, 1985; Rosen, 1987). In some target cells binding of polyclonal antibodies directed against the insulin receptor results in an action similar to the binding of the ligand itself, although the detailed mechanism of this reaction has yet to be clarified.

B. IGF-II Receptor

The IGF-II receptor is structurally distinct from the insulin and IGF-I receptors, as shown in Fig. 1. In most cell and tissue preparations examined so far, the IGF-II receptor binds the homologous ligand with high affinity, binds IGF-I with low affinity, and does not bind insulin (Ewton *et al.*, 1987; Rosenfeld *et al.*, 1987; Roth, 1988). The receptor does not possess intrinsic kinase activity, and thus does not autophosphorylate after ligand binding. Data obtained from the sequence of the cDNA predict a structure with a single transmembrane region, an extracellular domain that comprises 93% of the receptor molecule, and a relatively small cytoplasmic domain of 18 kDa (Morgan *et al.*, 1987). Evidence from structural studies (Roth *et al.*, 1987; Oshima *et al.*, 1988), immunological cross-reactivity (MacDonald *et al.*, 1988; Tong *et al.*, 1988), ligand binding affinities, and stoichiometry (von Figuera and Hasilik, 1986) has shown that the IGF-II receptor is identical to the cation-independent mannose-6-phosphate (M6P) receptor. These and other studies have demonstrated that this receptor binds IGF-II and M6P at distinct binding sites. IGF-II, however, does not bind to the cation-dependent M6P receptor (Tong *et al.*, 1988). Both M6P receptors bind M6P-containing glycoproteins (lysosomal enzymes), and target them to the lysosomes. Since the mitogenic effect of IGF-II in some target cells is mediated following its binding to the IGF-I receptor (Mottola and Czech, 1984; Furlanetto *et al.*, 1987), the functional significance of the IGF-II binding site remains open to question. Regardless of its biological role, receptor internalization, translocation to lysosomes, and recycling back to the membranes constitute a route integral to the cellular fate of both lysosomal enzymes and IGF-II.

IV. Preimplantation Embryos

A. Expression of IGFs and Their Receptors in Preimplantation Embryos

The preimplantation stage of mammalian development provides the opportunity for studying metabolism, gene expression, and the early stages of differentiation. It has proven possible to culture the embryos from a wide variety of species *in vitro,* although the ease with which zygotes can be cultured to the blastocyst stage varies considerably among species. The mouse provides a convenient model system, partly due to the ease of obtaining and culturing relatively large numbers of embryos. Another advantage is that the genetics of this species have been studied intensively for most of this century. Consequently, there is more genetic information available for the mouse than for any other mammalian species.

Despite the advantages mentioned above, there are still formidable barriers to the study of polypeptide growth factors and their receptors in the early embryo. For example, the classical biochemical approach to discriminate between IGF-I and insulin receptors is to measure binding affinities by means of Scatchard plot analysis. Such an approach is not feasible using the mouse preimplantation embryo because of the limited amount of material available. Table I shows the volume, DNA, mRNA, and protein content of mouse embryos at various preimplantation stages.

The use of molecular techniques is one approach to the problem of limited material for experimentation. In particular, the polymerase chain reaction has proven to be very useful. In this technique the use of a

Table I Volume, DNA, mRNA, and Protein Content per Embryo in Several Preimplantation Stages of Development

Stage	Volume (nl)[a]	DNA (pg)[b]	mRNA (pg)[c]	Protein (ng)[d]
Fertilized ovum	0.192	8	23	27.8
Two-Cell	0.158	17	8	26.1
Eight-Cell	0.138	50	14	23.4
32-Cell (blastocyst)	0.219	194	37	23.9

[a] Data from Lewis and Wright (1935).
[b] Data calculated from Piko and Taylor (1987).
[c] Calculated by Schultz (1986), using data from Piko and Clegg (1982).
[d] Data from Brinster (1967).

thermostable DNA polymerase allows the selective enrichment of a specific DNA sequence by a factor of 10^6 (Saiki *et al.*, 1988). A modification of the polymerase chain reaction has been devised recently that employs reverse transcriptase to detect the presence of mRNA transcripts. Using this mRNA phenotype method, maternally derived platelet-derived growth factor and transforming growth factor (TGF-α and TGF-β) mRNA transcripts have been detected in mouse oocytes (Rappolee *et al.*, 1988). As the embryonic genome became activated (at the two-cell stage in the mouse), transcripts for the growth factors could be detected in cleavage stage embryos.

Another approach to cellular localization of receptors is autoradiography. The binding of a labeled ligand to its receptor can be assessed by light-microscopic examination. Specificity of binding and incorporation can be measured by incubating the sample in an excess of unlabeled ligand and measuring the displacement of the label. In addition, specificity can be demonstrated by the use of more than one labeled ligand.

Using light-microscopic autoradiography, [^{125}I]insulin binding to preimplantation mouse embryos was shown to be displaceable by excess unlabelled IGFs, providing evidence for the presence of IGF receptors. The IGF receptors appear to be developmentally regulated and to be expressed first at the morula stage (Mattson *et al.*, 1988). When blastocysts are grown in a medium containing amino acids, they will hatch from the zona pellucida, and if provided with an appropriate medium, they will "implant" on a plastic or glass surface. The implanted embryos continue to proliferate and differentiate, with the cells of the inner cell mass clearly distinguishable from the underlying trophoblast cells (Gwatkin, 1966). Using this system in conjunction with autoradiography, Mattson *et al.* (1988) showed that receptors that bind both [^{125}I]IGF-I and [^{125}I]IGF-II could be detected on the cells of the inner cell mass and the trophectoderm. Specificity for each of the IGFs was confirmed by displacement of the labeled ligand by excess unlabeled peptide. It is of interest to note that in their culture system Mattson *et al.* (1988) could detect no difference in the binding of IGFs to the cells of the trophectoderm, as compared with binding to the inner cell mass.

More recently, Rappolee *et al.* (1989) have obtained results at the mRNA level to support the concept that IGFs act in very early development. These investigators showed that, although IGF-I and insulin transcripts were not detectable in stages up to and including the blastocyst stage, IGF-II transcripts could be detected in mouse embryos at the two-cell stage, after activation of the embryonic genome. On the other hand, mRNA transcripts for the IGF-I, IGF-II, and insulin receptors appeared during cleavage stages and increased in amount through the blastocyst stage. These results support previous speculation that growth factors may play an important role in the preimplantation stages of mammalian development.

B. Expression of Insulin and Its Receptor in Preimplantation Embryos

Another effective method for identifying surface molecules in small tissue samples is the use of immunological probes. Antibodies provide both sensitivity and specificity and have been used extensively in the study of surface molecules on mammalian embryos. This approach was adopted by Rosenblum *et al.* (1986), who showed that insulin binding could be detected first on the surface of mouse embryos at the morula stage of development. These experiments provided the first evidence that cells of the mouse embryos are capable of binding insulin in a developmentally regulated manner. Further evidence that this binding is receptor mediated, rather than a consequence of the development of the embryonic endocytotic system (Fleming and Pickering, 1985), was provided by autoradiographic studies. Grain counts on sections of oocytes and preimplantation cleavage stages showed that specific binding of insulin to the cells of the preimplantation embryos could be detected first at the morula stage (Fig. 2), and displacement with excess unlabeled ligand demonstrated that the

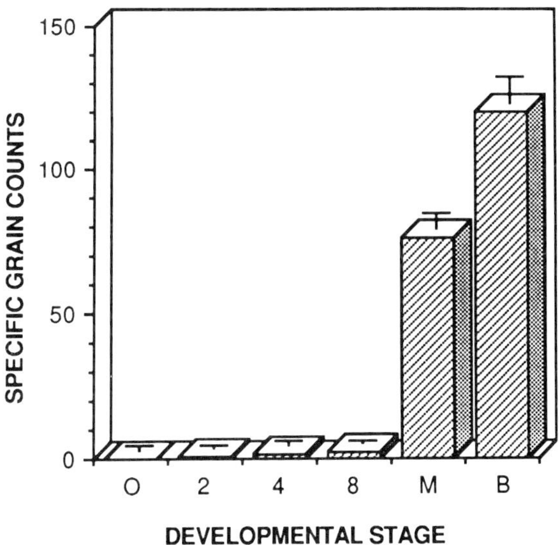

Fig. 2 Specific cell-associated [^{125}I]insulin grain counts on mouse oocytes and preimplantation developmental stages. Counts represent the average grain counts per oocyte or embryo; background grain counts were subtracted to give specific cell-associated counts. Bars represent the standard error of the mean. 0, 2, 4, 8, Number of cells; M, morula stage; B, blastocyst stage. (Data from Mattson *et al.*, 1988.)

binding was receptor mediated. The finding that the increased number of grains associated with the morula and blastocyst stages reached a plateau at physiological levels of hormone also provided evidence that insulin binding by embryos at these early embryonic stages was mediated by receptor-mediated endocytosis. These investigators showed that, in addition to incubation with excess unlabeled insulin, a mixture of IGF-I and IGF-II was capable of displacing labeled insulin bound to the cleavage stage embryo, although to a lesser extent. When blastocyst outgrowths were examined, all three peptides were found to be bound in a receptor-mediated fashion, and there was no apparent difference in relative binding to the cells of the trophectoderm or the inner cell mass.

Numerous studies have shown that insulin may be visualized readily at the ultrastructural level by means of labeling with either ferritin or colloidal gold. Taking advantage of this, Heyner *et al.* (1989b) have shown that occupied insulin receptors may be visualized on preimplantation mouse embryos at the morula and blastocyst stages, using colloidal gold-labeled insulin in conjunction with high-resolution electron microscopy. Embryos at the two- and four-cell stages showed no evidence of insulin binding. At the eight-cell stage binding of the labeled ligand to the surface membrane showed embryo-to-embryo variation, with some embryos exhibiting binding and others not. However, at the morula and blastocyst stages, there was clear evidence of gold–insulin binding to the plasma membrane and translocation of the ligand by means of coated pits to cytoplasmic organelles. In addition, detection of gold particles in cells of the inner cell mass suggested that the polar trophectoderm may act as a transporting epithelium, transporting insulin from the external medium to the inner cell mass. Control embryos that were incubated with an equivalent concentration of gold-labeled bovine serum albumin (BSA) showed no evidence of internalization of gold particles. Because the gold–insulin was stabilized with BSA, the BSA controls provided evidence that uptake was specific to the hormone. Figure 3 shows high-resolution micrographic details of the endocytotic pathway of gold-labeled insulin in the mouse blastocyst. The initial event is accumulation of the ligand in areas of thickened plasma membrane (Fig. 3A), followed by uptake of the ligand via coated pits (Fig. 3B) and translocation of gold-labeled insulin mediated by coated and uncoated vesicles (Fig. 3C), with accumulation of the ligand in endosomes, dense bodies, and multivesicular bodies (Fig. 3D).

Immunocytochemical studies with gold-labeled antibody directed against the ligand were performed in order to demonstrate that insulin that had been internalized by the embryo remained immunologically intact (Heyner *et al.*, 1989b). These studies confirmed that immunologically intact insulin could be detected in all cells of the mouse blastocyst. Furthermore, although insulin could be detected in blastocysts obtained fresh

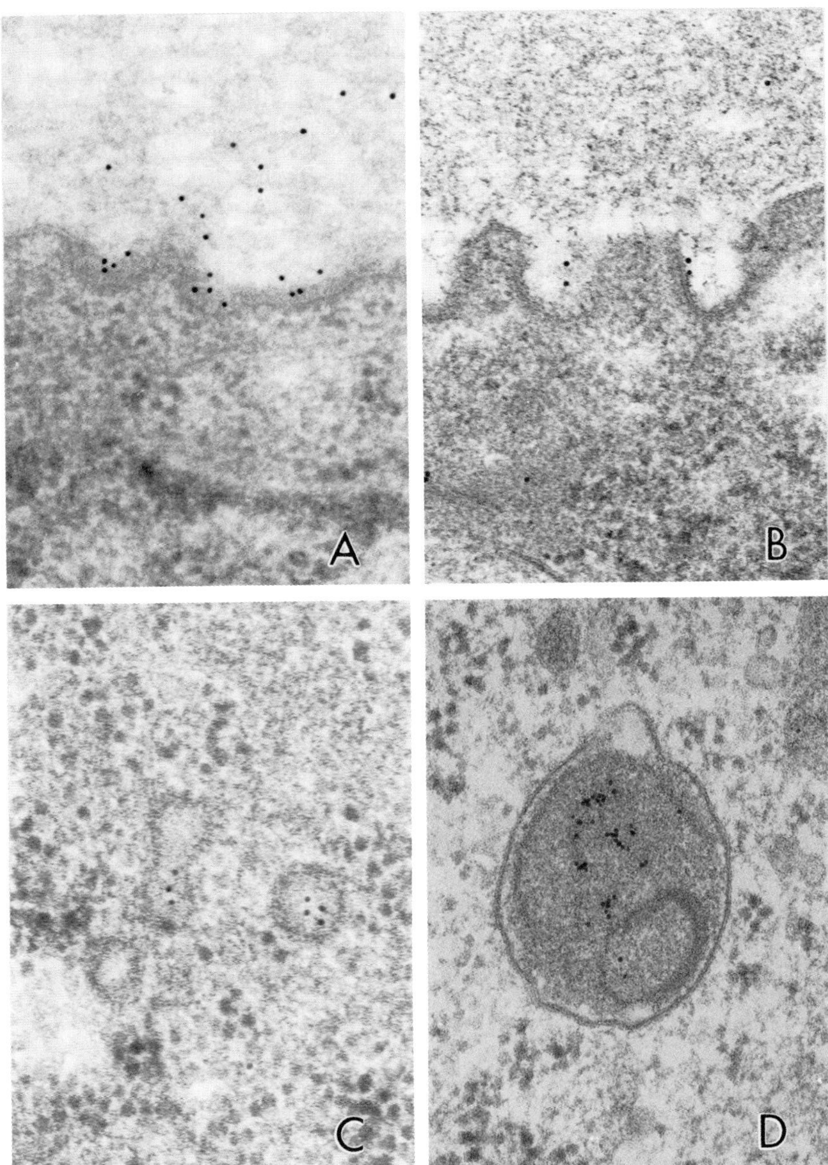

Fig. 3 High-resolution electron-microscopic detail of the binding and uptake of gold-labeled insulin by mouse blastocysts. (A) Accumulation of labeled ligand in regions of thickened plasma membrane. (B) Ligand uptake via coated pits. (C) Gold-labeled insulin in coated vesicular structures. (D) Ligand accumulation within dense bodies.

from the reproductive tract, no insulin could be visualized in embryos that were incubated overnight in medium lacking the hormone. These results suggested that the insulin detected within mouse embryos flushed from the reproductive tract was maternal insulin, and that the embryo does not synthesize the hormone during preimplantation development. This hypothesis was further supported by the additional observation that insulin could be detected within the maternal reproductive tract using immunocytochemical methods (Heyner *et al.,* 1989b).

Little is known of the function of insulin in early mammalian development. In addition to the classic metabolic effects of insulin in various differentiated cells, such as muscle and adipose cells, insulin promotes DNA synthesis and proliferation of a number of cell types in culture. It was of particular interest, therefore, to evaluate the effect of insulin on nucleic acid synthesis in preimplantation mouse embryos. Embryonic stages (two-cell, eight-cell, morula, and blastocyst) were incubated for 1 hour in the presence or absence of physiological levels of insulin. This was followed by a 2-hour incubation in [^{3}H]thymidine or [^{3}H]uridine, with or without insulin, respectively. Insulin significantly increased the rate of synthesis of RNA and DNA at the morula and blastocyst stages of development. The incubation of intact embryos with insulin had no effect on the rate of appearance of labeled precursor in the trichloroacetic acid (TCA)-soluble pool of cellular components. However, there were 8% and 27% increases, respectively, in the rate of [^{3}H]thymidine incorporation into the TCA-insoluble fraction, and 54% and 110% increases, respectively, in the incorporation of [^{3}H]uridine into the TCA-insoluble fraction, when morula and blastocyst stage embryos were incubated for 1 hour in a medium containing physiological levels of insulin, followed by a 2-hour incubation in a medium containing the labeled precursor. Earlier stage embryos did not demonstrate significant responses to insulin, a result that is consonant with the absence of expression of receptors that bind insulin.

C. Teratocarcinoma Cells: Models of Preimplantation Embryos

Teratocarcinomas are malignant tumors that develop spontaneously in the gonads and are formed experimentally when genital ridges or primordial germ cells are transplanted in certain strains of mice (Graham, 1977). These tumors possess malignant embryonal carcinoma (EC) stem cells and differentiated derivatives of these cells. EC cells can be maintained in culture and may be induced to undergo differentiation either by the addition of an agent such as retinoic acid or by appropriate culture conditions.

A number of investigators have used teratocarcinoma cell lines as models of the early embryo, because EC cells can differentiate into a variety of cell types that express biochemical, immunological, and morphological markers characteristic of the early stages of embryogenesis (Graham, 1977). In addition, certain EC cell lines can be "rescued" when injected into the blastocoel cavity and will participate in normal development to give rise to fully functional differentiated tissues (Brinster, 1974; Mintz and Illmensee, 1975; Papaioannou *et al.*, 1975). The obvious advantage of teratocarcinomas is that they can be grown in the large quantities required for detailed biochemical analysis. On the other hand, because EC cells display a transformed phenotype, experimental results using these cells as a model for the embryo must be interpreted cautiously.

Teratocarcinomas express receptors for a number of growth factors and produce growth factors to which they can respond in an autocrine manner (reviewed by Rizzino, 1989). A number of differences have been observed between cell lines examined for the expression of IGF and insulin receptors. Thus, while Heath *et al.* (1981) and Heath and Shi (1986) demonstrated receptors for IGFs on PC13 EC cells, they were unable to demonstrate insulin receptor binding. The reported insulin-stimulated growth response was presumed to be due to the expression of IGF-I receptors. However, when these cells were induced to differentiate by the administration of retinoic acid, the differentiated derivative cells (PC13END) expressed large numbers of insulin receptors, while the apparent number of unoccupied IGF receptors fell by 60%. Because the decrease in IGF receptors was accompanied by the expression of both IGF molecules and soluble binding proteins, the authors suggested that the drop in detectable receptors reflected occupation of a fraction of the receptors by endogenous IGF. This suggestion was strengthened by the observation that multiplication of PG13END cells is highly density dependent, which implies that endogenously produced IGF promotes cell proliferation.

In another mouse EC line, OTT-6050, high-affinity receptors for MSA (rodent IGF-II) have been identified (Salomon, 1980). Similarly, F9 cells, originally derived from OTT-6050, also express receptors capable of binding MSA and insulin (Nagarajan *et al.*, 1982). When these cells were grown in a serum-free medium, insulin was capable of stimulating their growth by acting through the insulin receptor (Nagarajan and Anderson, 1982). Another teratoma-derived cell line, 1246-3A, of mesodermal origin, synthesizes and secretes insulin-related factor (IRF) into the culture medium. This is an autocrine factor that is immunologically and biochemically similar to pancreatic insulin, but can be distinguished from IGF-I or IGF-II by radioimmunoassay (Yamada and Serrero, 1988). It stimulates proliferation of an insulin-dependent cell line and competes with [^{125}I]insulin for binding to cells. The data obtained from studies of teratocarcinoma cells provide evidence that they express growth factor receptors and some growth factors that can regulate cellular proliferation in an autocrine manner. Taken together, data derived from the study of EC cells support the concept that they express a complex system of interactive networks to control growth in which the insulin family of peptides may play a key role.

V. Postimplantation Embryos

A. Expression of IGFs and Their Receptors in Postimplantation Stages

There is significantly more tissue in fetal, compared with embryonic, stages of mammalian development, and therefore more detailed biochemical studies are feasible. Furthermore, *in situ* hybridization with specific cDNA probes provides the means to demonstrate tissue and cellular localization of synthesis of the ligand and its homologous receptor. There have been several detailed recent reports of the localization of mRNAs for IGFs in fetal stages. Smith *et al.* (1987) have studied mouse developmental stages encompassing most of the period of organogenesis, from day 9 through day 12. The results of these studies indicate that mouse embryonic tissues at this time span possess both IFG-I and IGF-II receptors. In addition, embryos possess extractable immunoreactive IGFs and IGF-binding proteins. Heath and Shi (1986) explanted embryonic and extraembryonic tissues of the 9.5 days post coitum mouse embryo and metabolically labeled them with [^{35}S]methionine. Culture supernatants were treated with a polyclonal antibody that recognized prohormone forms of IGF-II, as well as IGF-binding protein. The results of immunoprecipitation showed that IGF-like molecules and their cognate binding proteins were expressed in culture by amnion and extraembryonic yolk sac mesoderm, but there was no evidence for the expression of IGF-like molecules or their binding proteins by either parietal yolk sac or visceral endoderm. The authors suggest that IGF molecules and the cognate binding proteins are expressed solely by early postimplantation tissues of extraembryonic mesodermal origin.

Mouse limb buds grown as organ cultures from the blastema stage to well-differentiated cartilage and bone (19 days) have been examined by means of a ^{125}I-labeled hormone binding assay. Both IGF-I and IGF-II receptors were found to be present in limb buds at all stages of development. The number of type I receptors decreased with development, while type II receptors increased. However, investigation of the functional relationship between the IGFs revealed that, despite the increase in IGF-II receptor number, IGF-II receptor responsiveness to exogenous hormone, as estimated by cellular proliferation, was lost. In contrast, IGF-I receptor density decreased as the tissue differentiated, but responsiveness to the hormone increased. The authors suggested that these results may support the concept of a switch between IGF-I and IGF-II during development

(Bhaumick and Bala, 1987). In a subsequent study IGF-II and insulin at similar concentrations (0.1–1 μg/ml) stimulated glucose uptake by mouse limb bud tissue. They also stimulated incorporation of glucose into glycogen, and increased glycogen synthetase activity of the limb buds irrespective of the differentiation stage of the tissues. In contrast, IGF-I had little or no effect. The authors interpreted their findings to suggest a regulatory role of IGF-II for glucose metabolism in developing limb buds that complements or overlaps with that of insulin. The absence of an effect of IGF-II or insulin on CO_2 production suggested that they may regulate glucose metabolism at the level of glycogen synthesis (Bhaumick and Bala, 1988).

Postimplantation rat embryos were examined by means of *in situ* hybridization in order to detect mRNAs coding for IGF-I and IGF-II (Beck *et al.*, 1987). Oligodeoxynucleotide probes were used for tissue localization, and the results were confirmed by means of Northern blots. IGF-II transcripts seemed to predominate throughout development. They were found in a number of mesodermally derived cells in the process of differentiation; for example, chondrocytes were heavily labeled until differentiation was complete, at which time the label decreased to background levels. IGF-II was also expressed strongly in the liver and the yolk sac. These results confirmed the results of Heath and Shi (1986), who detected synthesis of IGF-II by fetal mouse tissues. Although most of the sites that were positive for IGF-II transcripts were negative for IGF-I transcripts, faint positive signals for IGF-I transcripts were obtained in some mesodermal tissues as development proceeded. The patterns of IGF-II gene expression obtained by Beck *et al.* (1987) have been confirmed by Stylianopoulou *et al.* (1988). In addition, the latter investigators described positive hybridization signals in neural crest derivatives of the cephalic region and in the embryonic pituitary. No other tissues of ectodermal origin expressed IGF-II. Rotwein *et al.* (1987) used a sensitive solution hybridization assay to determine the steady-state levels of IGF mRNAs during midgestation in the rat. IGF-I mRNA could be detected by day 11 and rose approximately eightfold over the subsequent 48 hours, whereas IGF-II mRNA, also detectable at day 11, remained relatively constant over the subsequent 3 days.

Immunoreactive IGF-II is present at a high level in the serum of fetal rats, although its level decreases 95–99% to typical adult levels by 3 weeks of age (Moses *et al.*, 1980). Similarly, the developmental variation of the IGF-II level in the serum is correlated with the level of hybridizable IGF-II RNA in the liver (Whitfield *et al.*, 1984; Rechler *et al.*, 1985). To determine whether the developmental pattern of IGF-II ligand and RNA expression observed in serum and liver, respectively, is common to other rat tissues, Brown *et al.* (1986) estimated the levels of IGF-II mRNA in a variety of rat tissues of different ages by hybridization of slot blots to a rat IGF-II cDNA probe. IGF-II mRNA could be detected in 11 of 13 fetal (16 or 21 days' gestation) or neonatal (2 days' post-partum) rat tissues. High levels were observed in muscle, skin, lung, liver, intestine, and thymus, while signals were lower in brain stem, cerebral cortex, kidney, and hypothalamus. In three tissues—lung, thymus, and kidney—a marked decrease was observed after birth, and by 11 days IGF-II mRNA was virtually undetectable in these tissues. In contrast, muscle, heart, skin, intestine, and liver showed high levels of IGF-II mRNA, which remained elevated at 2 days' post partum. Except for in the liver, IGF-II was undetectable in rat tissues by 11 days post partum; IGF-II mRNA was not detectable in the liver at 22 days. In the cerebral cortex and the hypothalamus IGF-II mRNA could be detected into adult life. In all tissues positive for IGF-II mRNA, multiple species of the RNA were detected, and the authors attributed this finding to alternative mRNA processing.

Similar studies of fetal IGF expression have been carried out in humans. Scott *et al.* (1985) used tissue from human first-trimester therapeutic abortions to isolate RNA for dot blots, and Northern blot analysis to detect IGF-II mRNA. Transcripts for IGF-II were found in the adrenal gland, liver, kidney, and striated muscle taken from 7- to 10-week human fetuses. More recently, Han *et al.* (1987a) used *in situ* hybridization in conjunction with ^{32}P-labeled synthetic oligodeoxynucleotide probes to IGF-I and IGF-II. IGF-I and IGF-II mRNAs were found in connective tissues and in cells of mesenchymal origin in various organs and tissues of conceptuses between 16 and 20 weeks of gestation. In a subsequent study Han *et al.* (1987b) used immunocytochemical methods to identify immunoreactive somatomedin/IGF-positive cells in prostaglandin-induced human fetal abortuses of 12–20 weeks' gestation. Cells that stained positively for IGF included hepatocytes, liver-derived hematopoietic cells, columnar epithelia from the pulmonary airways, intestine, kidney, adrenal cortex, dermal cells, skeletal and cardiac muscle fibers, and pancreatic acinar and islet cells. The liver contained the greatest proportion of reactive cells, while the thymus and the spleen contained the fewest positive cells. Due to cross-reactivity of the reagents, IGF-I immunoreactivity could not be distinguished from that of IGF-II. However, parallel *in situ* hybridization studies revealed that mRNAs encoding IGF-I and IGF-II were localized predominantly in fibroblastic and mesenchymal cells. The connective tissues that were rich in IGF mRNA were localized adjacent to immunoreactive cells. The juxtaposition of cells that synthesize IGFs with those that may respond to the IGFs prompted the authors to suggest a paracrine mode of action for the IGF peptides.

B. Expression of Insulin and Its Receptor in Postimplantation Stages

Insulin receptor expression has been examined in postimplantation stages of a number of mamalian embryos. Thus, Smith *et al.* (1987) showed that insulin receptors are widespread in mouse tissues between days 9 and 12 of gestation, although the insulin receptors are fewer in number than IGF receptors. The visceral yolk sac, which was an exception, expressed more insulin receptors than IGF receptors.

Unterman *et al.* (1986) studied insulin receptor expression in rat embryos and extraembryonic membranes. Short-term cultures (24 or 48 hours) of rat conceptuses excised on day 9.5 of gestation were studied by radiolabeled ligand binding, photoaffinity labeling, and electrophoresis. These methods showed that insulin-specific binding sites could be detected on embryonic tissues and extraembryonic membranes (yolk sac, amnion, and allantoic placentas were homogenized together). When measured in the presence of an anti-insulin receptor antibody, insulin binding was inhibited by ~75% in embryos and 92% in membranes. This result suggests that most, if not all, of the insulin binding was to the insulin receptor. When yolk sac tissue was analyzed separately, it contained the highest density of receptors at this stage of development.

In the rabbit the occurrence of the insulin receptor was studied in liver and brown adipose tissue of developing fetuses. The structure of the binding domain (α subunit) was analyzed after covalent labeling with a ^{125}I-photoreactive insulin analog. The structure of the tyrosine kinase domain (β subunit) and the transmission of the hormonal signal from the α to the β subunit were analyzed by stimulating autophosphorylation by the addition of insulin. Fetuses were examined on days 20, 25, and 30 post coitum; a functional insulin receptor was detected in the liver of day 20 rabbit fetuses and was conserved to adulthood. Similar results were found with brown adipose tissue, and the expression of the insulin receptor was confirmed by its immunoreactivity with anti-receptor antibodies (Peyron *et al.*, 1985).

VI. Discussion

During the past 5 years, evidence from a number of developmental systems has accumulated to show that the insulin family of peptides and their receptors are expressed very early in development. It will be of interest to discover the range of species that express these ligands and receptors during embryogenesis.

High-resolution electron microscopy has demonstrated that insulin is concentrated and internalized by means of receptors that accumulate in coated pits (Heyner *et al.*, 1989b). Analysis of the cell surface for gold-labeled insulin distribution using quantitative morphometry after 45 minutes' incubation with insulin revealed an approximately fourfold concentration of the ligand in coated pits. Other studies of insulin uptake by cultured cells have shown that insulin is internalized by noncoated pinocytotic invaginations (Smith *et al.*, 1988). These results suggest that rapid intracellular translocation of this hormone may be important in the early mouse embryo. This suggestion is supported by functional studies that showed increased syntheses of DNA and RNA in the presence of insulin. Further support of a development role for insulin comes from experiments in which mice treated with streptozotocin, to render them diabetic, produced embryos that lagged developmentally when their cell number and protein synthetic rates were compared with embryos from untreated mice (Harvey and Kaye, 1988).

Studies of energy metabolism in preimplantation embryos have shown that pyruvate, but not glucose, meets the energy requirement of the embryo up to the eight-cell stage (Wordinger and Brinster, 1976). At the blastocyst stage glucose becomes the preferred energy substrate and predominates during periimplantation development. It may be biologically significant that insulin binds to the preimplantation mouse embryo at the morula stage, just as glucose becomes the preferred substrate. It is tempting to relate insulin binding and glucose transport at this stage of development, but data regarding the effects of insulin on glucose transport into the early mouse embryo are conflicting. Gardner and Kaye (1984) found that uptake of 3,0-methylglucose, a nonmetabolizable glucose analog, by mouse blastocysts was increased by 60% above controls when pharmacological concentrations of insulin were present in culture media. In contrast, Gardner and Leese (1988) were unable to demonstrate that concentrations of insulin up to ten times greater than physiological concentrations had a statistically significant effect on glucose transport into mouse blastocysts.

Pritchard *et al.* (1987) demonstrated increased incorporation of [^{3}H]uridine into RNA when mouse embryos at the morula stage were incubated in the presence of physiological levels of insulin. Heyner *et al.* (1989b) confirmed and extended these results by showing that insulin added in physiological amounts to preimplantation mouse embryos in culture stimulated the synthesis of both RNA and DNA, and that this effect was first discernible at the morula stage. This anabolic effect of insulin agrees with earlier studies by Wales *et al.* (1985). These investigators studied the effects of insulin in the culture medium on the incorporation of radioactive glucose into the acid-soluble or -insoluble glycogen pool of mouse embryos at the morula–early blastocyst stage. Although insulin did not have any effect on the turnover of label in acid-soluble glycogen pools of the embryo, it did stimulate incorporation of glucose into acid-insoluble marcomolecules. The authors concluded that their results provided evidence that the anabolic effects of this hormone are expressed as early as the blastocyst stage of development.

The precise role(s) of the IGFs in development remains unclear. A number of studies have documented the expression of IGF-II and its receptor at midgestation in tissues of mesodermal origin, notably cartilage.

However, there are a number of inconsistencies with respect to the ontogeny and level of expression of IGF-I versus IGF-II in the studies outlined in the previous sections of this chapter. Some of these differences may be ascribed to differing experimental techniques, and there may be species differences as well. In general, IGF-II has been considered to stimulate growth in nondifferentiated, but not differentiated, tissue. IGF-I has been considered to act primarily to regulate stem cell growth and differentiation. Following differentiation, the proliferating tissues are postulated to become sensitive to a number of hormones, among them insulin. One of the difficulties of interpreting some of the studies cited is that exogenous hormone effects may be masked by autocrine production. Thus, in the studies by Bhaumick and Bala (1987), the decreased number of IGF-II receptors and concurrent increased responsiveness may reflect occupancy of some receptors by IGF-II produced by the same cells and acting in an autocrine mode. This suggestion is reinforced by the studies by Heath and Shi (1986) with murine teratocarcinoma cells. The results of these investigations revealed a high level of complexity in the regulation of cellular proliferation, mediated via a complex interactive network involving an IGF autocrine loop. There is no reason to believe that such interactions are restricted to teratocarcinoma cells; they represent, in all likelihood, a general developmental phenomonen.

Studies at molecular and cellular levels in pre- and postimplantation embryos from several mammalian species have provided persuasive evidence for the expression of IGF-I and IGF-II receptor mRNA and protein. In addition, IGF-II has been detected at very early stages in the mouse embryo. The presence of both IGF receptors as well as the insulin receptor on most cells makes it difficult to determine which receptor mediates a particular biological response, in light of the known ligand cross-reactivity. To add a further complication, the IGFs are known to circulate not as free ligands, but bound to carrier proteins. The role played by these binding proteins is not fully understood, but in studies of cultured human fibroblasts, binding proteins could be detected on the cell surface at times when the cells were responsive to the peptide. This suggests that the binding protein may be involved in delivery of the ligand to the surface receptor (Clemmons *et al.*, 1986). It is of particular interest to note that Smith *et al.* (1987) detected IGF-binding proteins from mouse embryo homogenates (days 9–12), visceral yolk sac (day 10), and blastocysts. The embryo and yolk sac tissues also expressed the IGF receptor. In light of the autoradiographic data of Mattson *et al.* (1988) that demonstrated the presence of IGF receptors at the morula stage, and studies by Rappolee *et al.* (1989) that showed the expression of IGF-II mRNA as early as the two-cell stage, it is surprising that IGF receptor expression on the blastocyst was not detected. However, the detection of the binding protein in the embryo suggests that further analyses are needed to discriminate between the expression of receptors and the binding proteins of the corresponding ligands.

It is clear from this brief review that many unanswered questions remain with respect to the significance of the insulin family of peptides in early mammalian development. Although we are beginning to understand the functional role of insulin in the earliest stages of mammalian development, no function has been ascribed to the IGFs in preimplantation development. Of particular interest is the role of IGF-II in early development. This ligand, which may act in an autocrine fashion in the preimplantation mouse embryo, is one of the earliest products of the embryonic genome; its receptor is expressed approximately three cell cycles later.

Molecular and cellular biology offer promising new techniques and approaches for exploring and elucidating the functional integration of growth factor pathways and their developmental consequences. Examples of new techniques include methods such as the microinjection of antisense RNA, for defining the role of specific transcriptional events, and new experimental approaches at the cellular level that involve the use of antibodies directed against specific receptor domains. Studies of this nature are needed to unravel the precise manner in which the insulin family of peptides acts independently, interdependently, or synergistically to regulate cellular proliferation and/or differentiation in mammalian embryogenesis.

Acknowledgments

We would like to thank Robert M. Smith for the preparation of Fig. 3 and for his critical comments on the manuscript. These studies were supported in part by National Institutes of Health grant HD23511.

References

Bassas, L., de Pablo, F., Lesniak, M., and Roth, J. (1985). *Endocrinology (Baltimore)* **117,** 2321–2329.

Beck, F., Samani, N. J., Penschow, J. D., Thorley, B., Tregear, G. W., and Coghlan, J. P. (1987). *Development* **101,** 175–184.

Bhaumick, B., and Bala, R. M. (1987). *Biochim. Biophys. Acta* **927,** 117–128.

Bhaumick, B., and Bala, R. M. (1988). *Biochem. Biophys. Res. commun.* **152,** 359–367.

Blundell, T. L., and Humbel, R. E. (1980). *Nature (London)* **287,** 781–787.

Blundell, T. L., and Wood, S. P. (1975). *Nature (London)* **257,** 197–203.

Blundell, T. L., Bedarkar, S., Rinderknecht, E., and Humbel, R. E. (1978). *Proc. Natl. Acad. Sci. U.S.A.* **75,** 180–184.

Brinster, R. L. (1967). *J. Reprod. Fertil.* **13,** 413–420.

Brinster, R. L. (1974). *J. Exp. Med.* **140,** 1049–1056.

Brown, A. L., Graham, D. E., Nissley, S. P., Hill, D. J., Strain, A. J., and Rechler, M. M. (1986). *J. Biol. Chem.* **261,** 13144–13150.

Clemmons, D. R., Elgin, R. G., Han, V. K. M., Casella, S. J., D'Ercole, A. J., and Van Wyk, J. J. (1986). *J. Clin Invest.* **77,** 1548–1558.

Daughday, W. H., Hall, K., Raben, M., Salmon, W. D., Van den Brande, J. L., and Van Wyk, J. J. (1972). *Nature (London)* **235,** 107.

de Pablo, F. (1989) *In* "Growth Factors in Early Development" (I. Y. Rosenblum and S. Heyner, eds.), pp. 71–90. CRC Press, Boca Raton, Florida.

Ebina, Y., Ellis, L., Jarnagin, K., Edery, M., Graf, L., Clauser, E., Ou, J.-H., Masiarz, F., Kan, Y. W., Goldfine, I. D., Roth, R. A., and Rutter, W. J. (1985). *Cell (Cambridge, Mass.)* **40,** 747–758.

Ewton, D. Z., Falen, S. L., and Florini, J. R. (1987). *Endocrinology (Baltimore)* **120,** 115–123.

Fleming, T. P., and Pickering, S. J. (1985). *J. Embryol. Exp. Morphol.* **89,** 175–208.

Froesch, E. R., Schmid, C., Schwander, J., and Zapf, J. (1985). *Annu. Rev. Physiol.* **47,** 443–467.

Furlanetto, R. W., DiCarlo, J. N., and Wisehart, C. (1987). *J. Clin. Endocrinol. Metab.* **64,** 1142–1149.

Gardner, D. K., and Leese, H. J. (1988). *Development* **104,** 423–429.

Gardner, H., and Kaye, P. L. (1984). *Program Annu. Meet. Aust. Soc. Reprod. Biol., 16th, Melbourne* p. 107.

Graham, C. F. (1977). *In* "Concepts in Mammalian Embryogenesis" (M. I. Sherman, ed.), pp. 315–394. MIT Press, Cambridge, Massachusetts.

Gwatkin, R. B. L. (1966). *J. Cell. Physiol.* **68,** 335–344.

Han, V. K. M., D'Ercole, A. J., and Lund, P. K. (1987a). *Science* **236,** 193–197.

Han, V. K. M., Hill, D. J., Strain, A. J., Towle, A. C., Lauder, J. M., Underwood, L. E., and D'Ercole, A. J. (1987b). *Pediatr. Res.* **22,** 245–249.

Harvery, M. B., Beebe, L. F. S., and Kaye, P. L. (1988) *Diabetes Int. Symp.* Auckland, New Zealand.

Heath, J. K., and Shi, W.-K. (1986). *J. Embryol. Exp. Morphol.* **95,** 193–212.

Heath, J. K., Bell, S., and Rees, A. R. (1981). *J. Cell Biol.* **91,** 293–297.

Heyner, S., Mattson, B. A., Smith, R. M., and Rosenblum, I. Y. (1989a). *In* "Growth Factors in Early Development" (I. Y. Rosenblum and S., Heyner, eds.), pp. 91–112. CRC Press, Boca Raton, Florida.

Heyner, S., Rao, L. V., Jarett, L., and Smith, R. M. (1989b). *Dev. Biol.* **134,** 48–58.

Kasuga, M., Sasaki, N., Kahn, C. R., Nissley, S. P., and Rechler, M. M. (1983). *J. Clin. Invest.* **72,** 1459–1469.

Klapper, D. G., Svoboda, M. E., and Van Wyk, J. J. (1983). *Endocrinology (Baltimore)* **112,** 2215–2217.

Lewis, W., and Wright, E. (1935). *Contrib. Embryol. Carnegie Inst.* **25,** 113–144.

MacDonald, R. G., Pfeffer, S. R., Coussens, L., Tepper, M. A., Brocklebank, C. M., Mole, J. E., Anderson, J. K., Chen, E., Czech, M. P., and Ullrich, A. (1988). *Science* **239,** 1134–1137.

Marquardt, H., Todaro, G. J., Henderson, L. E., and Oroszlan, S. (1981). *J. Biol. Chem.* **256,** 6859–6863.

Mattson, B. A., Rosenblum, I. Y., Smith, R. M., and Heyner, S. (1988). *Diabetes* **37,** 585–589.

Mintz, B., and Illmensee, K. (1975). *Proc. Natl. Acad. Sci. U.S.A.* **72,** 3585–3589.

Morgan, D. O., Edman, J. C., Standring, D. N., Fried, V. A., Smith, M. C., Roth, R. A., and Rutter, W. J. (1987). *Nature (London)* **329,** 301–307.

Moses, A. C., Nissley, S. P., Short, P. A., Rechler, M. M., White, R. M., Knight, A. B., and Higa, O. Z. (1980). *Proc. Natl. Acad. Sci. U.S.A.* **77,** 3649–3653.

Mottola, C., and Czech, M. P. (1984). *J. Biol. Chem.* **259,** 12705–12713.
Nagarajan, L., and Anderson, W. B. (1982). *Biochem. Biophys. Res. Commun.* **106,** 974–980.
Nagarajan, L., Nissley, S. P., Rechler, M. M., and Anderson, W. B. (1982). *Endocrinology* (*Baltimore*) **110,** 1231–1237.
Oshima, A., Nolan, C. M., Kyle, J. W., Grubb, J. H., and Sly, W. S. (1988). *J. Biol. Chem.* **263,** 2553–2562.
Papaioannou, V. E., McBurney, M. W., Gardner, R. L., and Evans, M. J. (1975). *Nature* (*London*) **258,** 70–73.
Petruzzelli, L., Herrara, R., Garcia, R. and Rosen, O. M. (1985). *J. Biol. Chem.* **260,** 16072–16075.
Peyron, J. F., Samson, M., Van Obberghen, E., Brandenburg, D., and Fehlmann, M. (1985). *Diabetologia* **28,** 369–372.
Piko, L., and Clegg, K. B. (1982). *Dev. Biol.* **89,** 362–378.
Piko, L., and Taylor, K. D. (1987). *Dev. Biol.* **123,** 364–374.
Pritchard, M. L., Haydock, S. W., Wikarczuk, M. L., Farber, M., and Heyner, S. (1987). *Biol. Reprod.* **36,** Suppl. 1, 77.
Rappolee, D. A., Brenner, C. A., Schultz, R., Mark, D., and Werb, Z. (1988). *Science* **241,** 1823–1825.
Rappolee, D. A., Schultz, G. A., Pederson, R. A., and Werb, Z. (1989). *J. Cell Biol.* **107,** 234a.
Rechler, M. M., and Nissley, S. P. (1985). *Annu. Rev. Physiol.* **47,** 425–442.
Rechler, M. M., Zapf, J., Nissley, S. P ., Froesch, E. R., Moses, A. C., Podskalny, J. M., Schilling, E. E., and Humbel, R. E. (1980). *Endocrinology* (*Baltimore*) **107,** 1451–1459.
Rechler, M. M., Bruni, C. B., Whitfield, H. J., Yang, Y., W.-H., Frunzio, R., Graham, D. E., Coligan, J. E., Terrell, J. E., Acquaviva, A. M., and Nissley, S. P. (1985). *Cancer Cells* **3,** 131–138.
Rizzino, A. (1989). *In* "Growth Factors in Early Development" (I. Y. Rosenblum and S. Heyner, eds.), pp. 113–134. CRC Press, Boca Raton, Florida.
Rosen, O. M. (1987). *Science* **237,** 1452–1458.
Rosenblum, I. Y., Mattson, B. A., and Heyner, S. (1986). *Dev. Biol.* **116,** 261–263.
Rosenfeld, R. G., Conover, C. A., Hodges, D., Lee, P. D. K., Misra, P., Hintz, R. L., and Li, C. H. (1987). *Biochem. Biophys. Res. Commun.* **143,** 199–205.
Roth, R. A. (1988). *Science* **239,** 1269–1271.
Roth, R. A., Stover, C., Hari, J., Morgan, D. O., Smith, M. C., Sara, V., and Fried, V. (1987). *Biochem. Biophys. Res. Commun.* **149,** 600–606.
Rotwein, P., Pollock, K. M., Watson, M., and Milbrandt, J. D. (1987). *Endocrinology* (*Baltimore*) **121,** 2141–2144.
Saiki, R. K., Gelfand, D. H., Stoffel, S., Scharf, S. J., Higuchi, R., Horn, G. T., Mullis, K. B., and Erlich, H. A. (1988). *Science* **239,** 487–494.
Salomon, D. (1980). *Exp. Cell Res.* **128,** 311–321.
Schultz, G. A. (1986). *In* "Experimental Approaches to Mammalian Embryonic Development" (J. Rossant and R. A. Pederson, eds.), pp. 239–265.
Scott, J., Cowell, J., Robertson, M. E., Priestley, L. M., Wadey, R., Hopkins, B., Pritchard, J., Bell, G. I., Rall, L. B., Graham, C. F., and Knott, T. J. (1985). *Nature* (*London*) **317,** 260–262.
Smith, E. P., Sadler, T. W., and D'Ercole, A. J. (1987). *Development* **101,** 73–82.
Smith, R. M., Goldberg, R. I., and Jarett, L. (1988). *J. Histochem. Cytochem.* **36,** 359–365.
Stylianopoulou, F., Efstratiadis, A., Herbert, J., and Pintar, J. (1988). *Development* **103,** 497–506.

Tong, P. Y., Tollefsen, S. E., and Kornfeld, S. (1988). *J. Biol. Chem.* **263,** 2585–2588.

Ullrich, A., Bell, J., Chen, E., Herrera, R., Petruzzelli, L. M., Dull, T. J., Gray, A., Coussens, L., Liao, Y., Tsubokawa, M., Mason, A., Seeburg, P. H., Grunfeld, C., Rosen, O. M., and Ramachandran, J. (1985). *Nature (London)* **313,** 756–761.

Ullrich, A., Gray, A., Tam, A., Yang-Feng, T., Tsubokawa, M., Collins, C., Henzel, W., LeBon, T., Kathuria, S., Chen, E., Jacobs, S., Francke, U., Ramachandran, J., and Fujita-Yamaguchi, Y. (1986). *EMBO J.* **5,** 2503–2512.

Unterman, T., Goewert, R. R., Baumann, G., and Freinkel, N. (1986). *Diabetes* **35,** 1193–1199.

von Figuera, K., and Hasilik, A. A. (1986). *Annu. Rev. Biochem.* **55,** 167–193.

Wales, R. G., Khurana, N. K., Edirisinghe, W. R., and Pike, I. L. (1985). *Aust. J. Biol. Sci.* **38,** 421–428.

Whitfield, H. J., Bruni, C. B., Frunzio, R., Terrell, J. E., Nissley, S. P., and Rechler, M. M. (1984). *Nature (London)* **312,** 277–280.

Wilson, D. M., Thomas, J. A., Hamm, T. E., Wyche, J., Hintz, R. L., and Rosenfeld, R. G. (1987). *Endocrinology (Baltimore)* **120,** 1896–1901.

Wordinger, R. J., and Brinster, R. L. (1976). *Dev. Biol.* **53,** 294–296.

Yamada, Y., and Serrero, G. (1988). *Proc. Natl. Acad. Sci. U.S.A.* **85,** 5936–5940.

Yang Feng, T. L., Francke, U., and Ullrich, A. (1985). *Science* **228,** 728–731.

6

Nerve Growth Factor and the Issue of Mitosis in the Nervous System

I. B. Black, E. DiCicco-Bloom, and C. F. Dreyfus
Division of Developmental Neurology
Department of Neurology
Cornell University Medical College
New York, New York 10021

I. Introduction

Intercellular signaling is ubiquitous in biology, mediating colony formation in unicellular organisms (Klein *et al.*, 1988) and integrating cellular and system functions in metazoa. One subset of signals, growth factors, has been the focus of increasing interest, since they appear to regulate function of multiple biological systems. Indeed, growth factors have been invoked in such disparate generic processes as normal ontogeny, wound healing,

Current Topics in Developmental Biology, Vol. 24

atherosclerosis, and neoplastic transformation. Intercellular signaling in general and growth factors in particular are of critical importance in the nervous system, which is largely devoted to specialized intercellular communication. Nevertheless, the function of growth factors in the nervous system, and even the terminology employed, may be confusing to the uninitiated. These difficulties arise both from the intrinsic complexity of the nervous system and from the unique role that neuroscientific study has played in the discovery of growth factors.

The human brain consists of approximately 100 billion neurons, each with roughly 10,000 synaptic connections. In a system of such structural complexity, organization itself has been the subject of intense study. What factors confer specificity of connections and communication? The enormity of the biological problem has challenged generations of scientists. One critical clue was discovered nearly 40 years ago. An activity that supported survival and process outgrowth of selected neurons was defined, as described below extensively. The purified activity was termed "nerve growth factor" (NGF) (see Levi-Montalcini and Angeletti, 1968, for a review), and the molecule became the model for numerous other growth factors that followed. However, the conflation of NGF with other growth factors has led to a degree of confusion.

Modern cellular and molecular biologies have now defined numerous growth factors and growth factor families, the subject of the present volume. The newer growth factors, by general accord, are mitogenic, regulating cell division, presumably through interaction with specific cell surface receptors. Paradoxically, extensive evidence suggests that NGF, the prototypical growth factor, is not mitogenic for neurons (see Section X). Rather, NGF appears to primarily affect neuron survival, process elaboration, and connectivity, processes of particular importance in the nervous system.

Emerging evidence indicates that growth factors entirely distinct from NGF regulate neuronal mitosis. In sum, the classic growth factor, NGF, is not apparently directly mitogenic for neurons, whereas other factors do regulate neuronal mitosis. In concert, these multiple factors contribute to the normal development and function of the nervous system. Consequently, in this brief review we focus on the twin issues of NGF and neuronal mitogenesis in the nervous system. We hope to disentangle the problems of neuronal mitosis and NGF function in the nervous system; however, the regulation of mitosis is placed in the context of neural system complexity. Therefore, we begin with a specific view, emphasizing that NGF helps foster specific patterns of connectivity and thereby fosters its subsequent actions on survival and phenotypic expression. Our view stresses the inextricable interrelationships of NGF, connectivity, neuron survival, and differentiation. In this context we stress recent work that is beginning to define the regulation of neuronal mitosis.

II. NGF and the Nervous System

The unique design of the nervous system places particularly stringent requirements on underlying ontogenetic processes. The system is organized for point-to-point and population-to-population communication over distances that may be measured in meters. Specific, highly selective connections are established during development and maintained through maturity. What mechanisms confer such specificity and selectivity? NGF appears to play an important role. The factor is elaborated by targets and appears to contribute to the preservation of specific connections. In turn, appropriate connection to specific targets provides innervating neurons with access to NGF, which is necessary for survival and which fosters expression of differentiated phenotypic products. Conversely, inappropriate connections may be eliminated due to the absence of available target NGF or the presence of afferents unresponsive to the agent. During maturity, ongoing exposure to NGF maintains connectivity and circuit integrity. In sum, NGF functions at the nexus of connectivity, survival, and differentiation. We develop the view that NGF helps to foster connectivity, which then promotes survival and differentiation through the mediation of NGF itself.

After briefly considering the discovery of NGF, we review relatively well-delineated actions in the peripheral nervous system (PNS), before examining emerging information concerning NGF in the brain.

III. Discovery of NGF: A Brief History

The discovery and characterization of NGF have been recently celebrated (Marx, 1986; Levi-Montalcini, 1987), providing an opportunity to describe this early episode in the growth factor field. Nearly a half-century ago a mouse sarcoma was transplanted into the chick embryo, or onto the chorioallantoic membrane, with astonishing results. Sensory and sympathetic ganglia in the PNS markedly increased in size (Bueker, 1948; Levi-Montalcini and Angeletti, 1968). Simultaneously, ganglionic neural processes invaded the tumor parenchyma and ramified massively. Levi-Montalcini and Hamburger postulated that the tumor elaborated a diffusible factor that affected neural growth (Levi-Montalcini and Hamburger, 1951, 1953). The putative factor was christened the "nerve growth factor" (Cohen *et al.*, 1954), beginning a remarkable scientific saga.

Subsequent studies supported the contention that the activity was diffusible. Using techniques that were to become critical in the field, sensory or sympathetic ganglia were grown in culture in the presence of the tumor or its extract. The studies of cultured cells replicated the results obtained *in vivo:* Neurite outgrowth was dramatically enhanced (Levi-Montalcini *et al.,* 1954).

Cohen (1960) pursued the formidable task of purifying the putative factor. A number of tissues were screened as potential sources of activity, and the adult male mouse submaxillary gland was found to contain extraordinary levels. This fortunate discovery allowed purification and ultimate characterization (Cohen, 1960; Varon *et al.,* 1967, 1968; Bocchini and Angeletti, 1969; Angeletti *et al.,* 1971a, 1973ab). Extensive work has indicated that biological activity is associated with the β subunit of NGF, a dimer of covalently linked, identical peptides, each containing 118 amino acids of known sequence (Angeletti and Bradshaw, 1971; Angeletti *et al.,* 1971a, 1973a,b; Bradshaw, 1978; Greene and Shooter, 1980). The dimer is contained in a multisubunit storage complex, 7S NGF, consisting of an α–γ_2–β_1 composition, stabilized by zinc ions. In a sense identification of the salivary source was fortuitous, since extensive subsequent study has indicated that, in virtually all targets, NGF is a rare gene product (Heumann *et al.,* 1984; Shelton and Reichardt, 1984). The biological significance of the high salivary levels of the protein remains to be elucidated.

Nevertheless, the existence of a rich biological source of NGF permitted approaches that fostered a number of critical insights. Antisera were generated against NGF, allowing classical depletion experiments (Cohen, 1960). Treatment with antisera *in vivo* prevented normal development of peripheral sympathetic and sensory neurons (Levi-Montalcini and Booker, 1960a; Levi-Montalcini, 1972), suggesting that NGF was necessary for normal development. Although the physiological route of action was unclear, the diffusible agent was tacitly assumed to act through humoral mechanisms.

The development of sensitive radioimmunoassays for NGF protein, and Northern blot and nuclease protection assays for the mRNA, permitted further insights regarding the route of action. In early studies Hendry and colleagues (1974a,b), demonstrated that [^{125}I]NGF injected into targets *in vivo* resulted in the labeling of afferent sympathetic neurons. The new molecular techniques confirmed the impression that NGF is synthesized in targets of responsive neurons: Both message and protein were detectable in specific targets and faithfully reflected the density of innervation (Heumann *et al.,* 1984; Shelton and Reichardt, 1984).

The model emerging from the foregoing studies involved synthesis of NGF by targets, binding to high-affinity receptors on innervating nerve terminals, internalization, and retrograde transport to the cell body, where critical physiological actions are mediated. We may now discuss these contentions in greater detail, focusing initially on the well-studied PNS.

IV. NGF and the Peripheral Nervous System

A. Cell Survival

As in virtually every organ system, cells in the nervous system undergo massive developmental death, up to 80% degenerating in some populations (Glucksmann, 1951; Cowan *et al.*, 1984). Target-derived NGF plays a critical role in the regulation of survival of responsive populations. Extensive data support this contention. For example, treatment of neonatal mice or rats with anti-NGF antiserum results in virtually complete degeneration of neurons in the sympathetic nervous system through NGF deprivation (Levi-Montalcini and Booker, 1960a; Levi-Montalcini, 1972). Sensory neurons, on the other hand, require NGF in the embryo, and exposure to maternal antibodies results in sensory degeneration (Gorin and Johnson, 1979; Johnson *et al.*, 1980). Moreover, both sensory and sympathetic neurons require NGF for survival in culture, suggesting that the agent acts directly on the neuronal populations (Levi-Montalcini and Booker, 1960a; Sabatini *et al.*, 1965; Coughlin *et al.*, 1977; Chun and Patterson, 1977a,b).

Administration of NGF to postnatal animals prevents developmental neuronal death, resulting in a marked increase in cell number in sympathetic ganglia (Hendry and Campbell, 1976). While early studies raised the possibility that mitosis might actually be enhanced, subsequent investigations indicated that the effect on neuron number is entirely attributable to increased survival (Hendry, 1967; Zaimis, 1971; see also Yankner and Shooter, 1982).

In turn, the effects of NGF on survival are intimately related to connectivity. For example, axotomy of developing sympathetic neurons, which prevents retrograde transport from targets, results in degeneration (Angeletti and Levi-Montalcini, 1970; Hendry, 1975a). NGF treatment prevents axotomy-induced neuronal death (Hendry, 1975b; Levi-Montalcini *et al.*, 1975). Stated differently, successful connection with an appropriate target and access to NGF appear to prevent developmental death. It may be inferred that those neurons failing to make adequate target connections fail to survive due to absence of the sustaining factor. In this manner NGF selects for those neurons that have made appropriate connections to targets, and against those neurons contacting inappropriate targets or making aberrant connections. However, the final common pathway is selective survival, not enhanced mitosis.

B. NGF and Nerve Process Outgrowth

While NGF plays a role in connectivity and consequent survival, the relationship of the factor to initial neurite outgrowth and axon pathfinding is far less clear. Emerging evidence suggests that membrane-bound cell adhesion molecules and extracellular matrix surface adhesion molecules play critical roles in growth cone guidance (Edelman, 1983; Hynes, 1987; Jessell, 1988; Tomaselli *et al.,* 1988). Nevertheless, NGF may also be an important contributory factor.

The early work by Levi-Montalcini and Hamburger was extremely provocative in this regard (Levi-Montalcini and Hamburger, 1951, 1953). As discussed, implantation of the NGF-producing sarcoma into chicks resulted in massive ingrowth of sympathetic and sensory neurites, suggesting that the factor exerted a tropic, or neurite guidance, influence. Moreover, the repeated injection of NGF into the brain medulla oblongata elicited profuse invasion by sympathetic fibers that entered the spinal cord from the PNS and ascended to the brain stem (Levi-Montalcini, 1976). Consequently, NGF appeared to be capable of attracting neurites from distant populations, and the possibility of operation through gradients was raised.

Studies in culture strengthened the contention that NGF exerts tropic effects (Campenot, 1977). Sympathetic ganglia in culture preferentially elaborated neurites toward cocultured targets which are densely innervated *in vivo* (Chamley and Dowel, 1975; Ebendal and Jacobson, 1977) and which produce NGF (Heumann *et al.,* 1984). In even more compelling experiments cultured sensory neurites turned toward a capillary source of NGF (Gundersen and Barrett, 1979, 1980). Finally, in cultures of dissociated sensory neurons, processes grew toward higher concentrations of NGF in a gradient (Letourneau, 1978).

While the foregoing evidence suggested to many researchers that NGF may elicit initial neurite outgrowth and guidance to targets, as well as fostering connectivity and survival, this contention is subject to a number of difficulties. For example, on theoretical grounds alone sympathetic and sensory targets are distributed throughout the body, and multiple NGF gradients could hardly confer the specificity of innervation that routinely occurs during development (Black, 1978). In addition, a number of studies suggest that early embryonic neurons, that do elaborate neurites, do not require NGF and are not responsive to the agent.

Cultured early embryonic mouse sympathetic neurons do not require NGF for survival, but develop absolute dependence at later stages (Coughlin, *et al.,* 1977). Circumstantial evidence suggests that the early neurons may require other, as yet unidentified, factors (Coughlin *et al.,* 1981). This general contention is supported by more recent work. For example, trigeminal sensory neurons express NGF receptors only after neurites reach the target maxillary process (Davies *et al.,* 1987). Further, NGF protein and mRNA are expressed by targets only subsequent to afferent trigeminal innervation. Consequently, in sympathetic neurons and in at least some sensory neurons, NGF does not seem to be responsible for initial neurite elaboration and guidance. It would appear to be more likely that NGF mediates proximate interactions between axon terminal and target, once the fiber is in the field of innervation.

C. NGF and Neuronal Differentiation

Establishment of appropriate target innervation not only allows responsive neurons to survive, but also fosters differentiation. These effects also appear to be attributable, at least in part, to actions of NGF. Generally, early ultrastructural studies suggested that NGF elicited a marked increase in protein synthesis: The Golgi apparatus and the nucleolus enlarged, and the Nissl substance increased (Angeletti *et al.*, 1971b; Schwab and Thoenen, 1975). Direct biochemical measures supported this view, indicating that protein and RNA syntheses are elevated by NGF exposure (Levi-Montalcini and Angeletti, 1968; Amaldi, 1971; Huff *et al.*, 1978). Moreover, uptake of amino acids, purines, pyrimidines, glucose, and a number of ions increase (Horii and Varon, 1975, 1977; Skaper and Varon, 1983). In general terms, then, NGF markedly stimulates neuronal metabolic activity. These changes are attendant to enhanced expression of specific neuronal products in receptive neurons.

NGF increases the synthesis of specific transmitter-related molecules. The neuropeptides, substance P, somatostatin, vasoactive intestinal polypeptide, and cholecystokinin increase in sensory neurons upon exposure to the protein (Kessler and Black, 1980; Otten and Lorez, 1983; Hayashi *et al.*, 1985). Conversely, the noradrenergic biosynthetic enzymes, tyrosine hydroxylase and dopamine-β-hydroxylase, increase in sympathetic neurons (Thoenen *et al.*, 1971; Hendry, 1977; MacDonnell *et al.*, 1977; Otten *et al.*, 1977). It may be concluded that target innervation, with consequent exposure to NGF, promotes maturation of neurons, as well as allowing survival. It is presently unclear whether different molecular mechanisms underlie survival and differentiation. Available evidence does suggest that NGF enhances the expression of differentiated products already expressed, rather than eliciting expression of entirely new molecular species (Chun and Patterson, 1977a,b).

Finally, NGF increases the receptivity of neurons to afferent innervation. For example, administration of anti-NGF antiserum to animals reduces afferent synaptic contacts on sympathetic neurons and decreases synaptic responsiveness (Nja and Purves, 1978). Moreover, current work indicates that NGF regulates the molecular architecture of the synapse in sympathetic ganglia. Treatment of rats with NGF increases the specific postsynaptic density protein in sympathetic neurons (Wu and Black,

1989). In aggregate, these observations indicate that NGF regulates afferent as well as efferent connections of responsive neurons. In this manner NGF may regulate the development of distant and proximate components of a neural pathway.

Early events in the cascade mediating NGF actions include the early appearance of the c-*fos* oncogene product, suggesting that rapid transcriptional events may be involved (Greenberg *et al.,* 1986). However, the mechanisms by which the NGF signal is transduced into the variegated cellular effects described above remain one of the outstanding questions in the area.

D. NGF and Maintenance of Pathway Integrity

In addition to fostering connectivity during development, abundant evidence suggests that ongoing action of the factor is necessary for the maintenance of pathways and their components during maturity. For example, treatment of adult rats with anti-NGF antisera or antibodies, which interfere with NGF action, decreases substance P in sensory neurons and norepinephrine in sympathetic neurons (Bjerre *et al.,* 1974; Gorin and Johnson, 1979; Schwartz *et al.,* 1982; Rich *et al.,* 1984). These are early signs of dysfunction due to NGF deprivation. Indeed, sympathetic neurons ultimately atrophy, lose synaptic contacts, and in many cases die after antibody treatment (Levi-Montalcini, 1972; Nja and Purves, 1978). These observations indicate that ongoing presence of NGF is critical for the maintenance of normal function in the adult.

However, the biological reality is far more complex and interesting than a simple all-or-none affair. Treatment of adults with NGF results in neuronal hypertrophy, a generalized increase in protein synthesis, and elevated transmitter products (Angeletti *et al.,* 1971b; Thoenen and Barde, 1980). These fascinating experiments suggest that NGF is limiting in the adult and that neurons are capable of more exuberant function, if exposed to supranormal levels of the protein. Therefore, available physiological levels of NGF in the adult maintain normal, not maximal, function. Consequently, NGF, and perhaps yet undiscovered analogous factors, may maintain not only individual pathways, but also delicate balances among pathways. During maturity, as well as development, then, NGF does maintain function, but within rather narrow limits imposed by physiological levels of the agent.

Actions of the trophic agent on lesioned pathways in adults further illustrate the nature of function during maturity. Axonal transection or chemical lesion of sympathetic neurons in adults, which separates cell bodies from target NGF, induces neuronal atrophy and, in some cases, death (Bjerre *et al.*, 1973, 1974; Hendry, 1975a; Purves, 1975; Nja and Purves, 1978). Treatment with NGF largely prevents the degenerative process (Bjerre *et al.*, 1973; Hendry, 1975b; Purves and Nja, 1976; Nja and Purves, 1978): Loss of synapses is inhibited and decreases in transmitter are largely reduced, although cell loss still occurs. Moreover, exogenous NGF enhances the regrowth of axons to targets (Bjerre *et al.*, 1973). Conversely, treatment with anti-NGF antiserum inhibits axon regeneration (Bjerre *et al.*, 1974). NGF may thus play a role in the reestablishment of pathway connections after illness and injury in the adult, recapitulating developmental regulation.

V. NGF and the Central Nervous System

While it is abundantly clear that NGF plays a physiological role in the PNS, potential actions in the central nervous system (CNS) have been discerned only recently. Although NGF and the CNS have been studied for decades, actions have defied detection. Difficulties arose in part from unwarranted preconceptions that were, nevertheless, instructive. Early work in the PNS focused heavily on catecholaminergic sympathetic neurons and on noradrenergic molecular markers, as described. Responses were so dramatic that it was tacitly assumed that if any brain neurons were NGF responsive, they would be catecholaminergic. Decades of work, often employing the most ingenious approaches, failed to unequivocally uncover an effect of NGF on any central catecholaminergic population (e.g., Thoenen *et al.*, 1987; Whittemore and Seiger, 1987; Springer, 1988). In retrospect, however, extensive work in the PNS had indicated that there is no orthodox correlation between transmitter phenotype and NGF responsiveness. To date, there is no evidence that transmitters confer the capacity to express high-affinity NGF receptors.

While initial efforts were unrewarded, studies in the last half-decade suggest that NGF does play a role in the brain after all. The new observations have attracted considerable interest, since the trophic agent appears to regulate cholinergic neurons in the basal forebrain (bf) and the striatum, populations that degenerate in Alzheimer's and Huntington's diseases, respectively (Rossor *et al.*, 1984; Conneally, 1984). Nevertheless, if information concerning the PNS is incomplete, that for the CNS is patently primitive. We summarize a rapidly expanding field, but refer the reader to a number of excellent reviews (Thoenen *et al.*, 1987; Whittemore and Seiger, 1987; Springer, 1988).

To help orient the unfamiliar reader, we begin with a brief summary that emphasizes parallels to NGF action in the PNS. Several lines of evidence suggest that bf cholinergic neurons derive NGF from the target hippocampus to which they project. The bf neurons are located in the medial septum and the diagonal band of Broca. NGF protein and mRNA have been detected in the hippocampus, indicating that the trophic molecule is synthesized in the target (Korsching *et al.*, 1985; Whittemore *et al.*, 1986; Shelton and Reichardt, 1986). The NGF binds to specific high-affinity receptors located on the terminals of bf neurons (Hefti *et al.*, 1986; Richardson *et al.*, 1986; Raivich and Kreutzberg, 1987; Dreyfus *et al.*, 1989) and undergoes retrograde transport from the hippocampus to the perikarya in the bf (Schwab *et al.*, 1979). Available evidence suggests that the NGF may influence survival and function of the cholinergic bf neurons (see Section V,A).

A. NGF and Neuron Survival

Whereas NGF definitively regulates neuron survival in the PNS, present information is suggestive, but incomplete, for brain populations. Perhaps the most provocative evidence is derived from *in vivo* studies in which the bf–hippocampus system has been transected. Surgery results in a loss of choline acetyltransferase- and acetylcholinesterase-positive neurons, the presumed cholinergic populations (Hefti *et al.*, 1984; Williams *et al.*, 1986; Kromer, 1987). Neuronal loss is associated with deficits in spatial memory, a function normally subserved by this system (Stein and Will, 1983). Administration of NGF prevents the apparent decrease in cholinergic cells (Hefti, 1986; Williams *et al.*, 1986; Kromer, 1987) and significantly improves the derangement of cognitive function (Stein and Will, 1983). While these results are highly suggestive, interpretation is not without difficulties. Since NGF normally increases cholinergic enzyme activities used to identify cholinergic neurons in these studies, the enzymes may not constitute indifferent cholinergic markers for morphometric investigation. For example, NGF may simply increase cholinergic enzymes to threshold levels of detectability in multiple populations, which then masquerade as "rescued" neurons. This difficulty may be circumvented by the development of novel NGF-independent markers for the populations in question.

Experiments with anti-NGF antibodies have been even less satisfying. Injection into the developing brain has yielded no consistent effects on bf neuron survival (Gnahn *et al.*, 1983). Lack of observable effects may have been attributable to a lack of adequate penetration and access to critical sites. Alternatively, the presence of multiple additional survival factors in the brain *in vivo* may compensate for a relative deficit of NGF. In this regard, use of a stringent culture system may provide insights unobtainable from the unmodified *in vivo* system (Hartikka and Hefti, 1988).

B. NGF and Brain Neurite Outgrowth

While information remains scant, preliminary studies have raised the possibility that NGF may influence neurite elaboration in cultured cells. Exposure of dissociated bf cholinergic neurons to exogenous NGF apparently enhanced neuritic extension (Hartikka and Hefti, 1988). It will be important to obtain confirmation of these studies and to extend observations to the living animal before the physiological relevance of these intriguing results can be adequately evaluated. Of course, these studies raise the possibility that NGF influences the establishment of connections in the brain, as in the PNS.

C. NGF and Brain Neuron Differentiation

Administration of NGF to neonatal rats via the intraventricular route suggests that the agent fosters differentiation *in vivo* (Gnahn *et al.*, 1983; Johnston *et al.*, 1987). Experiments performed in culture (Honegger and Lenoir, 1982; Martinez *et al.*, 1987; Hartikka and Hefti, 1988) support this contention and suggest that NGF acts directly on these neurons. In fetal bf explant culture NGF exposure dramatically increases choline acetyltransferase and acetylcholinesterase, suggesting that the trophic agent increases multiple differentiated traits in brain neurons, as in the PNS (Martinez *et al.*, 1987). Moreover, in dissociated bf neuron cultures, cholinergic neurons express high-affinity NGF receptors, indicating that the neurons can respond directly to the agent (Bernd *et al.*, 1988; Dreyfus *et al.*, 1989). In principle, then, target-derived NGF may influence differentiation of innervating, afferent populations, as in the PNS.

This formulation is consistent with a number of additional observations derived from studies *in vivo*. bf Afferents and targets exhibit remarkable synchrony. Just as developing bf fibers contact the target hippocampus, NGF synthesized by the hippocampus increases simultaneously, while NGF receptors and mRNA expressed by bf neurons increase markedly (Buck *et al.*, 1987, 1988; Yan and Johnson, 1988). The notable coincidence of expression of NGF and receptors in target and innervating neurons suggests that the factor plays a role in the formation of functional connections.

In summary, though still sketchy, emerging evidence suggests that NGF mediates the development and consequences of connectivity in the brain, as well as in the PNS. Still, no evidence supports the contention that NGF influences neuronal mitosis. We must turn elsewhere to identify neuronal mitogens.

VI. NGF and Early Studies of Neuronal Precursor Proliferation

The foregoing section has described several rather novel aspects of neural ontogeny. Although component processes underlying nervous system development, including cell survival, process elaboration, adhesion and guidance, and cell connection, are not unique to neurons, these processes are brought to a high art during neural ontogeny. Remarkably, the most well-characterized neuronal growth factor, NGF, participates in many, if not all, of these processes. However, in contrast to the traditional view of growth factors, NGF is not a classical mitogen (Levi-Montalcini and Booker, 1960b; Hendry and Campbell, 1976; Thoenen and Barde, 1980). In fact, a widely held misconception regarding NGF function in the nervous system is that the trophic protein serves to stimulate neuronal division. This is not the case in the neuronal populations examined thus far (Hendry and Campbell, 1976; DiCicco-Bloom and Black, 1988a; Wu *et al.*, 1988), as we describe. Moreover, the term "growth factor" tends to be used in a generic, not mitogenic, sense in neurobiology. For example, growth factors may serve trophic functions, promoting neuronal survival and maintaining mature function, or tropic roles, eliciting directional process outgrowth (Varon and Bunge, 1978).

If NGF does not regulate the generation of neurons, what does? Before addressing the question of neuronal mitosis, or more correctly neuronal precursor or neuroblast mitosis, we briefly review *in vivo* studies describing the process of neurogenesis. Initial investigations of precursor proliferation in cell culture are then described. Finally, we present recent evidence demonstrating that specific mechanisms regulating neuroblast mitosis can be identified, using a fully defined neuronal culture system. In turn, insights into mechanisms regulating neuroblast division may shed light on relationships among the ontogenetic processes of neuroblast mitosis and survival and, ultimately, neural system formation.

The study of early brain development in avian and mammalian species has documented the process of neurogenesis extensively (Jacobson, 1978; Schacher, 1985). From these data, the chronology and geometry of neuronal production have been well characterized for both PNS and CNS populations (Hamburger and Levi-Montalcini, 1949; Cowan, 1973; Hamburger, 1975; Carr and Simpson, 1978a; Hamburger *et al.*, 1981). Although neuronal production occurs in apparent excess quantitatively (Hamburger and Levi-Montalcini, 1949; Hamburger, 1975; Hamburger *et al.*, 1981), the striking reproducibility of neuronal generation suggests that the process is precisely regulated (Cowan, 1973; Frederiksen and McKay, 1988; Rakic, 1988).

Early investigations on the control of neuroblast generation *in vivo* examined the role of target organs to which neurons projected. Classical studies initially suggested that targets may influence neuronal production (Hamburger and Levi-Montalcini, 1949; Prestige, 1967). Further, the stimulatory effects of NGF, a target-derived factor, were initially thought to be mitogenic (Levi-Montalcini and Booker, 1960b; Thoenen and Barde, 1980), as discussed above. However, these studies failed to distinguish potential mitogenic actions from survival-promoting effects. Clear evidence that target molecules did not influence neuronal precursor division was derived from systems in which target-dependent survival was temporally distinct from the phase of neuroblast production (Cowan, 1973; Landmesser and Pilar, 1974; Hamburger, 1975; Carr and Simpson, 1978b; Wright and Smolen, 1987). Nevertheless, distinguishing molecules that support the survival of dividing precursors from those that directly regulate the cell cycle continues to be a critical problem.

More recently, the potential mitogenic roles of hormones, including thyroid and growth hormones, and endogenous monoamine neurotransmitters have been examined in early brain development *in vivo* (LeGrand, 1977; Lauder, 1983). Although physiological brain growth required normal activity of these agents, potential direct mitogenic effects were obscured by the complexities of the maternal–fetal unit and the undefined fetal microenvironment. Consequently, several investigators turned to the more rigorous conditions provided by tissue culture to examine neuronal precursor proliferation.

Since neuroblast mitosis is restricted to early brain development, fetal or embryonic neural tissue was initially employed to study precursor proliferation (Schrier, 1973; Honegger *et al.*, 1979; Pettmann *et al.*, 1979). However, cultured neuronal precursors exhibited surprisingly restricted proliferative capacities (Honegger *et al.*, 1979; Pettmann *et al.*, 1979; Juurlink and Fedoroff, 1982). Cultured neuroblasts withdrew from the cell cycle within days, apparently reflecting the well-characterized developmental time course of precursor mitosis *in vivo* (Sensenbrenner *et al.*, 1980; Lenoir and Honegger, 1983; Barakat and Sensenbrenner, 1988). Efforts to enhance proliferation of neuroblasts in cell culture, by using higher concentrations of serum, actually decreased cell division (Barakat *et al.*, 1983, 1983–1984, 1984a). Alternatively, DNA synthesis was stimulated by exposure to brain extracts, suggesting that important *in vivo* mitogens might be isolated (Barakat *et al.*, 1982, 1984a). However, identification of purines as the active agents in these extracts suggested that medium composition had not been optimized (Barakat *et al.*, 1983, 1984b). Nevertheless, these early studies demonstrated the feasibility, in principle, of using culture techniques to study neuroblast mitosis.

Although several systems supporting dividing neuroblasts were developed, the identification of specific regulatory agents was hampered by the presence of serum-containing media (Pettmann *et al.,* 1979; Sensenbrenner *et al.,* 1980; Barakat *et al.,* 1983, 1983–1984, 1984a). To address this limitation, fully defined media were evolved, permitting identification of hormones and mitogenic growth factors that influenced dividing neuroblasts. For example, insulin, insulinlike growth factor-I and -II (IGF-I and -II), basic fibroblast growth factor (bFGF), acidic FGF [(aFGF), also called endothelial cell growth factor], and triiodothyronine all exerted effects (Raizada *et al.,* 1980; Yang and Fellows, 1980; Lenoir and Honegger, 1983; Enberg *et al.,* 1985; Gensberger *et al.,* 1987; Shemer *et al.,* 1987; Wu *et al.,* 1988). However, in many cases interpretations have been confounded by the presence of undefined nonneuronal cells which may have indirectly mediated stimulatory effects.

Relatively homogeneous neuronal populations have now been obtained by using a number of different strategies. Several specific neuronal mitogens have been tentatively defined, including IGFs and FGF (Gensberger *et al.,* 1987; DiCicco-Bloom and Black, 1988a; Wu *et al.,* 1988; see also Chapter 3 of this volume). In summary, the use of identified populations in fully defined media is now permitting delineation of multiple mechanisms regulating neuroblast mitosis.

VII. Unique Nervous System Characteristics Require Novel Experimental Approaches

Investigation of mitotic regulation in the nervous system involves a number of novel strategies. The nervous system exhibits several unique characteristics, including limited proliferative capacity, the requirement for trophic factor support, and striking cellular heterogeneity. Consequently, it has not been possible to apply strictly traditional methodologies to the study of neuronal cell division. The following section briefly discusses these peculiarly neural characteristics and describes a new fully defined model system for the study of neuroblast mitosis.

A. Neuronal Precursors Exhibit Limited Cell Division

Soon after birth, neuronal production ceases in the mammalian brain, suggesting that a quiescent stem cell population is not maintained, in contrast to most other tissues (Jacobson, 1978; Schacher, 1985). Easily accessible quantities of neuronal precursors are, therefore, not available. Consequently, investigators turned to embryonic sources and discovered an additional constraint: Cultured neuronal precursors rapidly withdrew from the cell division cycle (Honegger *et al.*, 1979; Pettmann *et al.*, 1979; Sensenbrenner *et al.*, 1980; Lenoir and Honegger, 1983; Barakat and Sensenbrenner, 1988). Further, culture conditions optimal for nonneuronal cells (e.g., serum-containing media) reduced neuroblast proliferation (Barakat *et al.*, 1983, 1983–1984, 1984a). Consequently, the absence of a logarithmic growth phase in neuroblast cultures precluded the use of clonal cell selection techniques to purify populations and optimize medium components. Moreover, reinitiation of DNA synthesis in a quiescent neuroblast population has yet to be elicited.

B. Neurons Require Trophic Growth Factors for Survival

The very issue of trophism raises a fundamental problem in the study of neuroblast mitosis. The availability of NGF from target sources *in vivo* determines whether neurons live or die (Thoenen and Barde, 1980; Hamburger *et al.*, 1981), as described extensively. Fundamentally, then, growth factors studied in cultured cells may promote the survival of dividing neuroblasts or actually stimulate entry into the mitotic cycle. Both categories of action yield apparent evidence of increased mitosis per se. In contrast, in nonneuronal systems culture conditions ensuring optimal survival have already been established, eliminating the possibility of confounding trophic with mitogenic effects. Consequently, culture paradigms for neuroblasts must distinguish between these alternative activities.

C. Nervous System Tissue Is Strikingly Heterogeneous

A purified cellular population is a basic requirement for the elucidation of molecular mechanisms. However, the remarkable cellular heterogeneity of nervous system tissue has made the task of isolating a pure neuronal population difficult in the extreme. For example, a diversity of mesenchymal cells is present in neural tissue, as in other organs. However, the contribution of mesenchymal cells is small compared to that of the glial cell population, representing approximately half of the component cells of the brain (Jacobson, 1978; Kandel and Schwartz, 1985). Moreover, as the major structural and reparative cell of the nervous system, glia possess a marked capacity for proliferation, both *in vivo* and *in vitro* (Cassel *et al.*, 1982; Sobue *et al.*, 1983; Kandel and Schwartz, 1985). However, the most formidable aspect of nervous system heterogeneity is represented by the primary elements themselves, the neurons. There is a multiplicity of neuronal cell types, even within a localized brain area. Although the study of

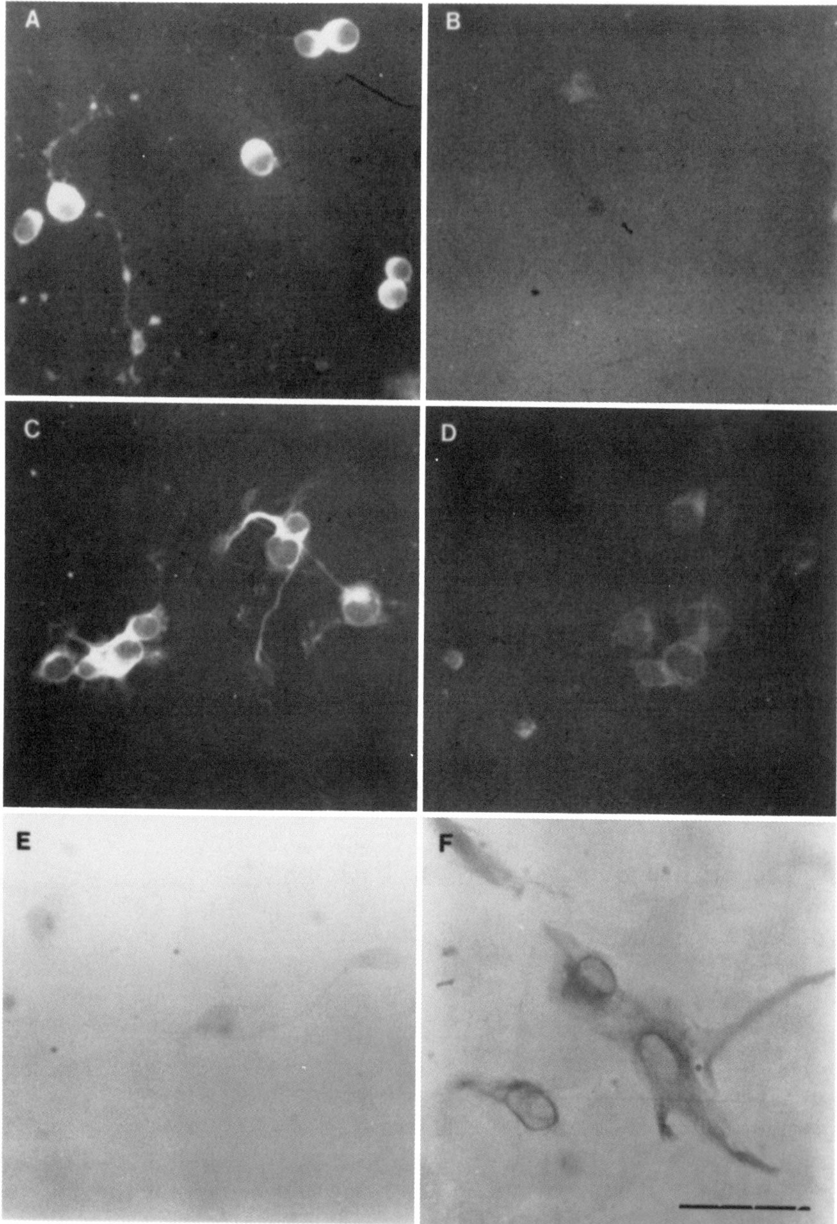

Fig. 1 Immunocytochemical staining of cultured cells from embryonic sympathetic ganglia. Ganglia at embryonic day 15.5 were dissociated and cultured in a fully defined serum-free medium. At 48 hours cultures were fixed and processed for immunocytochemistry. Intense tyrosine hydroxylase fluorescence is localized to the cell cytoplasm and long varicose processes (A). Neurofilament staining is distributed eccentrically in round cells, in punctate

neuronal typology remains active, we presently lack adequate experimental markers (Kandel and Schwartz, 1985). Consequently, the difficulty in identifying neuronal subtypes further complicates the analysis of population numbers. Use of a fully defined neuronal population minimizes confounding typological issues.

The foregoing nervous system characteristics require novel experimental approaches to study neuroblast mitosis. We developed a fully defined neuronal culture system composed of a virtually pure population of embryonic rat sympathetic neuroblasts (DiCicco-Bloom and Black, 1988a). Specifically, we used the dissociated superior cervical ganglion, a well-characterized peripheral structure of neural crest origin. This system has several particular advantages: (1) the cultured embryonic precursor cells undergo mitosis in a fully defined medium (DiCicco-Bloom and Black, 1988a); (2) young neuroblasts that do not yet require NGF are used, allowing culture in the absence of the confusing trophic variable (Coughlin *et al.*, 1977, 1981; Coughlin and Collins, 1985); (3) the proliferating sympathetic precursors express a number of recognizable neuronal traits that identify the cells (Rothman *et al.*, 1978, 1980); (4) the nonneuronal population, quantitatively small at this age (Cochard and Paulin, 1984; Roufa *et al.*, 1986), fails to proliferate in the fully defined tissue culture conditions (Cassel *et al.*, 1982; Sobue *et al.*, 1983; Mirsky and Jessen, 1986), eliminating a critical confounding variable.

VIII. Identified Neuroblasts Divide in Culture

To ensure that we were studying neuroblast mitosis, cells in our culture system were initially defined immunocytochemically. Sympathetic neuroblasts were obtained after dissociation of gestational day 15.5 rat embryo ganglia and were cultured in a fully defined medium on polylysine- and fibronectin-coated culture dishes (DiCicco-Bloom and Black, 1988a). At 48 hours virtually all of the cells exhibited the neurotransmitter enzyme, tyrosine hydroxylase (TH), immunocytochemically (Fig. 1). Tyrosine hydroxylase is the rate-limiting enzyme in the catecholamine transmitter biosynthetic pathway. In addition, a large majority of the cells also expressed the 160-kDa subunit of neurofilament, the neuron-specific inter-

fashion, and extends linearly in cells with processes (C). Specific primary antibodies were excluded in processing the controls for tyrosine hydroxylase (B) and neurofilament (D). No specific glial fibrillary acidic protein peroxidase staining is observed in sympathetic cultures (E), whereas nonneuronlike cells from serum-containing cultures of brain at embryonic day 18.5 exhibit an intense fibrillary reaction product (F). Bar = 5 μm. (From DiCicco-Bloom and Black, 1988a; reprinted with permission.)

mediate filament. In contrast, none of the cells expressed glial fibrillary acidic protein, a marker for the glial population in these ganglia. Consequently, these cultures were composed of a virtually pure neuronal population, allowing the study of neuron-specific mitogens (DiCicco-Bloom and Black, 1988a).

To characterize neuroblast mitosis, several complementary approaches were used. First, we observed mitotic stages in living cells, by phase microscopy. Second, time-lapse photography revealed that approximately 20% of the cells initially plated had divided by 48 hours of incubation (Fig. 2). Third, [^{3}H]thymidine incorporation was assessed by scintillation spectroscopy and autoradiography. Approximately one third of the tyrosine hydroxylase-positive neuroblasts exhibited silver grains specifically localized to the nucleus (labeling index, 33%), an index of DNA synthesis (Fig. 3). Definitive identification of mitotic populations eliminated many of the interpretative difficulties described above.

IX. Insulin Regulates the Neuroblast Mitotic Cycle

Considerable evidence indicates that hormones and growth factors regulate cell division in diverse nonneuronal systems. To define the role of hormones in neuroblast mitosis, we cultured cells in a control medium or in a medium lacking one of five individual components. DNA synthesis was quantitatively estimated by scintillation spectroscopy of culture acid precipitates. The deletion of insulin reduced [^{3}H]thymidine incorporation to one quarter of its original value. Moreover, the insulin effect differed significantly from that after deletion of one of the other components, including progesterone, putrescine, transferrin, and selenium, suggesting that insulin was critically required for neuroblast mitosis (DiCicco-Bloom and Black, 1988a).

To further characterize the effects of insulin, a dose–response curve was prepared. Increasing doses of insulin produced up to a fourfold rise in [^{3}H]thymidine incorporation, with a plateau at 5–10 μg/ml (Fig. 4A), suggesting that insulin stimulated mitosis via a saturable, receptor-mediated mechanism.

To define insulin specificity, a number of growth factors and hormones were examined for mitogenic activity. Platelet-derived growth factor, transforming growth factor-β, interleukin-2, dexamethasone, growth hormone, and thyroxine were all without effect (unpublished observations), suggesting that insulin is a highly specific neuroblast mitogen. A number of these agents were similarly ineffective in a fully defined chick neuroblast system, in which insulin stimulated cell division (Wu *et al.*, 1988).

To determine whether insulin stimulated DNA synthesis selectively or

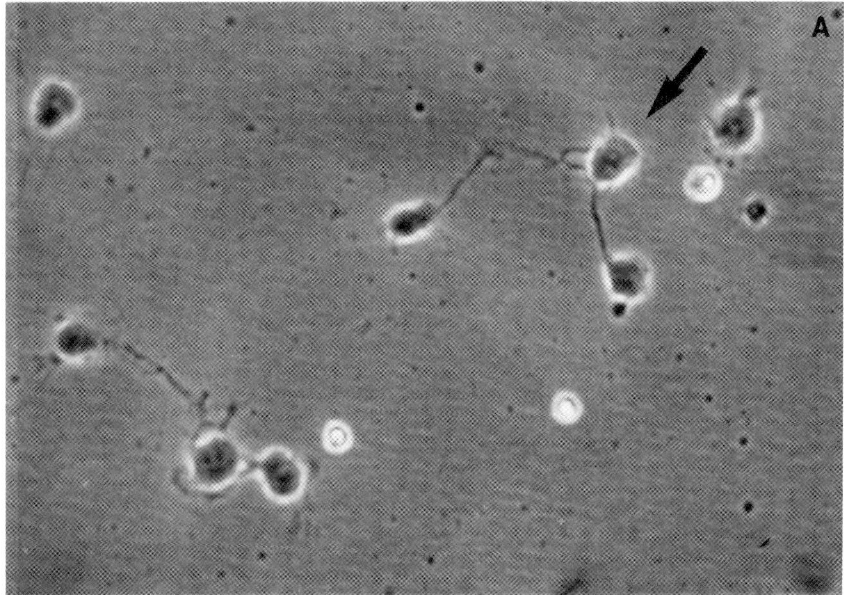

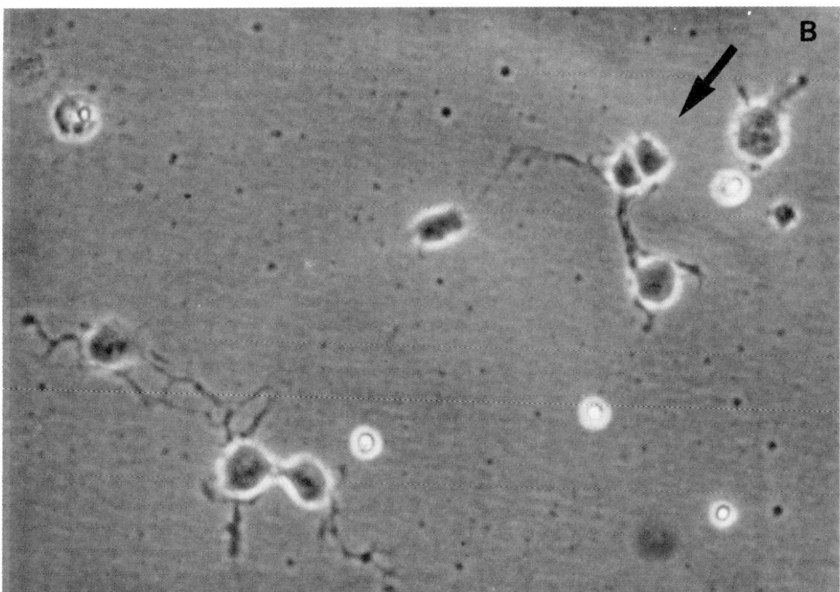

Fig. 2 Time-lapse photograph of dissociated sympathetic ganglia cultures. Neuroblasts were cultured as in Fig. 1. Serial phase photomicrographs of cultures were obtained at 4, 8, 16, 24, and 48 hours. (A) A number of neuroblasts have already elaborated processes at 16 hours (arrow). (B) By 24 hours one of these neuroblasts (arrow) has undergone cell division.

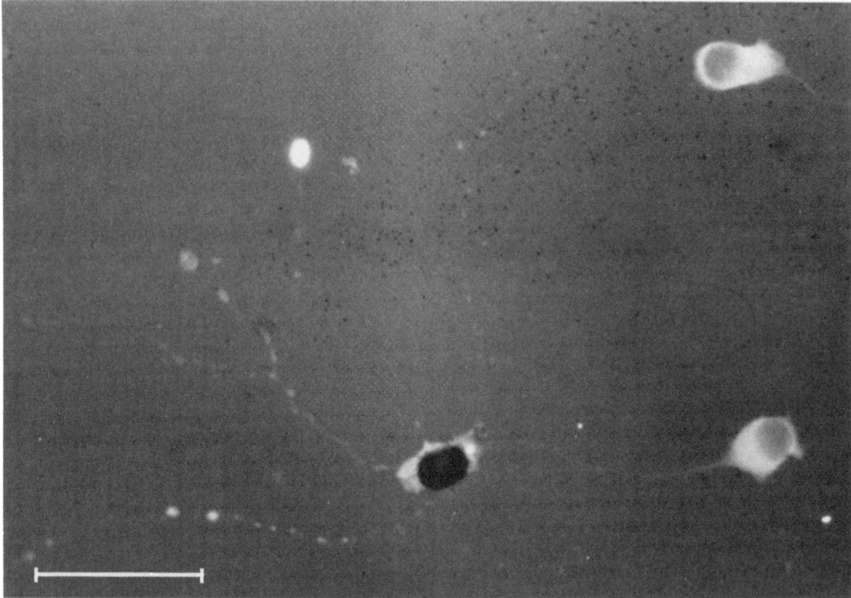

Fig. 3 Combined tyrosine hydroxylase immunocytochemistry and [^{3}H]thymidine autoradiography of dissociated ganglia cultures. Cells were cultured as in Fig. 1, except for the addition of [^{3}H]thymidine (1 μCi/ml) for the final 24 hours of incubation. At 48 hours cultures were processed for combined tyrosine hydroxylase immunocytochemistry and autoradiography and assayed for the labeling index. Three tyrosine hydroxylase-positive cells are shown. One cell (lower center) also exhibits dense black silver grains localized to the nucleus. Bar = 5 μm. (From DiCicco-Bloom and Black, 1988a; reprinted with permission.)

enhanced *all* metabolic processes, protein synthesis was examined. While insulin stimulated DNA synthesis, the hormone did not alter the incorporation of [^{3}H]leucine into total cellular protein (unpublished observations). In contrast, NGF elicited a fivefold increase in [^{3}H]leucine incorporation, indicating that the neuroblasts were capable of responding to other metabolic signals in the absence of insulin. Consequently, insulin selectively stimulated mitosis and did not simply exert a generalized effect on cellular metabolism. In sum, these observations indicated that insulin stimulated neuroblast DNA synthesis in a highly specific and selective manner, consistent with previous observations in mixed-cell systems (Raizada *et al.*, 1980; Yang and Fellows, 1980; Lenoir and Honegger, 1983; Enberg *et al.*, 1985).

While these observations suggested that insulin was mitogenic for neurons, other explanations warranted consideration. For example, as discussed above, insulin may serve as a neuronal trophic factor, a function previously ascribed to the hormone (Bottenstein *et al.*, 1980; Aizenman *et*

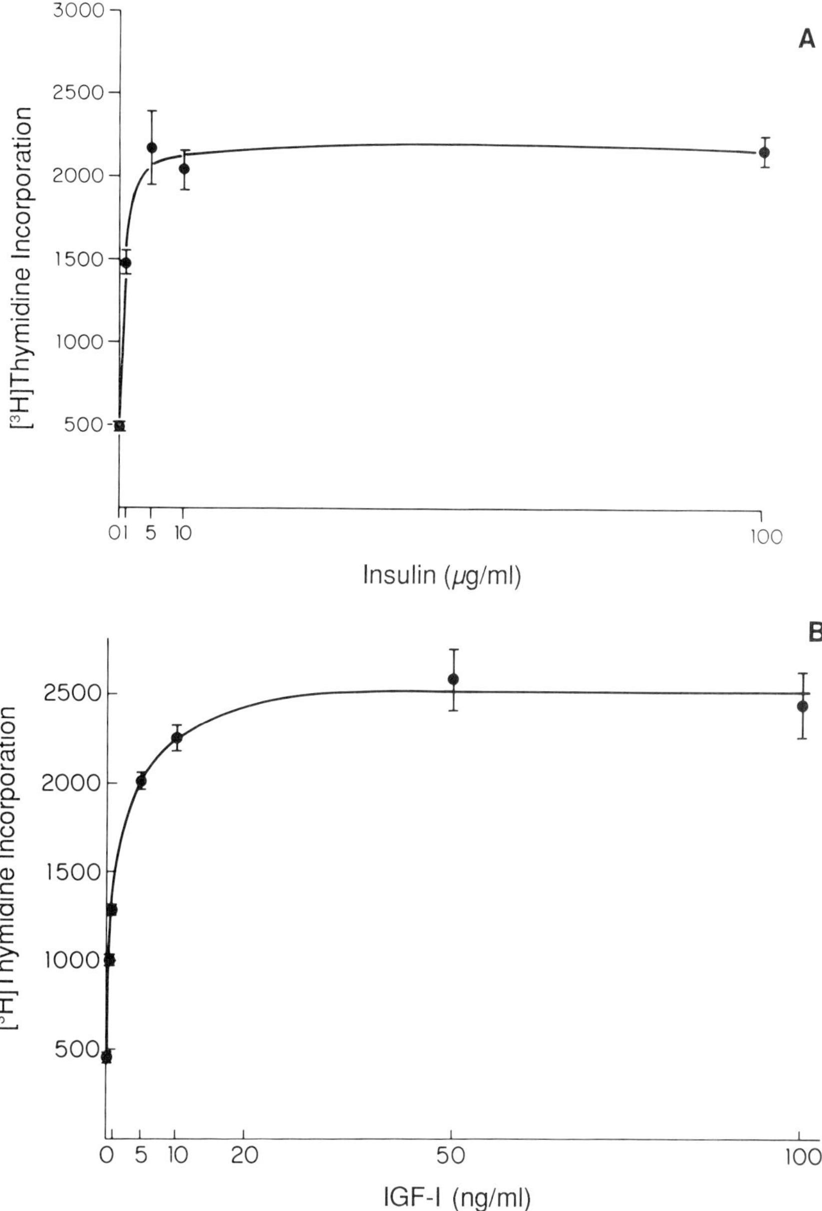

Fig. 4 The effect of IGFs on [^{3}H]thymidine incorporation. Cultures were incubated for 48 hours with various concentrations of insulin (A) or IGF-I (B). [^{3}H]Thymidine (1 μCi/ml) was added after 24 hours of incubation, and incorporation into culture acid precipitates was assayed 1 day later. Each experimental value represents the mean incorporation of three culture dishes (calculated after subtracting blank; range, 25–50 cpm) and is expressed as counts per minute [mean $\pm$ SEM (vertical bars)]. Note that insulin was used in microgram-per-milliliter concentrations, whereas IGF-I was used in nanogram-per-milliliter concentrations. (From DiCicco-Bloom and Black, 1988a; reprinted with permission.)

al., 1986; Aizenman and deVellis, 1987; Recio-Pinto and Ishii, 1988). In turn, increased DNA synthesis may reflect improved culture conditions, with enhanced survival and overall metabolism. However, the lack of effect on protein synthesis suggested that insulin did not simply stimulate all metabolic processes. Moreover, specific culture parameters were selected that minimized the contributions of potential changes in cell survival (DiCicco-Bloom and Black, 1988a).

Since insulin did not simply provide trophic support for cultured neuroblasts, the stimulation of DNA synthesis might reflect effects on the cell cycle. To determine whether insulin in fact played a role in mitotic regulation, the labeling index of the neuroblast population was defined. Insulin more than doubled the labeling index at 48 hours, indicating that increased DNA synthesis reflected an increased proportion of cultured neuroblasts entering the mitotic cycle (Fig. 5). It was tentatively concluded, then, that insulin served a regulatory role in neuroblast mitosis (DiCicco-Bloom and

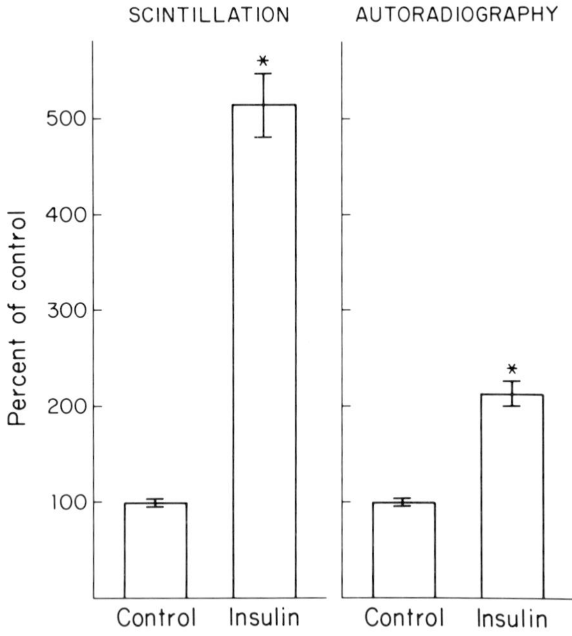

Fig. 5 Assessment of insulin-stimulated [^{3}H]thymidine incorporation by spectroscopy and labeling index. Cultures were incubated for 48 hours without insulin (control) or with insulin (10 μg/ml). [^{3}H]Thymidine incorporation was assessed in sister cultures, either by scintillation spectrometry, as in Fig. 4, or by combined immunocytochemistry and autoradiography, as in Fig. 3, and is expressed as a percentage of the control (mean ± SEM). The data were derived from three independent experiments. *, Differs from the control, at $p < 0.005$. (From DiCicco-Bloom and Black, 1988a; reprinted with permission.)

Black, 1988a). Similar conclusions were drawn in recent studies of a fully defined avian neuronal system (Wu *et al.*, 1988).

X. NGF Does Not Regulate the Mitotic Cycle of Cultured Neuroblasts

Development of the mitotic neuroblast system provided the unique opportunity to directly examine the effects of NGF on the cell division cycle. Specifically, we determined whether NGF altered ongoing DNA synthesis or, more importantly, the number of neuroblasts that entered the cell cycle. Since multiple mitogenic factors may interact to control cell division, the effects of NGF were examined in the absence and the presence of several doses of insulin (Rozengurt, 1986). NGF had no effect on the labeling index of neuroblasts cultured in the control medium (Fig. 6). In contrast, insulin more than doubled the proportion of neuroblasts entering the cycle. Moreover, even in cultures treated with insulin, NGF exerted no effect on the labeling index, suggesting that NGF served as neither a positive nor a negative mitogenic signal in this population (DiCicco-Bloom and Black, 1988a).

Although NGF did not alter the cell cycle, the trophic protein was not without effect. Indeed, NGF increased protein synthesis fivefold in these cultures. Further, the factor increased neurite outgrowth and complexity, enhanced apparent tyrosine hydroxylase TH immunofluorescence, and

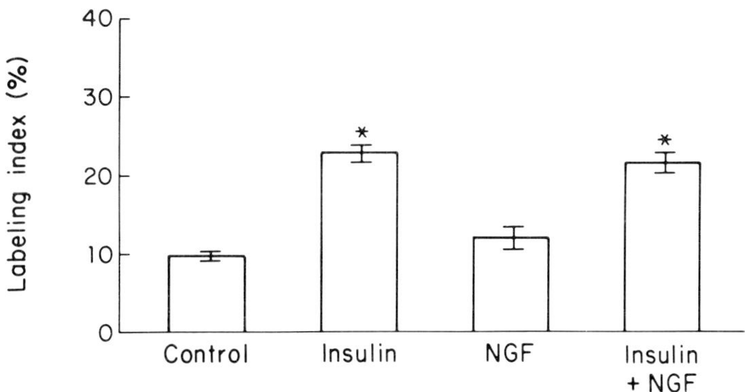

Fig. 6 The effect of NGF on [^{3}H]thymidine incorporation. Cultures were incubated for 48 hours in a control medium or in a medium containing insulin (10 μg/ml), NGF (10 U/ml), or insulin plus NGF. [^{3}H]Thymidine incorporation was assessed by determination of the labeling index, as in Fig. 3. The results are expressed as the mean ± SEM. *, Differs from control, at $p < 0.005$. (From DiCicco-Bloom and Black, 1988a; reprinted with permission.)

increased cell body size in responsive neuroblasts, all well-characterized effects of the trophic protein (Thoenen and Barde, 1980). Therefore, although NGF serves a trophic function for these neuroblasts, the protein does not appear to play a role in mitotic regulation (Honegger and Lenoir, 1982; DiCicco-Bloom and Black, 1988a). Similarly, in a fully defined avian system NGF had no effect on central neuroblast DNA synthesis (Wu *et al.*, 1988).

Although NGF does not stimulate the division of central or peripheral neuroblasts, the factor is not devoid of mitogenic effects. NGF stimulates the proliferation of several nonneuronal cell types, including tumor cell lines, adrenal chromaffin cells, and lymphoid cells (Burstein and Greene, 1982; Lillien and Claude, 1985; Ignatius *et al.*, 1985; Thorpe and Perez-Polo, 1987; Stemple *et al.*, 1988). It is hardly surprising that defined growth factors have cell-specific actions. Indeed, the absence of an NGF influence on neuroblast division indirectly supports the contention that insulin is a highly specific neuronal mitogen.

XI. IGF-I Is a Highly Potent Neuronal Mitogen

Insulin is only one of a family of growth factors, including IGF-I and IGF-II, that regulate cell division and intermediary metabolism in a variety of tissues (Froesch *et al.*, 1985; King and Kahn, 1985; Moses and Pilistine, 1985; see also Chapter 5 of this volume). Early studies indicated that IGFs acted on responsive tissues over long distances, as (endocrine) hormones. More recent developmental studies, however, suggest that IGFs are produced and act locally, regulating histogenesis, in a paracrine and/or autocrine mode (Sporn and Roberts, 1985; Soares *et al.*, 1986; Rotwein *et al.*, 1987; Smith *et al.*, 1987). Furthermore, extensive evidence indicates that insulin family members bind to homologous as well as heterologous receptors, eliciting cellular responses (Froesch *et al.*, 1985; King and Kahn, 1985; Moses and Pilistine, 1985). Indeed, in diverse nonneuronal systems, relatively high micromolar concentrations of insulin, such as those that stimulate neuroblasts, act via the IGF-I receptor. To define the role of IGF-I in neuroblast mitosis, a dose–response analysis was performed. IGF-I, at nanomolar concentrations, reproduced the fivefold stimulation of DNA synthesis observed with insulin (Fig. 4B). Moreover, there was a striking difference in potency. The EC_{50} for IGF-I was 1 ng/ml, whereas that of insulin was approximately 100 ng/ml (Fig. 4B), indicating that IGF-I was at least 100-fold more potent than insulin. In contrast, incubation of cultures with 100 ng/ml of IGF-II increased [^{3}H]thymidine incorporation only 53% (data not shown) (DiCicco-Bloom and Black, 1988a). Consequently, although all insulin family members stimulated neuroblast DNA synthesis, IGF-I was the most potent, suggesting that the IGF-I receptor mediates the neuroblast mitogenic response in cell culture.

The foregoing observations in culture are completely consistent with recent observations made *in vivo*. Many studies suggest that IGFs play a role in neuronal development. High-affinity insulin and IGF binding occurs early in brain development and is maximal during the period of most active neuronal production (Sara *et al.*, 1983; Hendricks *et al.*, 1984 Basses *et al.*, 1985; Van Schravendijk *et al.*, 1986). Further, insulin and IGF receptors have been isolated from the developing brain (Burgess *et al.*, 1987; Shemer *et al.*, 1987; Ocrant *et al.*, 1988), suggesting that immature neuroblasts possess the necessary apparatus to respond to IGFs. Moreover, the embryonic brain apparently elaborates these important fetal mitogens. IGF gene expression and IGF protein have been detected in developing brain (Soares *et al.*, 1986; Beck *et al.*, 1987; Rotwein *et al.*, 1988) and embryonic neural cultures, respectively (D'Ercole *et al.*, 1980; Clarke *et al.*, 1986). These observations suggest that IGFs are synthesized locally in the brain, regulating neural ontogeny in a autocrine and/or paracrine fashion.

Although the present observations indicate that IGFs may regulate neuronal production, studies with postmitotic neurons suggest that IGFs serve a neurotrophic function during brain development as well. For example, in a number of neuronal culture systems, IGFs promote neuronal survival and neurotransmitter phenotypic expression (Honegger *et al.*, 1979; Aizenman *et al.*, 1986; Aizenman and deVellis, 1987). In addition, IGFs elicit neuritic process elaboration from peripheral neurons, in conjunction with NGF, apparently independently of effects on neuronal survival (Recio-Pinto and Ishii, 1988). From a broader perspective, then, the diverse effects of IGFs on dividing and differentiating neuroblasts suggest that the developmental state of the neuron may define the repertoire of responses elicited by growth factors.

XII. Multiple Factors May Interact to Regulate Neuroblast Mitosis

The epigenetic regulation of neuroblast mitosis raises the possibility that other extracellular signals may also play a role. What might these factors be? One approach involves examination of the effects of other growth factors identified in neural tissue. For example, aFGF, bFGF, and epidermal growth factor have been isolated from neural preparations (Gospodarowicz, 1985 and Chapter 3 of this volume; Lakshmanan *et al.*, 1986). Moreover, FGF supports the proliferation of neuronal precursors (Gensberger *et al.*, 1987). Using the sympathetic neuroblast system, we have found that epidermal growth factor also increases the proportion of neuroblasts entering the mitotic cycle (manuscript in preparation), suggesting that multiple growth factors may interact in mitotic regulation, as occurs in nonneuronal systems.

To pursue the possibility of multiple signals, we recently examined the effects of a potentially novel neuronal mitogen, neuronal depolarization. Depolarizing stimuli, including elevated extracellular K^+ and the voltage-dependent sodium channel agonist, veratridine, both increased DNA synthesis and doubled the labeling index of cultured neuroblasts (DiCicco-Bloom and Black, 1988b; Pincus *et al.*, 1988). Moreover, blockade of the Na^+ channel, using tetrodotoxin, or the voltage-sensitive Ca^{2+} channel, using nitrendipine, prevented the depolarization effects. Consequently, fluxes via respective voltage-sensitive ion channels apparently mediated depolarization-induced mitosis. In contrast, ion fluxes via voltage-sensitive channels were not required for IGF-induced mitogenesis (Table I) (DiCicco-Bloom and Black, 1988b; Pincus *et al.*, 1988). These observations suggest that neuronal depolarization may use different signal transduction pathways in responsive cells. Although these effects were documented in the culture dish, they may be relevant to the dividing neuroblast population in the embryo: Presynaptic neurotransmission has been documented in these ganglia 2 days before we dissect the ganglia for these studies (Rubin, 1985). Thus, nerve impulse activity may play a role in determining the size of the target neuronal population in the embryo (Rothman *et al.*, 1978, 1980; Rubin, 1985).

Table I Effects of Na^+ Channel Antagonist Tetrodotoxin on Mitogenic Stimuli[a]

	[^{3}H]Thymidine incorporation (cpm, mean ± SEM)
Control	1274 ± 41
+ TTX	1088 ± 17
Veratridine	3097 ± 125[b]
+ TTX	1178 ± 51
IGF-I	3512 ± 179[b]
+ TTX	3448 ± 184[b]

[a] Cells cultured in the control medium or in the presence of veratridine (2μm) or IGF-I (40 ng/ml) were incubated with or without TTX (10 n*M*) and assayed for incorporation as in Fig. 4. TTX, Tetrodotoxin.

[b] Differs from the control, at $p < 0.005$.

XIII. Prospects

In aggregate, these studies suggest that multiple factors and signals regulate neuroblast proliferation. Observations suggest, moreover, that orthodox distinctions among traditional growth factors, neurotransmitters, and hormones may be inadequate. Indeed, the single-molecule insulin functions as a growth factor, transmitter, and hormone. Further, recent work indicates that the gastrointestinal hormones, which also serve as neurotransmitters, are potent mitogens for specific populations (Zachary *et al.*, 1987). We anticipate that novel mitogens may be identified by the study of neural hormones, transmitters, trophic factors, and growth factors in the future.

More generally, it is apparent that multiple epigenetic factors regulate the development and maintenance of the nervous system. While apparently discrete processes, such as mitosis, may be regulated by multiple intercellular signals, any signal may influence manifold processes. Thus, NGF may regulate survival, connectivity, and phenotypic expression. Elucidation of the relationship among different ontogenetic processes and signals may yield a clearer understanding of the principles underlying ontogeny and mature function.

References

Aizenman, Y., and deVellis, J. (1987). *Brain Res.* **406,** 32–42.
Aizenman, Y., Weichsel, M. E., and deVellis, J. (1986). *Proc. Natl. Acad. Sci. U.S.A.* **83,** 2263–2266.
Amaldi, P. (1971). *J. Neurochem.* **18,** 827–832.
Angeletti, R. H., and Bradshaw, R. A. (1971). *J. Cell Biol.* **67,** 118–125.
Angeletti, P. U., and Levi-Montalcini, R. (1970). *Proc. Natl. Acad. Sci. U.S.A.* **65,** 114–121.
Angeletti, R. H., Bradshaw, R. A., and Wade, R. D. (1971a). *Biochemistry* **10,** 463–469.
Angeletti, P. O., Levi-Montalcini, R., and Caramia, F. (1971b). *J. Ultrastruct. Res.* **36,** 24–36.
Angeletti, R. H., Hermodson, M. A., and Bradshaw, R. A. (1973a). *Biochemistry* **12,** 100–115.
Angeletti, R. H., Mercanti, D., and Bradshaw, R. A. (1973a). *Biochemistry* **12,** 90–100.
Auburgėr, G., Heumann, R., Hellweg, R., Korsching, S., and Thoenen, H. (1987). *Dev. Biol* **120,** 322–328.
Barakat, I., and Sensenbrenner, M. (1988). *Dev. Neurosci.* **10,** 173–179.
Barakat, I., Sensenbrenner, M., and Vincedan, J. (1982). *Neurochem. Res.* **7,** 287–300.
Barakat, I., Sensenbrenner, M., and Labourdette, G. (1983). *Neurosci. Lett.* **41,** 325–330.
Barakat, I., Labourdette, G., and Sensenbrenner, M. (1983–1984). *Dev. Neurosci.* **6,** 169–183.
Barakat, I., Courageot, J., Devilliers, G., and Sensenbrenner, M. (1984a). *Neurochem. Res.* **9,** 263–271.

Barakat, I., Sensenbrenner, M., and Labourdette, G. (1984b). *J. Neurosci. Res.* **11,** 117–129.

Bassas, L., DePablo, F., Lesniak, M. A., and Roth, J. (1985). *Endocrinology (Baltimore)* **117,** 2321–2329.

Beck, F., Samani, N. J., Penschow, J. D., Thorley, B., Tregear, G. W., and Coghlan, J. P. (1987). *Development* **101,** 175–184.

Bernd, P., Martinez, H. J., Dreyfus, C. F., and Black, I. B. (1988). *Neuroscience* **26,** 121–129.

Bjerre, B., Bjorklund, A., and Mobley, W. (1973). *Z. Zellforsch. Mikrosk. Anat.* **146,** 15–43.

Bjerre, B., Bjorklund, A., and Edwards, D. C. (1974). *Cell Tissue Res.* **148,** 441–476.

Black, I. B. (1978). *Annu. Rev. Neurosci.* **1,** 183–214.

Bocchini, V., and Angeletti, P. U. (1969). *Proc. Natl. Acad. Sci. U.S.A.* **64,** 787–794.

Bottenstein, J. E., Skaper, S. D., Varon, S. S., and Sato, G. H. (1980). *Exp. Cell Res.* **125,** 183–190.

Bradshaw, R. A. (1978). *Annu. Rev. Biochem.* **47,** 191–216.

Buck, C. R., Martinez, H. I., Black, I. B., and Chao, M. V. (1987). *Proc. Natl. Acad. Sci. U.S.A.* **84,** 3060–3063.

Buck, C. R., Martinez, H. J., Chao, M. V., and Black I. B. (1988). *Dev. Brain Res.* **44,** 259–268.

Bueker, E. D. (1948). *Anat. Rec.* **102,** 369–390.

Burgess, S. K., Jacobs, S., Cuatrecassas, P., and Sahyoun, N. (1987). *J. Biol. Chem.* **262,** 1618–1622.

Burstein, D. E., and Greene, L. A. (1982). *Dev. Biol.* **94,** 477–482.

Campenot, R. B. (1977). *Proc. Natl. Acad. Sci. U.S.A.* **74,** 4516–4519.

Carr, V. M., and Simpson, S. B. (1978a). *J. Comp. Neurol.* **182,** 727–740.

Carr, V. M., and Simpson, S. B. (1978b). *J. Comp. Neurol.* **182,** 741–756.

Cassel, D., Wood, P. M., Bunge, R. P., and Glaser, L. (1982). *J. Cell. Biochem.* **18,** 433–445.

Chamley, J. H., and Dowel, J. J. (1975). *Exp. Cell Res.* **90,** 1–7.

Chun, L. L.-Y., and Patterson, P. H. (1977a). *J. Cell Biol.* **75,** 705–711.

Chun, L. L.-Y., and Patterson, P. H. (1977b). *J. Cell Biol.* **75,** 712–718.

Clarke, D. W., Mudd, L., Boyd, F. T., Fields, M., and Raizada, M. K. (1986). *J. Neurochem,* **47,** 831–836.

Cochard, P., and Paulin, D. (1984). *J. Neurosci.* **4,** 2080–2094.

Cohen, S. (1960). *Proc. Natl. Acad. Sci. U.S.A.* **46,** 302–311.

Cohen, S. R., Levi-Montalcini, R., and Hamburger, V. (1954). *Proc. Natl. Acad. Sci. U.S.A.* **40,** 1014–1018.

Conneally, P. M. (1984). *Am. J. Hum. Genet.* **36,** 506–526.

Coughlin, M. D., and Collins, M. B. (1985). *Dev. Biol.* **110,** 392–401.

Coughlin, M. D., Boyer, D. M., and Black, I. B. (1977). *Proc. Natl. Acad. Sci. U.S.A.* **74,** 3438–3442.

Coughlin, M. D., Bloom, E. M., and Black, I. B. (1981). *Dev. Biol.* **82,** 56–68.

Cowan, W. M. (1973). *In* "Development and Aging in the Nervous System" (M. Rockstein, ed.), pp. 19–41. Academic Press, New York.

Cowan, W. M., Fawcett, J. W., O'Leary, D. D. M., and Stanfield, B. B. (1984). *Science* **225,** 1258–1265.

Davies, A. M., Bandtlow, C., Heumann, R., Korsching, S., Rohrer, H., and Thoenen, H. (1987). *Nature (London)* **326,** 353–358.

D'Ercole, I. A., Applewhite, G. T., and Underwood, L. E. (1980). *Dev. Biol.* **75,** 315–328.

DiCicco-Bloom, E., and Black, I. B. (1988a). *Proc. Natl. Acad. Sci. U.S.A.* **85,** 4066–4070.
DiCicco-Bloom, E., and Black, I. B. (1988b). *Soc. Neurosci.* **14,** 767.
Dreyfus, C. F., Bernd, P., Martinez, H. J., Rubin, S. J., and Black, I. B. (1989). *Exp. Neurol.* (in press).
Ebendal, T., and Jacobson, C.-O. (1977). *Exp. Cell Res.* **105,** 379–387.
Edelman, G. M. (1983). *Science* **219,** 450–457.
Enberg, G., Tham, A., and Sara, V. R. (1985). *Acta Physiol. Scand.* **125,** 305–308.
Frederiksen, K., and McKay, R. D. G. (1988). *J. Neurosci.* **8,** 1144–1151.
Froesch, E. R., Schmid, C., Schwander, J., and Zapf, J. (1985). *Annu. Rev. Physiol.* **47,** 443–467.
Gensburger, C., Labourdette, G., and Sensenbrenner, M. (1987). *FEBS Lett.* **217,** 1–5.
Glucksmann, A. (1951). *Biol. Rev. Cambridge Philos. Soc.* **26,** 59–86.
Gnahn, H., Hefti, F., Heumann, R., Schwap, M. E., and Thoenen, H. (1983). *Dev. Brain Res.* **9,** 45–52.
Gorin, P. D., and Johnson, E. M. (1979). *Proc. Natl. Acad. Sci. U.S.A.* **76,** 5382–5386.
Gospodarowicz, D. (1985). *In* "Control of Animal Cell Proliferation" (A. L. Boynton and H. L. Leffert, eds.), pp. 61–90. Academic Press, Orlando, Florida.
Greenberg, M. E., Ziff, E. B., and Greene, L. A. (1986). *Science* **234,** 80–83.
Greene, L. A., and Shooter, E. (1980). *Annu. Rev. Neurosci.* **3,** 353–402.
Gundersen, R. W., and Barrett, J. N. (1979). *Science* **206,** 1079–1080.
Gundersen, R. W., and Barrett, J. N. (1980). *J. Cell Biol.* **87,** 546–554.
Hamburger, V. (1975). *J. Comp. Neurol.* **160,** 535–546.
Hamburger, V., and Levi-Montalcini, R. (1949). *J. Exp. Zool.* **111,** 457–502.
Hamburger, V., Brunso-Bechtold, J. K., and Yip, J. W. (1981). *J. Neurosci.* **1,** 60–71.
Hartikka, J., and Hefti, F. (1988) *J. Neurosci.* **8,** 2967–2985.
Hayashi, M., Edgar, D., and Thoenen, H. (1985). *Dev. Biol.* **108,** 49–55.
Hefti, F. (1986). *J. Neurosci.* **6,** 2155–2162.
Hefti, F., Dravid, A., and Hartikka, J. (1984). *Brain Res.* **293,** 305–311.
Hefti, F., Hartikka, J., Salvietierra, A., Weiner, W. J., and Mash, D. C. (1986). *Neurosci. Lett.* **69,** 37–45.
Hendricks, S. A., dePablo, F., and Roth, J. (1984). *Endocrinology (Baltimore)* **115,** 1315–1323.
Hendry, I. A. (1967). *Rev. Neurosci.* **2,** 149–194.
Hendry, I. A. (1975a). *Brain Res.* **90,** 235–244.
Hendry, I. A. (1975b). *Brain Res.* **94,** 87–97.
Hendry, I. A. (1977). *Brain Res.* **134,** 213–223.
Hendry, I. A., and Campbell, J. (1976). *J. Neurocytol.* **5,** 351–360.
Hendry, I. A., Stach, R., and Herrup, K. (1974a). *Brain Res.* **82,** 117–128.
Hendry, I. A., Stockel, K., Thoenen, H., and Iversen, L. L. (1974b). *Brain Res.* **68,** 103–121.
Heumann, R., Korsching, S., Scott, J., and Thoenen, H. (1984). *EMBO J.* **3,** 3183–3189.
Honegger, P., and Lenoir, D. (1982). *Dev. Brain Res.* **3,** 229–238.
Honegger, P., Lenoir, D., and Favrod, P. (1979). *Nature (London)* **282,** 305–308.
Horii, Z. I., and Varon, S. (1975). *J. Neurosci. Res.* **1,** 361–375.
Horii, Z. I., and Varon, S. (1977). *Brain Res* **124,** 121–133.
Huff, K., Lakshmann, J., and Guroff, G. (1978). *J. Neurochem.* **31,** 599–609.
Hynes, R. O. (1987). *Cell (Cambridge, Mass.)* **48,** 549–554.
Ignatius, M. J., Chandler, C. R., and Shooter, E. M. (1985). *J. Neurosci.* **5,** 343–351.
Jacobson, M. (1978). "Developmental Neurobiology." Plenum, New York.
Jessell, T. M. (1988). *Neuron* **1,** 3–13.

Johnson, E. M., Gorin, P. D., Brandeis, L. D., and Pearson, J. (1980). *Science* **210,** 916–918.

Johnston, M. V., Rutkowski, J. L., Warner, B. H., Long, J. B., and Mobley, W. C. (1987). *Neurochem. Res.* **12,** 985–994.

Juurlink, B. H., and Fedoroff, S. (1982). *In Vitro* **18,** 179–182.

Kandel, E. R., and Schwartz, J. H. (1985). "Principles of Neural Science." Elsevier, New York.

Kessler, J. A., and Black, I. B. (1980). *Proc. Natl. Acad. Sci. U.S.A.* **77,** 649–652.

King, G. L., and Kahn, C. R. (1985). *In* "Control of Animal Cell Proliferation" (A. L. Boynton and H. L. Leffer, eds.). pp. 201–249. Academic Press, Orlando, Florida.

Klein, P. S., Sun, T. J., Saxe, C. L., III, Kimmel, A. R., Johnson, R. L., and Devreotes, P. N. (1988). *Science* **241,** 1467–1472.

Korsching, S., Auburger, G., Heumann, R., Scott, J., and Thoenen, H. (1985). *EMBO J.* **4,** 1389–1393.

Kromer, L. F. (1987). *Science* **235,** 214–216.

Lakshmanan, J., Weichsel, M. E., Jr., and Fisher, D. A. (1986). *J. Neurochem.* **46,** 1081–1085.

Landmesser, L., and Pilar, G. (1974). *J. Physiol.* (*London*) **241,** 715–736.

Lauder, J. M. (1983). *Psychoneuroendocrinology* **8,** 121–155.

LeGrand, J. (1977). *In* "Brain: Fetal and Infant" (S. R. Berenberg, ed.), pp. 137–164. Nijhoff, The Hague.

Lenoir, D., and Honegger, P. (1983). *Dev. Brain Res.* **7,** 205–213.

Letourneau, P. C. (1978). *Dev. Biol.* **66,** 183–196.

Levi-Montalcini, R. (1972). *In* "Immunosympathectomy" (G. Steiner and E. Schonbaum, eds.), pp. 55–78. Elsevier, Amsterdam.

Levi-Montalcini, R. (1976). *Prog. Brain Res.* **45,** 235–256.

Levi-Montalcini, R. (1987). *EMBO J.* **6,** 1145–1154.

Levi-Montalcini, R., and Angeletti, P. U. (1968). *Physiol. Rev.* **48,** 534–569.

Levi-Montalcini, R., and Booker, B. (1960a). *Proc. Natl. Acad. Sci. U.S.A.* **46,** 373–384.

Levi-Montalcini, R., and Booker, B. (1960b). *Proc. Natl. Acad. Sci. U.S.A.* **46,** 384–391.

Levi-Montalcini, R., and Hamburger, V. (1951). *J. Exp. Zool.* **116,** 321–362.

Levi-Montalcini, R., and Hamburger, V. (1953). *J. Exp. Zool.* **123,** 233–388.

Levi-Montalcini, R., Meyer, H., and Hamburger, V. (1954). *Cancer Res.* **14,** 49–57.

Levi-Montalcini, R., Aloe, L., Mugnaini, E., Oesch, F., and Thoenen, H. (1975). *Proc. Natl. Acad. Sci. U.S.A.* **72,** 595–599.

Lillien, L. E., and Claude, P. (1985). *Nature* (*London*) **317,** 632–634.

MacDonnell, P. C., Tolson, N., and Guroff, G. (1977). *J. Biol. Chem.* **252,** 5859–5863.

Martinez, H. J., Dreyfus, C. F., Jonakait, G. M., and Black, I. B. (1987). *Brain Res.* **412,** 295–301.

Marx, J. L. (1986). *Science* **234,** 543–544.

Mirsky, R., and Jessen, K. R. (1986). *In* "Neurofibromatosis" (A. E. Rubenstein, R. P. Bunge, and D. E. Housman, eds.), Vol. 486, pp. 132–146. New York Acad. Sci., New York.

Moses, A. C., and Pilistine, S. J. (1985). *In* "Control of Animal Cell Proliferation" (A. L. Boynton and H. L. Leffert, eds.), pp. 91–119. Academic Press, Orlando, Florida.

Nja, A., and Purves, D. (1978). *J. Physiol.* (*London*) **277,** 53–75.

Ocrant, I., Valentino, K. L., Eng, L. F., Hintz, R. L., Wilson, D. M., and Rosenfeld, R. G. (1988). *Endocrinology* (*Baltimore*) **123,** 1023–1034.

Otten, U., and Lorez, H. P. (1983). *Neurosci. Lett.* **34,** 153–158.

Otten, U., Schwab, M., Gagnon, C., and Thoenen, H. (1977). *Brain Res.* **133,** 291–303.

Pettmann, B., Louis, J. C., and Sensenbrenner, M. (1979). *Nature (London)* **281,** 378–380.

Pincus, D. W., DiCicco-Bloom, E., and Black, I. B. (1988). *Soc. Neurosci. Abstr.* **14,** 767.

Prestige, M. C. (1967). *J. Embryol. Exp. Morphol* **17,** 453–471.

Purves, D. (1975). *J. Physiol. (London)* **252,** 429–463.

Purves, D., and Nja, A. (1976). *Nature (London)* **260,** 535–536.

Raivich, G., and Kreutzberg, G. W. (1987). *Neuroscience* **20,** 23–36.

Raizada, M. K., Yang, J. W., and Fellows, R. E. (1980). *Brain Res.* **200,** 389–400.

Rakic, P. (1988). *Science* **241,** 170–176.

Recio-Pinto, E., and Ishii, D. N. (1988). *Neurochem. Int.* **12,** 397–414.

Rich, K. M., Yip, H. K., Osborne, P. A., Schmidt, R. E., and Johnson, E. M., Jr. (1984). *J. Comp. Neurol.* **230,** 110–118.

Richardson, P. M., Verge Issa, V. M. K., and Riopelle, R. I. (1986). *J. Neurosci.* **6,** 2312–2321.

Rossor, M. N., Iversen, L. L., Reynolds, G. P., Mountjoy, C. Q., and Roth, M. (1984). *Br. Med. J.* **288,** 961–964.

Rothman, T. P., Gershon, M. D., and Holtzer, H. (1978). *Dev. Biol.* **65,** 322–341.

Rothman, T. P., Specht, L. A., Gershon, M. D., Joh, T. H., Teitelman, G., Pickel, V. M., and Reis, D. I. (1980). *Proc. Natl. Acad. Sci. U.S.A.* **77,** 6221–6225.

Rotwein, P., Pollock, K. M., Watson, M., and Milbrandt, J. D. (1987). *Endocrinology (Baltimore)* **121,** 2141–2144.

Rotwein, P., Burgess, S. K., Milbrandt, J. D., and Krause, J. E. (1988). *Proc. Natl. Acad. Sci. U.S.A.* **85,** 265–269.

Roufa, D., Bunge, M. B., Johnson, M. I., and Cornbrooks, C. J. (1986). *J. Neurosci.* **6,** 790–802.

Rozengurt, E. (1986). *Science* **234,** 161–166.

Rubin, E. (1985). *J. Neurosci.* **5,** 697–704.

Sabatini, M. T., Pellegrino de Iraldi, A., and DeRobertis, E. (1965). *Exp. Neurol.* **12,** 370–383.

Sara, V. R., Hall, K., Misaki, M., Fryklund, L., Christensen, N., and Wetterberg, L. (1983). *J. Clin. Invest.* **71,** 1084–1094.

Schacher, S. (1985). *In* "Principles of Neural Science" (E. R. Kandel and J. H. Schwartz, eds.), pp. 729–742. Elsevier/North-Holland, New York.

Schrier, B. K. (1973). *J. Neurobiol.* **4,** 117–124.

Schwab, M. E., and Thoenen, H. (1975). *Cell Tissue Res.* **158,** 543–553.

Schwab, M. E., Otten, U., Agid, Y., and Thoenen, H. (1979). *Brain Res.* **168,** 473–483.

Schwartz, J. P., Pearson, J., and Johnson, E. M. (1982). *Brain Res.* **244,** 378–381.

Sensenbrenner, M., Wittendorp, E., Barakat, I., and Rechenmann, R. V. (1980). *Dev. Biol.* **75,** 268–277.

Shelton, D. L., and Reichardt, L. F. (1984). *Proc. Natl. Acad. Sci. U.S.A.* **81,** 7951–7955.

Shelton, D. L., and Reichardt, L. F., (1986). *Proc. Natl. Acad. Sci. U.S.A.* **83,** 2714–2718.

Shemer, J., Raizada, M. K., Masters, B. A., Ota, A., and LeRoith, D. (1987). *J. Biol. Chem.* **262,** 7693–7699.

Skaper, S. D., and Varon, S. (1983). *Brain Res.* **271,** 263–271.

Smith, E. P., Sadler, T. W., and D'Ercole, A. L. (1987). *Development* **101,** 73–82.

Soares, M. B., Turken, A., Ishii, D., Mills, L., Episkopou, V., Cotter, S., Zeithin, S., and Efstratiadis, A. (1986). *J. Mol. Biol.* **192,** 737–752.

Sobue, G., Kreider, B., Asbury, A., and Pleasure, D. (1983). *Brain Res.* **280,** 263–275.
Sporn, M. B., and Roberts, A. B. (1985). *Nature* (*London*) **313,** 745–747.
Springer, J. E. (1988). *Exp. Neurol.* **102,** 354–365.
Stein, D. G., and Will, B. E. (1983). *Brain Res.* **261,** 127–131.
Stemple, D. L., Mahanthappa, N. K., and Anderson, D. J. (1988). *Neuron* **1,** 517–525.
Thoenen, H., and Barde, Y.-A. (1980). *Physiol. Rev.* **60,** 1284–1335.
Thoenen, H., Angeletti, P. U., Levi-Montalcini, R., and Kettler, R. (1971). *Proc. Natl. Acad. Sci. U.S.A.* **68,** 1598–1602.
Thoenen, H., Bandtlow, C., and Heumann, R. (1987). *Rev. Physiol. Pharmacol.* **109,** 146–178.
Thorpe, L. W., and Perez-Polo, J. R. (1987). *J. Neurosci. Res.* **18,** 134–139.
Tomaselli, K. I., Neughebauer, K. M., Bixby, J. L., Lilien, J., and Reichardt, L. F. (1988). *Neuron* **1,** 33–43.
Van Schravendijk, C. F. H., Hooghe-Peters, E. L., Van den Brande, J. L., and Pipeleers, D. G. (1986). *Biochem. Biophys. Res. Commun.* **135,** 228–238.
Varon, S. S., and Bunge, R. P. (1978). *Annu. Rev. Neurosci.* **1,** 327–361.
Varon, S., Nomura, J., and Shooter, E. M. (1967). *Proc. Natl. Acad. Sci. U.S.A.* **575,** 1782–1789.
Varon, S., Nomura, J., and Shooter, E. M. (1968). *Biochemistry* **7,** 1296–1303.
Whittemore, S., and Seiger, A. (1987). *Brain Res. Rev.* **12,** 439–464.
Whittemore, S. R., Ebendal, T., Larkfors, L., Olson, L., Seiger, A., Stromberg, P., and Persson, H. (1986). *Proc. Natl. Acad. Sci. U.S.A.* **83,** 817–821.
Williams, L. R., Varon, S., Peterson, G. M., Wictorin, K, Fischer, W., Bjorklund, A., and Gage, F. H. (1986). *Proc. Natl. Acad. Sci. U.S.A.* **83,** 9231–9235.
Wright, L. L., and Smolen, A. J. (1987). *Int. J. Dev. Neurosci.* **5,** 305–311.
Wu, D. K., Maciag, T., and deVellis, J. (1988). *J. Cell. Physiol.* **136,** 367–372.
Wu, K., and Black, I. B. (1989). *J. Cogn. Neurosci.* (in press).
Yan, Q., and Johnson, E. M., Jr. (1988). *J. Neurosci.* **8,** 3481–3498.
Yang, J. W., and Fellows, R. E. (1980). *Endocrinology* (*Baltimore*) **107,** 1717–1724.
Yankner, B. A., and Shooter, E. M. (1982). *Annu. Rev. Biochem.* **51,** 845–868.
Zachary, I., Woll, P. I., and Rozengurt, E. (1987). *Dev. Biol.* **124,** 295–308.
Zaimis, E. (1971). *J. Physiol.* (*London*) **216,** 65P–66P.

7

Developmental Roles for Growth Factor-Regulated Secreted Proteins

Richard T. Hamilton
Department of Zoology
Iowa State University
Ames, Iowa 50011

Albert J. T. Millis
Center for Cellular Differentiation
Department of Biological Sciences
The University at Albany
State University of New York
Albany, New York 12222

I. Introduction

One of the most pronounced effects polypeptide growth factors produce in cultured fibroblasts and epithelial cells is the induction of glycoprotein synthesis and secretion (Nilsen-Hamilton *et al.*, 1980, 1982; Hamilton *et*

Current Topics in Developmental Biology, Vol. 24

al., 1985; Nilsen-Hamilton and Holley, 1983). Each cell type responds to polypeptide growth factors by generating a specific pattern of secreted proteins (Nilsen-Hamilton and Hamilton, 1982). Those patterns are characteristic of the differentiation and sometimes the growth state of the cell and could therefore be used for identification. The pronounced increase in the production of these secreted proteins in growth and differentiation suggests that they may function as autocrine or paracrine regulators of these events.

Among the secreted glycoproteins induced by growth factors are mitogen-regulated protein (MRP) (Nilsen-Hamilton *et al.*, 1980), also known as proliferin (Linzer and Nathans, 1984; Parfett *et al.*, 1985);[1] cathepsin L (CL), also known as major excreted protein (MEP) (Gottesman, 1978; Nilsen-Hamilton *et al.*, 1980; Denhardt *et al.*, 1986); fibronectin (Chen *et al.*, 1987; Ignotz and Massagué 1986; Blatti *et al.*, 1988); collagen (Roberts *et al.*, 1986; Penttinen *et al.*, 1988); and proteolytic enzymes (see Chapter 8 of this volume).

Polypeptide growth factors also stimulate cultured fibroblasts and epithelial cells to produce secreted glycoproteins, including collagenase (Chua *et al.*, 1985; Bauer *et al.*, 1985; Edwards *et al.*, 1987a), transin (Matrisian *et al.*, 1986), plasminogen activator inhibitor-I (Nilsen-Hamilton and Holley, 1983; Thalacker and Nilsen-Hamilton, 1987; Millis *et al.*, 1989), and a group of superinducible proteins that range in molecular weight from 12,000 to 63,000 (Nilsen-Hamilton *et al.*, 1982; Hamilton *et al.*, 1985).

This chapter focuses on MRP, the placental lactogens (PLs), CL, plasminogen activator, collagen, and fibronectin. The regulation of collagenase and other proteases is discussed in Chapter 8 of this volume. Many of the growth factor-induced secreted proteins are involved in forming the extracellular matrix (ECM); therefore, we also review the role these proteins play in this process. Additional perspectives on the role of growth factors in the formation of the ECM and the role of the ECM in development can be found in Chapters 4 and 8 of this volume. Because the secreted proteins are so tightly regulated by growth factors in culture systems, we expect that studies of their regulation and function in development will provide important new knowledge that will help us understand the contribution that growth factors make to developmental processes.

[1] Because MRP was the original name and because the name proliferin implies a function which has yet to be defined, we will use MRP throughout this review instead of the cumbersome MRP/PLF.

II. Mitogen-Regulated Protein

MRP was one of the first growth factor-regulated secreted glycoproteins to be discovered. Its level in Swiss 3T3 cells was raised 30-fold in the presence of epidermal growth factor (EGF) and fibroblast growth factor (FGF) (Nilsen-Hamilton *et al.*, 1980). Subsequently, MRP was found to be produced by the trophoblastic giant cells of the mouse placenta at a discrete stage of development (Jang *et al.*, 1987; Lee *et al.*, 1988).

In this section on MRP, we first review the studies done with cells in tissue culture, then we relate those findings to the results of studies done on MRP in the mouse.

A. Regulation of MRP Expression in Tissue Culture Cells

MRP is a glycoprotein with a median molecular weight of 34,000. It was discovered as a glycoprotein which is secreted after growing Swiss 3T3 cells are treated with serum and polypeptide growth factors (Nilsen-Hamilton *et al.*, 1980). Tumor promoters and serum stimulate 3T3 cells to synthesize and secrete MRP (Fienup *et al.*, 1986; Linzer and Nathans, 1983). MRP has sequence homology with the family of proteins consisting of prolactin, growth hormone, and PL (Parfett *et al.*, 1985). Therefore, it has also been called proliferin (Linzer and Nathans, 1984).

In 3T3 cells stimulated by serum or growth factors, increases in the amounts of MRP mRNA and secreted protein begin 4–6 hours after the addition of the stimulus (Nilsen-Hamilton *et al.*, 1980; Linzer and Nathans, 1983). The rate of MRP protein synthesis peaks at about 20 hours, remains elevated until about 28 hours, and then declines sharply (Nilsen-Hamilton *et al.*, 1980). MRP mRNA peaks 12–16 hours after 3T3 cells have been stimulated with serum (Linzer and Nathans, 1983) or growth factors (R. T. Hamilton, unpublished observations). Serum activates transcription of the MRP gene (Linzer and Mordacq, 1987).

Protein synthesis is required for the serum-inducible expression of MRP in BALB/c 3T3 cells (Linzer and Wilder, 1987) and for the growth factor-inducible expression of MRP in Swiss 3T3 cells (M. Nilsen-Hamilton, personal communication). This suggests that the regulation of MRP production requires the synthesis of a *trans*-acting regulator of transcription (Connor *et al.*, 1990).

Several factors also negatively regulate the production of MRP. These include oncogenic transformation of Swiss 3T3 cells by simian virus 40 (SV40) or Moloney sarcoma virus, which eliminate or severely decrease MRP expression (Nilsen-Hamilton *et al.*, 1980). Transforming growth factor-β (TGF-β) also negatively regulates the production of MRP and counteracts the increases in MRP mRNA and protein levels caused by growth factors and tumor promoters (Chiang and Nilsen-Hamilton, 1986, 1990). The amount of MRP is also negatively regulated by degradation in the lysosomes (Nilsen-Hamilton *et al.*, 1981, 1988). MRP is probably directed to the lysosomes by the mannose-6-phosphate (M6P) signal contained in its carbohydrate side chains (Lee and Nathans, 1988).

The mouse genome contains five or six MRP genes. At least two of these have slightly different sequences in the MRP coding region (Wilder and Linzer, 1986; Connor *et al.*, 1990). The different protein sequences seem to result in proteins with at least some difference in function. One form of MRP reduced the capacity of a myogenic cell line (10T1/2) to differentiate, while another form, differing by only three amino acid residues, was unable to alter the capacity of the myogenic cell line to differentiate.

Two forms of the MRP gene were cloned from BALB/c 3T3 cells and were found to be expressed in the placenta (Wilder and Linzer, 1986). Connor *et al.*, (1990) cloned the region 1.1 kb upstream from the transcription start site of a third form of the MRP gene. The region contains the following consensus sequences: two half-sites of the glucocorticoid receptor, two adjacent AP-1 binding sites, an AP-2 site, a cAMP-responsive element, a serum-responsive element of the heat-shock protein 70 gene, two octamer-binding sites, and five Sph sites [AAG(T/C)ATGCA]. By analogy with other growth factor-regulated genes, it is likely that the regulation of MRP expression by growth factors and tumor promoters is mediated through the *cis* elements, AP-1 and AP-2.

B. Developmental Expression of MRP

In the mouse, MRP mRNA is found only in the placenta (Linzer *et al.*, 1985; R. T. Hamilton *et al.*, unpublished observations). The MRP mRNA level peaks on the 10th day of gestation and declines slowly until day 16, when it reaches a stable minimum. Immunocytochemical staining shows that MRP is present in the trophoblastic giant cells of the fetal placenta between the 9th and 13th days of gestation (Jang *et al.*, 1987; Lee *et al.*, 1988; Nilsen-Hamilton *et al.*, 1988). *In situ* RNA hybridization of placental slices confirms that MRP mRNA is also localized in the trophoblastic giant cells (Lee *et al.*, 1988). These results suggest that giant cells are the source of the protein. The fraction of placental giant cells that stained for MRP was measured as a function of the gestational age. The percentage of placental giant cells containing MRP is 80–90% until day 12, and then it drops from about 70% to 20% between the 13th and 14th days (M. Nilsen-Hamilton, personal communication).

Evidently, MRP is produced in the placenta during the period of placental growth. It is also secreted into the maternal bloodstream during this time, where its concentration in the blood rises rapidly between gestational days 8 and 11, peaks at about 3.5–10 μg/ml on days 10–11, and then rapidly declines (Jang *et al.*, 1987; Lee *et al.*, 1988).

Potential mechanisms for the rapid decline in the MRP mRNA level at midgestation include: (1) the MRP mRNA level decreases on day 12, (2) the MRP protein is degraded in the lysosomes, and (3) MRP is rapidly removed from the fetus and the maternal circulation by binding to the M6P receptor. The first two proposed mechanisms are supported by observations of MRP regulation in cell culture. First, growth factors increase the rate of initiation of gene transcription (Linzer and Mordacq, 1987). Second, in Swiss 3T3 cells the amount of MRP in the cytosol and the amount secreted depend on the degree to which MRP is degraded in the lysosomes (Nilsen-Hamilton *et al.,* 1981, 1988). Furthermore, the related protein, prolactin, can be rapidly degraded in the pituitary lysosomes (Smith and Farquhar, 1966). The third proposed mechanism is supported by the observation that the level of expression of the M6P receptor in the fetal and maternal livers begins to increase during late gestation at about the same time as the amount of MRP in the placenta and in the maternal circulation begins to rapidly decline. Conversely, the level of M6P receptor in the fetal and maternal livers peaks at about day 16, when the level of MRP in the plasma is at its lowest (Lee and Nathans, 1988). However, at no time does circulating MRP contain M6P (M. Nilsen-Hamilton, personal communication). Therefore, the rapid decline in MRP levels cannot presently be explained by a hypothesis that postulates MRP clearance by binding to M6P receptors on the liver.

C. Stimulation of MRP Expression by EGF and TGF-α

In 3T3 cells the regulation of MRP synthesis involves transcriptional regulation (Nilsen-Hamilton *et al.*, 1980, 1987; Parfett *et al.*, 1985; Linzer and Mordacq, 1987). Experiments in which mouse cells were transfected with a construction composed of the upstream sequences of an MRP gene and the chloramphenicol acetyltransferase reporter gene demonstrated that serum induced transcriptional activity 20- to 40-fold.

MRP synthesis is increased by EGF and TGF-α (Nilsen-Hamilton *et al.*, 1980; L. Bendickson and M. Nilsen-Hamilton, unpublished observations). TGF-α is believed to be the fetal form of EGF and to have an important role in regulating fetal development (see Chapter 1 and 2 of this volume). TGF-α interacts strongly with the EGF receptor and is usually functionally equivalent to EGF. Using *in situ* RNA hybridization and Northern blot analyses, Han *et al.* (1987) found high levels of TGF-α mRNA in the rat maternal decidua during midgestation. They suggested that the decidual TGF-α was the source of high levels of this growth factor in the developing embryo. Decidual expression seemed to be induced after implantation, peaked at day 8, and then slowly declined through day 15. Also using *in situ* RNA hybridization, Wilcox and Derynck (1988) found that TGF-α mRNA was expressed in 9- and 10-day mouse fetuses but was absent in older fetuses. In contrast to Han *et al.* (1987), they found that the cells containing mRNA were the syncytiotrophoblasts of the placenta. The actual source of placental TGF-α (i.e., the maternal decidua or the fetal syncytiotrophoblasts) is still unresolved. The giant cells containing MRP are those in the basal zone, which is adjacent to the maternal decidua. The coordinate expression of MRP and TGF-α in the placenta at midgestation suggests that TGF-α acts as a paracrine regulator to induce expression of the MRP gene (Han *et al.*, 1987; Jang *et al.*, 1987; Nilsen-Hamilton, 1989; Nilsen-Hamilton *et al.*, 1988; Lee *et al.*, 1988). If TGF-α also stimulates placental proliferation, then the parallel increase in the production of MRP and placental weight could be coordinated by the action of TGF-α.

D. Inhibition of MRP Expression by TGF-β

In Swiss 3T3 cells TGF-β counteracts the stimulatory effect of EGF on the production of MRP protein (Chiang and Nilsen-Hamilton, 1986) and its transcript (Chiang and Nilsen-Hamilton, 1990). Because a large amount of TGF-β is present in the human placenta (Frolik *et al.*, 1983), it is likely that similar conditions exist in the mouse. Swiss 3T3 cells are most sensitive to inhibition of MRP synthesis by TGF-β when they are at high density and quiescent. Possibly, placental TGF-β is responsible for the inhibition of MRP expression in the placenta, as it is in dense cultures of quiescent 3T3 cells.

Our current hypothesis is that the basal decidua produces and secretes TGF-α, which stimulates the giant cells to synthesize MRP mRNA. TGF-β counteracts the increase in MRP mRNA caused by TGF-α. The MRP secreted by placental giant cells may bind to maternal and/or fetal cells, where it could function as a growth factor or a cytokine. All of the other members of the MRP gene family (e.g., growth hormone, prolactin, and PL) stimulate adult or fetal cells to produce insulinlike growth factor (IGF). (Atkison *et al.*, 1980; Clemmons *et al.*, 1981). MRP may induce specific fetal and maternal cells to produce IGF, which then helps to coordinate the growth of the fetus with that of maternal tissue required for fetal development (Nilsen-Hamilton, 1989).

E. Relationship between the Production of MRP and Cell Proliferation

The production of MRP and cell proliferation correlate. For example, (1) proliferating Swiss 3T3 cells exposed to growth factors proliferate and secrete MRP (Nilsen-Hamilton *et al.*, 1980), (2) MRP is produced in the growing placenta, but not when the placenta stops growing, (3) the expression of MRP is associated with the immortalization of mouse cells in culture (Parfett *et al.*, 1985; Edwards *et al.*, 1987b; Denhardt *et al.*, 1987a), and (4) mutant 3T3 cells resistant to the mitogenic activity of tumor promoters are no longer able to produce MRP in response to the tumor promoters when they are quiescent (Fienup *et al.*, 1986). These findings suggest that common pathways are activated when mitogenic agents stimulate MRP and DNA syntheses.

If MRP acts as a growth factor, it is more likely to act in an endocrine or a paracrine mode rather than as an autocrine growth factor. This proposal is based on the observations that anti-MRP antiserum does not inhibit growth factor-induced DNA synthesis in Swiss 3T3 cells (Fienup *et al.*, 1986) and a BALB/c 3T3 cell line that does not make MRP (Nilsen-Hamilton *et al.*, 1981) still responds to growth factors by increasing DNA synthesis (Parfett *et al.*, 1985). MRP could regulate placental cell proliferation or it could be produced as a consequence of the activity of another regulator. Currently, its function is not known.

III. PLs and Other Prolactinlike Polypeptides

The placenta makes several prolactinlike proteins. The PLs (Ogren and Talamantes, 1988) have recently been reviewed. The placenta also makes proliferin-related protein (Linzer and Nathans, 1985) and at least three forms of MRP (Linzer and Nathans, 1985; Wilder and Linzer, 1986; Connor *et al.*, 1990). Several of the MRP molecules have been found to differ in sequence by only two or three amino acids. Nevertheless, these apparently minor differences appear to be critical for function. For example, the expression of one type of MRP in myogenic 10T1/2 cell lines seemed to interfere with the capacity of the cells for myogenic differentiation. This is not true of another type of MRP (Wilder and Linzer, 1989).

PLs have been identified in the mouse: PL-I and PL-II. The level of PL-I is high in midgestation but then declines. By contrast, PL-II appears several days later, and it reaches its highest titer in late gestation (Soares and Talamantes, 1982). A proliferin-related transcript is also produced during midgestation; the peak of that message (day 12) occurs 2 days after the peak of MRP production (Linzer and Nathans, 1985). Although MRP and PL-I appear at identical times in mouse placental development, they can be distinguished by molecular weight (Nilsen-Hamilton *et al.*, 1980; Colosi *et al.*, 1987), antigenicity (Lee and Nathans, 1987), functional activity, and amino acid sequence (Colosi *et al.*, 1987; Lee and Nathans, 1988). It is not known whether growth factors regulate the expression of proliferin-related protein or the PLs exactly as they regulate MRP. However, EGF stimulates primary cultures of human placental cells to produce PL (Lai and Guyder, 1984). Also, EGF and FGF can rapidly induce prolactin expression (Evans *et al.*, 1978; Murdoch *et al.*, 1982).

Several functions have been attributed to the PLs. They are thought to regulate mammary gland secretory activity, maternal intermediary metabolism, fetal IGF production, and luteal progesterone production (Ogren and Talamantes, 1988). The effects of the PLs have long been thought to occur through their ability to interact with growth hormone and prolactin receptors. However, other mechanisms are possible, since specific receptors for ovine PL are present in fetal ovine liver (Freemark and Handwerger, 1986).

IV. Cathepsin L

CL (or MEP) is a glycoprotein containing M6P. It is a member of the lysosomal thiol or cysteine proteinase family, and it is induced by growth factors (Nilsen-Hamilton *et al.*, 1980; Gottesman and Sobel, 1980; Sahagian and Gottesman, 1982). In this review the acronym "MEP" refers specifically to procathepsin L, whereas the acronym "CL" is a more general terms that refers to all forms of the enzyme (Portnoy *et al.*, 1986; Mason *et al.*, 1987). CL was first purified from rat liver (Kirschke *et al.*, 1977) and is a very active protease. When tested *in vitro*, CL had the most potent collagenolytic and elastinolytic activities of any of the cathepsins (Mason *et al.*, 1986; Kirschke *et al.*, 1982).

The amino acid sequences of the human and mouse CLs are 70% homologous (Joseph *et al.*, 1988). CL has been purified from rat, rabbit, and human livers and all have similar catalytic properties. The mature forms of CL from each of these species contain heavy and light chains, with apparent molecular weights of about 25,000–29,000 and 5,000, respectively (Kirschke *et al.*, 1977; Mason *et al.*, 1984). The mouse contains four antigenically similar forms of CL, which have apparent molecular weights, as determined from electrophoretic mobility, of 43,000, 39,000, 29,000, and 20,000 (Hamilton *et al.*, 1990). Mouse fibroblasts in culture secrete the 39-kDa form of CL, procathepsin L, which is also known as MEP (Gal *et al.*, 1985; Denhardt *et al.*, 1986). The results from pulse-chase labeling experiments showed that 50–60% of the 39-kDa form of CL was secreted by transformed cells. Of the 40–50% remaining, about 5% was posttranslationally processed and the two lower-molecular-weight processed forms (i.e., 29,000 and 20,000) were not secreted. The light lysosomal/Golgi fraction contained the 39-kDa protein, and the 29- and 20-kDa proteins were in the heavy lysosomal fraction (Gal *et al.*, 1985). Presumably, the 29- and 20-kDa CLs are the mature, enzymatically active lysosomal forms of MEP.

Previously, it was reported that the rat kidney contains a large amount of CL (Bando *et al.*, 1986). Using Northern and slot-blot analyses, Hamilton *et al.* (1990) found that the mouse kidney and liver contains CL mRNA, but that the placenta contains more than five times the CL mRNA found in the kidney. Except for the kidney, all organs examined contain a single 2-kb species of CL mRNA. In addition, the kidney contains a 4-kb species of CL mRNA.

The secreted form of CL was discovered in metabolically radiolabeled Swiss 3T3 cells transformed by the mouse Kirsten sarcoma virus. The protein was named "major excreted protein," or MEP. Shortly afterward, using an antiserum raised against MEP by Gottesman (1978), MEP was found to be secreted along with MRP after proliferating Swiss 3T3 cells were treated with FGF or EGF (Nilsen-Hamilton *et al.*, 1980). Gal and Gottesman (1986) showed that the MEP of transformed cells and CL have similar proteinase activities. The sequence of the murine MEP cDNA established that it was CL (Denhardt *et al.*, 1986). At the same time, Portnoy *et al.* (1986) reported the cloning and characterization of a mouse cysteine proteinase from the macrophagelike cell line, J774. The sequences of the cDNAs from the mouse fibroblasts and the J774 cells were the same.

Besides CL, at least two other cathepsins are secreted by certain cells under the appropriate stimulus: cathepsins B and D. Recklies and Mort (1985) have suggested that the secreted forms of cathepsin B and CL are precursor forms of the lysosomal enzymes abnormally secreted by cells in culture. However, this explanation is unlikely, because the mouse placenta contains large amounts of the 39-kDa MEP at all stages of gestation.

The secretion of such large amounts of MEP, which is inactive at neutral pH (Mason *et al.*, 1987), by growth factor-stimulated cells and by the placenta raises several questions. For example, does MEP (procathepsin L) have a unique function? It might be a growth factor or a differentiation factor that interacts with specific placental receptors in a paracrine fashion. For example, the proteinase plasminogen activator binds to discrete sites on the cell surface (Apella *et al.*, 1987). Alternatively, CL might be secreted as a zymogen that requires further activation at an appropriate time in development.

Most studies on the regulation of CL have been done using cultured cells. The results of these studies provide the basis for the design of experiments to determine the function of CL in mouse development.

A. Control of CL Expression in Cultured Cells

1. Positive Effectors of CL Expression

The effectors reported to positively regulate the levels of CL secreted by cultured cells are oncogenic transformation, polypeptide growth factors, tumor promoters, lectins, cell density, ionophores, inhibitors of lysosomal proteinases, lysosomotropic agents, and alkalinization of the culture medium.

a. Oncogenic Transformation. To examine the relationship between the secretion of MEP and oncogenic transformation, Gottesman (1978) screened a series of derivatives of a BALB/c cell line. He reported that, for the nontransformed cell lines, less than 0.9% of their secreted protein is CL; 3T3 cells transformed by SV40 or chemicals and spontaneously transformed 3T3 cells secrete between 2.9% and 9.0% of the secreted protein as CL; and lines transformed by RNA tumor viruses secrete between 28% and 39% of the secreted protein as CL. The retroviral transforming agent most active in stimulating mouse cells to produce CL seems to be the *ras* oncogene protein, p21. Denhardt *et al.* (1987b) found a positive correlation among the extent of *ras* expression, metastatic potential, and the amount of CL produced in nine independently isolated lines of H-*ras*-transfected C3H 10T1/2 cells.

The question of whether CL expression is coupled to oncogenic transformation or to proliferation and invasiveness was further investigated by determining the CL gene expression in the placenta, which is a rapidly growing and invasive normal tissue. The mouse placenta expresses large amounts of the 39-kDa form of CL and its mRNA throughout gestation, and the temporal expression of the CL gene corresponds with the expression of the c-Ha-*ras* protooncogene during gestation of the mouse (Hamilton *et al.*, 1990). Therefore, the correlation of *ras* and CL expression may reflect a normal regulatory mechanism for the expression of CL.

b. Polypeptide Growth Factors. Several growth factors stimulate proliferating or quiescent 3T3 cell lines to synthesize and secrete CL. For example, FGF and EGF each raised the secreted levels of CL when added to growing Swiss 3T3 cells (Nilsen-Hamilton *et al.*, 1980). The culture produced maximum levels at 4.5–10 hours and continued to synthesize and secrete CL for at least 20.5 hours (Nilsen-Hamilton *et al.*, 1982). Nerve growth factor (Nilsen-Hamilton *et al.*, 1981) and platelet-derived growth factor (PDGF) (Scher *et al.*, 1983) also stimulated density-arrested

BALB/c 3T3 cells to synthesize CL. The results of nuclear run-on transcription experiments indicated that PDGF activates transcription of the CL gene (Rabin *et al.*, 1986).

c. Tumor Promoters. Tumor promoters are potent stimulators of CL expression. When stimulated by 12-*O*-tetradecanoylphorbol-13-acetate phorbol ester (TPA) NIH 3T3 cells synthesize and secrete CL, 3–4 hours after treatment, at rates five- to tenfold over basal rates. Phorbol dibenzoate was less potent than TPA and is a less potent tumor promoter than TPA. The biologically inactive TPA analogs, 4-*0* methyl TPA, phorbol, and myristic acid, had no effect on CL synthesis (Gottesman and Sobel, 1980). TPA stimulated a threefold increase in the synthesis of CL in cultures of mouse primary epidermal cells. This increase was greatest 6 hours after treatment. CL was also produced in increased amounts when TPA was applied to the skin of mice. However, based on the effects of antipromoters on MEP production by mouse skin, Gottesman and Yuspa (1981) concluded that CL synthesis was not sufficient for tumor promotion.

The increase in CL synthesis in response to TPA results from an increased level of CL mRNA (Gottesman and Sobel, 1980; Doherty *et al.*, 1985). An increase in the amount of CL mRNA was detected as early as 0.5 hour after TPA had been added to NIH 3T3 cells. The induction of CL expression required protein synthesis (Rabin *et al.*, 1986). This requirement for protein synthesis could be a requirement for synthesis of a transcriptional regulating protein, such as the c-*fos* protein. The involvement of c-*fos* has been demonstrated for transin, a metalloproteinase that is regulated similarly to CL (Kerr *et al.*, 1988).

2. Negative Regulation of CL Expression by TGF-β

TGF-β counteracted the increase in CL and its transcript that was induced by EGF (Chiang and Nilsen-Hamilton, 1986; J. Kyoung-Shim and R. T. Hamilton, unpublished observations). These findings show an inhibitory effect of TGF-β similar to that on MRP production, as discussed in Section II,D. This demonstrates further similarities between the regulation of CL and MRP.

B. Developmental Expression of CL

One of the earliest defined functions of the developing embryo is tissue invasion. The mouse trophoblast has been considered a "pseudomalignant" tissue, because it grows invasively into the uterine epithelium or other surrounding tissue (Kirby, 1965). The trophoblasts must invade the decidua before embryonic implantation and placental development can occur. Some of the molecular events needed for trophoblast invasion probably include chemotactic signals from the decidua and the secretion of proteases by the trophoblasts. CL could be one of the proteases involved. It is produced in large amounts by the mouse placenta and its predominant form in the placenta is also the 39-kDa secreted form (Hamilton *et al.*, 1990).

As in 3T3 cells (Gal *et al.*, 1985), three forms of CL (39,000, 29,000, and 20,000) exist in the placenta. The 39-kDa form predominates in amount (about ten times more than the other two forms). Using the biotin–streptavidin technique of immunohistochemistry, it was found the CL was present throughout gestation in the spongiotrophoblasts and trophoblastic giant cells.

Although CL is expressed throughout mouse placental development, two peaks of maximal expression occur, one in the period between days 8 and 12 and the other a sudden rise in expression just before parturition (Hamilton *et al.*, 1990). The first peak of expression coincides with the increase in size of the placenta and may signify the increased CL activity needed for trophoblast growth and uterine invasion. The second peak of CL expression, which occurs late in gestation, may signify increased activity contributing to the degeneration of tissue surrounding the placenta in preparation for birth.

Whatever CL's role in placental development, it is likely to be significant, because of the large amount of CL found in the placenta. In addition, the two peaks of activity suggest that the expression of CL is under developmental regulation. Results from tissue culture experiments (Section IV,A) and placental analysis (this section) suggest several possible developmental controls of CL expression. Positive control could be through expression of p21, the *ras* gene product, through TGF-α, or both. Negative control could be through degradation of the 39-kDa form of CL in the lysosomes, through TGF-β, or both. Concerning these hypotheses, Han *et al.* (1987), using *in situ* RNA hybridization and Northern blot analyses, found that the high levels of TGF-α in early mouse development resulted from expression in the maternal decidua. Decidual expression appeared to be induced after implantation, peaked at day 8, and then slowly declined through day 15. Wilcox and Derynck (1988) reported that TGF-α mRNA was expressed in 9- and 10-day fetuses, but was absent in older fetuses. In contrast to Han *et al.* (1987), they found TGF-α mRNA-containing cells in the syncytiotrophoblasts. Therefore, TGF-α could provide the signal for the first peak of CL expression in the placental trophoblasts. Whether the signal comes from the maternal decidua or the syncytiotrophoblasts will have to be resolved.

TGF-α exerts its mitogenic effect through the EGF receptors at the cell surface. Nexø *et al.* (1980) detected EGF receptors in mouse embryos in days 11.5–17.5 of gestation. Adamson and Meek (1984) measured the number and the affinity of EGF receptors in mouse placentas from the 11th day of gestation (day 0 represents fertilization plug). They found a reciprocal relationship between the number of EGF receptors and their affinity for EGF. The number of receptors rose during gestation, while the affinity declined. Despite the apparent decline in affinity of EGF receptors toward the end of gestation, receptors were present. Therefore, it is possible that TGF-α is responsible for the second peak of CL mRNA expression. However, another level of regulation of MEP expression has been identified in cultured cells. This regulation involves the growth state of the cells. As 3T3 cells become confluent and quiescent, the basal level of MEP expression increases (Nilsen-Hamilton, 1989). Thus, the peaks and troughs of MEP expression in placental development may result from the balance of TGF-α and TGF-β signals, expression of their receptors, and the growth state of the placenta.

V. Proteins of the ECM

A. Composition and Organization of the ECM

The cells of most tissues are either embedded in or attached to a collagenous ECM. The molecular composition and organization of the ECM of a specific tissue are believed to be critical for cellular differentiation and function (Hauschka and Konigsberg, 1966; Reddi and Anderson, 1976; Adamson, 1983). In general, ECMs are categorized as either interstitial matrix—such as those associated with soft connective tissues—or as basement membrane matrix, which is commonly associated with anchorage of endothelial cells (Ekblom *et al.*, 1986).

ECMs are constructed from constituents of body fluids (principally blood) and from macromolecules synthesized and secreted by cells adjacent to the ECM (Akiyama and Yamada, 1987; Hynes, 1985; Vaheri and Mosher, 1978). Once secreted, proteins are subsequently organized into the fibrous structure of the ECM. For many years the ECM was thought to function only as an inert site of cell anchorage. Recent evidence suggests that the ECM has an active role in embryological development, cell differentiation, tissue organization, and wound repair.

ECMs are composed of collagenous proteins, glycoproteins, proteoglycans, and other less abundant components—for example, polypeptide growth factors. They are heterogeneous in molecular composition and organization of the principal macromolecules. We concentrate on two of the matrix components here: fibronectin and collagens. The synthesis and secretion of each can be regulated in cultured cells by polypeptide growth factors; each appears to have a role in development and differentiation.

Cells interact with ECM proteins through a family of transmembrane receptors called integrins (Ruoslahti, 1988). The integrins interact with cytoskeletal proteins inside the cells and recognize a tripeptide Arg-Gly-Asp (RGD) sequence on extracellular proteins (Hynes, 1987; Ruoslahti and Pierschbacher, 1987). The integrins are composed of two homologous subunits (α and β) that interact with each other noncovalently, and their levels are regulated along with those of the ECM proteins.

B. Fibronectins

Fibronectins are high-molecular-weight glycoproteins (>450 kDa) associated with the cell surface, connective tissue matrix, basement membrane, and extracellular fluids (including plasma, amniotic fluid, and synovial fluid) (Yamada, 1983; Hakomori *et al.,* 1984; Ruoslahti, 1988). The fibronectin polypeptides are organized into disulfide-bonded dimers and multimers. There are several different forms of fibronectin that have similar biological activities (Yamada and Olden, 1978; Hynes, 1985). The different forms are evidently generated by alternative splicing of a primary RNA transcript derived from a single gene (Kornblihtt *et al.,* 1984, 1985; Schwartzbauer *et al.,* 1987; Hynes, 1985; Gutman and Kornblihtt, 1987; Zardi *et al.,* 1987), as well as by posttranslational modifications, such as glycosylation (Paul and Hynes, 1984; Hynes, 1985).

The interaction between fibronectin and ECM macromolecules is likely to be mediated through several regions of the polypeptide. The best studied is the RGD region, through which fibronectin binds to the integrin receptors on the cell surface. In addition to the RGD region, interaction between fibronectin and the ECM occurs through the 25-kDa amino-terminal domain, the collagen binding domain, and the domains for heparin and fibrin binding in the carboxy-terminal region of the polypeptide (McKeown-Longo and Mosher, 1985; Millis *et al.,* 1985).

That fibronectin contributes to cell differentiation is suggested by the finding that, when exogenous fibronectin is added to cultured cells, the path of their differentiation is altered. For example, when smooth muscle cells are treated with fibronectin, multicellular nodules form and the contractile phenotype is lost (Brennan *et al.,* 1983; Hedin and Thyberg, 1987). Cultured chondrocytes revert to fibroblastlike cells when grown on fibronectin-coated substrates (West *et al.,* 1979; Pennypacker *et al.,* 1979). Furthermore, synthetic peptides containing the RGD sequence inhibit embryonic morphogenesis (Ruoslahti *et al.,* 1985; Thiery *et al.,* 1985). It was proposed that the peptide containing RGD competed with fibronectin for the integrin cell surface receptor. This was thought to be evidence that fibronectin is the component of the ECM that regulates morphogenesis. However, other proteins found in the ECM, including laminin, also bind to integrin receptors (Ruoslahti, 1988).

C. Collagens

The collagens are the most abundant class of protein in animals and form a major component of the ECM. They clearly contribute to the structural integrity of the ECM, and recent evidence suggests that they have roles in development and cell differentiation (Hay, 1981). A good example of collagen's active role in cell organization and morphogenesis is the result of an experiment in which endothelial cells seeded in a three-dimensional collagen gel are transformed from cell monolayer to spherical, branched, and tubular structures (Yang *et al.*, 1980, 1982; Hall *et al.*, 1982).

The biosynthesis of the collagens is complex. At least ten types of collagen have been identified and each is composed of one or more of 17 different polypeptides (Bornstein and Sage, 1980; Crawford *et al.*, 1985; van der Rest *et al.*, 1985; Schmid and Linsenmayer, 1985; Berg, 1986). In addition, following translation, the collagens are extensively modified by hydroxylation and glycosylation. The predominant collagen forms—types I, II, III, and IV—are synthesized and secreted as high-molecular-weight precursors known as procollagens. The procollagens are proteolytically processed to collagen and organized into triple-helical structures that may be further incorporated into higher-order fibers (Fessler and Fessler, 1978).

Different forms of collagen have been correlated with specific types of cells or cellular structures (Kleinman *et al.*, 1981, 1984). For example, collagen types I and III are widely distributed in most interstitial ECMs and connective tissues, while type II collagen is enriched in cartilage and bone. Type IV collagen is sometimes referred to as basement membrane collagen, because of its strong association with basement membranes of the vascular and secretory gland systems.

D. ECM Proteins as Growth Factors

Recent studies indicate that several ECM proteins have growth factor activity. Laminin is a multidomain glycoprotein whose expression can be detected as early as the two-cell embryo (Timpl *et al.*, 1979; Martin and Timpl, 1987; Dziadek and Timpl, 1985). A region of the laminin protein, separate from the cell attachment site, has mitogenic activity for 3T3 cells and PAM212 cells (Panayotou *et al.*, 1989). Growth factor-like activities have been found for fibronectin (Bitterman *et al.*, 1983) and for another ECM protein, thrombospondin (Majack *et al.*, 1986; Lawler and Hynes, 1986). The laminin study was well controlled for contamination by EGF and suggests the possibility that ECM macromolecules can directly induce localized cell proliferation in developing tissues.

E. Regulation of ECM Protein Expression by Growth Factors in Cultured Cells

The effects of purified polypeptide growth factors on the synthesis and secretion of collagen and fibronectin were evaluated after their addition to cultures of fibroblasts and other cells. Table I summarizes the results of recent studies using the growth factors TGF-β, FGF, PDGF, and EGF. Neither fibronectin nor collagen synthesis was altered in cells exposed to FGF, EGF, or PDGF. Any apparent increase in protein synthesis was attributed to an increase in cell number resulting from the proliferative

Table I Response of Cultured Cells to Growth Factors[a]

Growth factor	Cell type	Fibronectin		Collagen		References
		Protein	mRNA	Protein	mRNA	
TGF-β	Fibroblast	+	+	+	+	Varga *et al.* (1987), Falanga *et al.* (1987), Ignotz *et al.* (1987), Raghow *et al.* (1897), Fine and Goldstein (1987), Wrana *et al.* (1986)
TGF-β	Endothelial cell		+			Muller *et al.* (1987)
TGF-β	Myoblast	+	+	+	+	Ignotz *et al.* (1987), Massagué *et al.* (1986)
TGF-β	Bone cell osteoblast			+	+	Pfeilschifter *et al.* (1987), Centrella *et al.* (1987)
TGF-β	Smooth muscle cell	0				Majack (1987), Millis and Hoyles (1988)
PDGF	Fibroblast			0/+		LeRoy *et al.* (1982), Narayanan and Page (1983)
PDGF	Bone cell osteoblast			−		Centrella *et al.* (1986), Canalis (1985)
PDGF	Smooth muscle cell	0				Millis *et al.* (1988)
FGF	Fibroblast			0		LeRoy *et al.* (1982)
FGF	Endothelial cell			−		Tseng *et al.* (1982)
FGF	Bone cell osteoblast			+/0		Canalis and Raisz (1980), Canalis (1985)
EGF	Fibroblast			0		LeRoy *et al.* (1982), Kumegawa *et al.* (1982)
EGF	Bone cell osteoblast			−/0		Hiramatsu *et al.* (1982), Canalis (1985)
EGF	Epithelial cell			+		Kumegawa *et al.* (1982)

[a] Cells respond via an increase (+) or decrease (−) in protein synthesis or steady-state mRNA levels. 0, No change in either protein or mRNA level.

effect of the factors. By contrast, TGF-β was an effective inducer of collagen and fibronectin syntheses, even in the absence of a concomitant effect on cellular proliferation.

TGF-β stimulates mesenchymal and epithelial cells to synthesize fibronectin and collagen, which are subsequently incorporated into the ECM (Ignotz and Massagué, 1986; Fine and Goldstein, 1987; Centrella *et al.*, 1987). TGF-β also stimulated endothelial cells to produce fibronectin and endothelial cells, myoblasts, and osteoblasts to produce collagen (Table I). Thrombospondin synthesis is also increased in mouse cells treated with TGF-β (Penttinen *et al.*, 1988), and osteopontin synthesis is increased in osteosarcoma cells treated with TGF-β (Noda *et al.*, 1988).

Treatment with TGF-β resulted in increased steady-state levels of fibronectin and collagen mRNAs (Ignotz *et al.*, 1987; Raghow *et al.*, 1987; Varga *et al.*, 1987). Increases in the mRNA levels for these ECM proteins accompany increases in the rates of protein synthesis (Centrella *et al.*, 1987; Ignotz *et al.*, 1987; Varga *et al.*, 1987; Penttinen *et al.*, 1988). TGF-β seems to raise the levels of fibronectin and collagen production by increasing transcription of the corresponding mRNAs. Using the methods of DNA transfection, deletion analysis, and site-directed mutagenesis, Rossi *et al.* (1988) showed that TGF-β activates the mouse α_2 collagen gene in 3T3 cells and rat osteosarcoma cells through a mechanism that involves the nuclear factor 1 binding site in the promoter region.

The mechanisms by which TGF-β increases fibronectin and collagen levels have not been established. The treatment of cells with TGF-β may result in activation of the collagen gene through transcriptional activation of the collagen promoter (Rossi *et al.*, 1988). TGF-β also increases the steady-state levels of fibronectin and collagen (types I and III). This latter effect is probably achieved through a posttranscriptional mechanism (Varga *et al.*, 1987; Penttinen *et al.*, 1988). At yet another level of regulation, treatment with TGF-β caused fibronectin to be incorporated into the ECM (Ignotz and Massagué, 1986; Madri *et al.*, 1988).

It is not yet clear whether the increase in fibronectin and collagen gene expression is a primary or secondary effect of TGF-β. In 3T3 cells the stimulation of fibronectin and collagen syntheses by TGF-β was inhibited by cycloheximide. The onset of stimulation of fibronectin gene expression by TGF-β in 3T3 cells has been shown to be delayed in some cells; maximum synthesis occurs 16–24 hours after TGF-β has been added to the 3T3 cells (Penttinen *et al.* 1988). These results suggest that other proteins must be synthesized before fibronectin is induced. However, the results by Penttinen *et al.* (1988) do not agree with those of Ignotz *et al.* (1987), who found that the increase in fibronectin mRNA levels in rat NRK-49 fibroblasts and L_6E_9 myoblasts treated with TGF-β was inhibited by actinomycin D, but not by cycloheximide.

As well as increasing the extracellular levels of ECM proteins, TGF-β

also caused increased expression of integrins, the fibronectin cell-surface binding sites that mediate ECM assembly (Allen-Hoffmann *et al.*, 1988). TGF-β increases expression of the integrins by increasing the amount of mRNA encoding each integrin subunit and by increasing the rate at which the β subunit of integrin is processed to its mature form (Ignotz and Massagué, 1987; Roberts *et al.*, 1988; Heino *et al.*, 1989).

In interpreting the role of growth factors in regulating fibronectin and collagen syntheses, one must consider that responses to growth factors can vary, depending on the composition of the ECM and the density of the cell population. Furthermore, TGF-β alters the ratio of fibronectin isoforms and favors the production of an isoform containing the ED-A sequence (Balza *et al.*, 1988). It also stimulates the production of other cytokines and proteolytic enzymes that affect ECM composition.

Growth factors also influence the types of collagen being synthesized, even under conditions in which net collagen production is constant. The treatment of fibroblasts with EGF resulted in a lowering of the type III : type I ratio (Steinman *et al.*, 1982). EGF also stimulated fibroblasts to synthesize type IV collagen, and at the same time the collagen became more stable (Salomon *et al.*, 1981). In osteoblastic cells EGF treatment resulted in a shift in the type III : type I collagen ratio (Osaki *et al.*, 1984; Hata *et al.*, 1984). EGF stimulated palatal shelf organ cultures to increase the rate of type V collagen synthesis (Silver *et al.*, 1984). In some endothelial cells cultured in the presence of FGF, the removal of FGF from the medium resulted in a change in culture morphology and associated changes in types I, III, and IV collagens (Tseng *et al.*, 1982). Other cellular responses to EGF and FGF and their possible developmental roles are discussed in Chapters 1–3 of this volume.

As well as regulating the protein content of the ECM, TGF-β also stimulates proteoglycan synthesis in adult human arterial smooth muscle cells (Chen *et al.*, 1987), in bovine cartilage organ cultures (Morales and Roberts, 1988), and in fibroblast, preadipocyte, and skeletal muscle myoblast cell lines (Bassols and Massagué, 1988).

F. Regulation of ECM Protein Expression by Growth Factors *in Vivo*

The collagen and fibronectin responses to TGF-β in cultured cells suggest that similar responses may occur *in vivo*. This is more difficult to demonstrate, as many cells produce growth factors and fibronectin and collagen are also available from local tissues and the circulation. However, injections of TGF-β into newborn mice induced angiogenesis and appeared to activate fibroblasts to produce collagen. These responses were not mimicked by EGF or PDGF (Roberts *et al.*, 1986). Injection of TGF-β into

Buffalo rats produced responses similar to those seen in mice (Sporn *et al.*, 1983).

The importance of fibronectin to developmental processes has been shown by using synthetic peptides containing the RGD sequence to block cell migration and morphogenesis in chicks (Thiery *et al.*, 1985) and to block gastrulation in *Drosophila* and in amphibians (Boucalt *et al.*, 1984; Naidet *et al.*, 1987).

In amphibians antibodies to the fibronectin receptor disrupted gastrulation (Darribere *et al.*, 1988). However, the steady-state levels of fibronectin mRNA remained constant from oogenesis through gastrulation (Kimelman and Kirschner, 1987). The combination of FGF and TGF-β induced amphibian mesoderm formation (Slack *et al.*, 1987), but they did not appear to act through increased transcription of fibronectin mRNA. The role of growth factors in amphibian development is discussed in Chapter 9 of this volume.

In addition to its role as a cell attachment protein, fibronectin may affect developmental processes that involve directed cell movement. For example, chick mesenchyme precartilage cells migrate rapidly through a collagen gel in response to fibronectin; the effect is variable using fibronectins from different sources (Newman *et al.*, 1985). The effect of fibronectin on cell movement may be by a mechanism that is independent of the cell attachment site (Bronner-Fraser, 1982; Newman, 1988).

The fibronectins and collagens are soluble proteins modified to less soluble forms. We have reviewed here the contribution polypeptide growth factors make to the synthesis and secretion of these molecules. Because the growth factors have pleiotropic effects, it may be some time before the signal-transduction pathways for the regulation of expression of ECM proteins are identified.

Another problem in sorting out the mechanism of growth factor action is that there are several isoforms of some ECM proteins. Most studies of the regulation of fibronectins by growth factors have not distinguished between the different fibronectin isoforms (Castellani *et al.*, 1986). Most often, the antibodies or cDNA probes used were against nonvariant regions of the fibronectin polypeptide or mRNA. Although the different fibronectin polypeptides seem to have the same function when tested on cells in culture, the possibility that they differ in function *in vivo* has not been excluded (Chandrasekhar *et al.*, 1983).

VI. Conclusions

The relationship between growth factors and the ECM has been made more clear since the discovery that growth factors stimulate fibroblasts to synthesize and secrete essential components of the ECM. We have reviewed here two of those components: fibronectin and collagen. Other growth factor-induced glycoproteins, such as plasminogen activators and collagenases, help to shape the ECM through their proteolytic activities. Whether CL acts similarly to degrade the ECM is not known. As discussed in this chapter, the secreted form of CL does not degrade collagen at neutral pH. To be degraded by CL, components of the ECM must be in an environment whose pH is less than 6. This low pH is present in lysosomes and could be achieved in an extracellular microenvironment.

The relationship between the ECM and growth regulation is paradoxical. To make the transition from the G_0 phase to the S phase in response to a growth factor, quiescent cells must adhere to the ECM, yet they bind less tightly to the ECM after they have been stimulated by the growth factor. Furthermore, oncogenically transformed cells are continually primed to proliferate, but do not require an ECM. It appears that many of the ECM components contain multifunctional domains which may be included or excluded from the various isoforms. The role of growth factors and growth factor-induced enzymes may be very subtle. For example, rather than simply degrading the ECM proteins to completion, proteolytic enzymes may function as activators of additional ECM functions.

We envision a sequence of events in which exogenous growth factors, acting in an autocrine or paracrine mode, induce enzyme production. The resulting enzymes act on ECM substrates to affect cell adhesion and migration and to release growth factor activities, such as the one associated with laminin. When studied in cell culture systems, the growth factor-induced proteins appear to be tightly regulated by growth factors. Similar modes of regulation are probably used *in vivo*. Further study of the effects of growth factors in developmental systems will provide additional information on their specific roles in embryogenesis and tissue organization.

Acknowledgments

U.S. Public Health Service grants GM34488 and HD24990 and a grant from the Iowa State University Biotechnology Council supported work done by R.T.H. described here. U.S. Public Health Service grant AG00697 and a grant from the American Heart Association supported work done by A.J.T.M.

References

Adamson, E. D. (1983). *In* "Collagen in Health and Disease" (M. Jauson and J. Weiss, eds.), pp. 218–243. Churchill Livingstone, London.

Adamson, E. D., and Meek, J. (1984). *Dev. Biol.* **103,** 62–70.

Akiyama, S. K., and Yamada, K. M. (1987). *Adv. Enzymol. Relat. Areas Mol. Biol.* **59,** 1–57.

Allen-Hoffmann, B. L., Crankshaw, C. L., and Mosher, D. F. (1988). *Mol. Cell. Biol.* **8,** 4234–4242.

Apella, E., Robinson, E. A., Ullrich, S. J., Stoppelli, M. P., Corti, A., Cassini, G., and Blasi, F. (1987). *J. Biol. Chem.* **262,** 4437–4440.

Atkison, P. R., Weidman, E. R., Bhaumick, B., and Bala, R. M. (1980). *Endocrinology (Baltimore)* **106,** 2006–2012.

Balza, E., Borsi, L., Allemanni, G., and Zardi, L. (1988). *FEBS Lett.* **228,** 42–44.

Bando, Y., Kominami, E., and Katunuma, E. (1986). *J. Biochem. (Tokyo)* **100,** 35–42.

Bassols, A., and Massagué, J. (1988). *J. Biol. Chem.* **263,** 12828–12831.

Bauer, E. A., Cooper, T. W., Huang, J. S., Altman, J., and Deuel, T. F. (1985). *Proc. Natl. Acad. Sci. U.S.A.* **82,** 4132–4136.

Berg, R. A. (1986). *In* "Regulation of Matrix Accumulation" (R. P. Mecham, ed.), pp. 29–52. Academic Press, New York.

Bitterman, P. B., Rennard, S. I., Adelberg, S., and Crystal, R. G. (1983). *J. Cell Biol.* **97,** 1925–1932.

Blatti, S. P., Foster, D. N., Ranganathan, G., Moses, H. L., and Getz, M. J. (1988). *Proc. Natl. Acad. Sci. U.S.A.* **85,** 1119.

Bornstein, P., and Sage, H. (1980). *Annu. Rev. Biochem.* **49,** 957–1003.

Boucalt, J.-C., Darribere, T., Poole, T. J., Aoyama, J., and Yamada, K. M. (1984). *J. Cell Biol.* **99,** 1822–1830.

Brennan, M. J., Millis, A. J. T., Mann, D. M., and Fritz, K. E. (1983). *Dev. Biol.* **97,** 391–397.

Bronner-Fraser, M. (1982). *Dev. Biol.* **91,** 50–63.

Canalis, E. (1985). *Clin. Orthop.* **193,** 246–263.

Canalis, E., and Raisz, L. G. (1980). *Metabolism* **29,** 108–114.

Castellani, P., Siri, A., Rosellini, C., Infusini, E., Borsi, L., and Zardi, L. (1986). *J. Cell Biol.* **103,** 1671–1677.

Centrella, M., Massagué, J., and Canalis, E. (1986). *Endocrinology* **119,** 2306–2312.

Centrella, M., McCarthy, T. L., and Canalis, E. (1987). *J. Biol. Chem.* **262,** 2869–2874.

Chandrasekhar, S., Sorrentino, J. A., and Millis, A. J. T. (1983). *Proc. Natl. Acad. Sci. U.S.A.* **80,** 4747–4751.

Chen, J.-K., Hoshi, H., and McKeehan, W. L. (1987). *Proc. Natl. Acad. Sci. U.S.A.* **84,** 5287–5291.

Chiang, C.-P., and Nilsen-Hamilton, M. (1986). *J. Biol. Chem.* **261,** 261–264

Chiang, C.-P., and Nilsen-Hamilton, M. (1990). Submitted for publication.

Chua, C. C., Geiman, D. E., Keller, G. H., and Ladda, R. L. (1985). *J. Biol. Chem.* **260,** 5213–5215.

Clemmons, D. R., Underwood, L. E., and Van Wyck, J. J. (1981). *J. Clin. Invest.* **67,** 10–17.

Colosi, P., Ogren, L., Thordarson, G., and Talamantes, F. (1987). *Endocrinology (Baltimore)* **120,** 2500–2506

Connor, A. M., Waterhouse, P., Khoka, R., and Denhardt, D. T. (1990). Submitted for publication.

Crawford, S. W., Featherstone, J. A., Holbrook, K., Yong, S. L., Bornstein, P., and Sage, H. (1985). *Biochem. J.* **227,** 491–502.

Darribere, T., Yamada, K. M., Johnson, K. E., and Boucalt, J.-C. (1988). *Dev. Biol.* **126,** 182–194.

Denhardt, D. T., Hamilton, R. T., Parfett, C. L. J., Edwards D. R., St. Pierre, R., Waterhouse, P., and Nilsen-Hamilton, M. (1986). *Cancer Res.* **46,** 4590–4593.

Denhardt, D. T., Edwards, D. R., Parfett, C. L. J., and Smith, J. (1987a). *In* "Molecular Mechanisms in the Regulation of Cell Behavior" (C. Waymouth, ed.), pp. 59–64. Liss, New York.

Denhardt, D. T., Greenberg, A. H., Egan, S. E., Hamilton, R. T., and Wright, J. A. (1987b). *Oncogene* **2,** 55–59.

Doherty, P. J., Hua, L., Liau, G., Gal, S., Graham, D. E., Sobel, M., and Gottesman, M. M. (1985). *Mol. Cell. Biol.* **5,** 466–473.

Dziadek, M., and Timpl, R. (1985). *Dev. Biol.* **111,** 372–382.

Edwards, D. R., Murphy, G., Reynolds, J. J., Whitham, S. E., Docherty, A. J. P., Angel, P., and Heath, J. K. (1987a). *EMBO J.* **6,** 1899–1905.

Edwards, D. R., Parfett, C. L. J., Smith, J. M., and Denhardt, D. T. (1987b). *Biochem. Biophys. Res. Commun.* **147,** 467–473.

Ekblom, P., Vestweber, D., and Kemler, R. (1986). *Rev. Cell Biol.* **2,** 27–47.

Evans, G. A., David, D. N., and Rosenfeld, M. G. (1978). *Proc. Natl. Acad. Sci. U.S.A.* **75,** 1294–1298.

Falanga, V., Tiegs, S. L., Alstadt, S. P., Roberts, A. P., and Sporn, M. B. (1987). *J. Invest. Dermatol.* **89,** 100–104.

Fessler, J. H., and Fessler, L. I. (1978). *Annu. Rev. Biochem.* **47,** 129–162.

Fienup, V. K., Jeng, M.-H., Hamilton, R. T., and Nilsen-Hamilton, M. (1986). *J. Cell. Physiol.* **129,** 151–158.

Fine, A., and Goldstein, R. H. (1987). *J. Biol. Chem.* **262,** 3897–3902.

Freemark, M., and Handwerger, S. (1986). *Endocrinology (Baltimore)* **118,** 613–617.

Frolik, C. A., Dart, L. L., Myers, C. A., Smith, D. M., and Sporn, M. B. (1983). *Proc. Natl. Acad. Sci. U.S.A.* **80,** 3676–3580.

Gal, S., and Gottesman, M. M. (1986). *Biochem. Biophys. Res. Commun.* **139,** 156–162.

Gal, S., Willingham, M. C., and Gottesman, M. M. (1985). *J. Cell Biol.* **100,** 535–544.

Gottesman, M. M. (1978). *Proc. Natl. Acad. Sci. U.S.A.* **75,** 2767–2771.

Gottesman, M. M., and Sobel, M. E. (1980). *Cell (Cambridge, Mass.)* **19,** 449–455.

Gottesman, M. M., and Yuspa, S. H. (1981). *Carcinogenesis,* **2,** 971–976.

Gutman, A., and Kornblihtt, A. R. (1987). *Proc. Natl. Acad. Sci. U.S.A.* **84,** 7179–7182.

Hakomori, S., Fukuda, M., Sekiguchi, K., and Carter, W. G. (1984). *In* "Extracellular Matrix Biochemistry" K. A. Piez and A. H. Reddi, eds.), pp. 229–244. Elsevier, New York.

Hall, H. G., Farson, D. A., and Bissell, M. J. (1982). *Proc. Natl. Acad. Sci. U.S.A.* **79,** 4672–4676.

Hamilton, R. T., Nilsen-Hamilton, R. T., and Adams, G. (1985). *J. Cell. Physiol.* **123,** 201–208.

Hamilton, R. T., Delgado, M. A., Kyoung-Shim, J., Denhardt, D. T., and Nilsen-Hamilton, M. (1990). Submitted for publication.

Han, V. K. M., Hunter, E. S., Pratt, R. M., Zendegui, J. G., and Lee, D. C. (1987). *Mol. Cell. Biol.* **7,** 2335–2343.

Hata, R., Hori, H., Nagai, Y., Tanaka, S., Kondo, M., and Hiramatsu, M. (1984). *Endocrinology (Baltimore)* **115,** 867–876.

Hauschka, D. S., and Konigsberg, I. R. (1966). *Proc. Natl. Acad. Sci. U.S.A.* **55,** 119–126.

Hay, E. D. (1981). *In* "Cell Biology of Extracellular Matrix" (E. D. Hay, ed.), pp. 379–409. Plenum, New York.

Hedin, U., and Thyberg, J. (1987). *Differentiation (Berlin)* **33,** 239–246.

Heino, J., Ignotz, R. A., Hemler, M. E., Crouse, C., and Massagué, J. (1989). *J. Biol. Chem.* **264,** 380–388.

Hiramatsu, M., Kumegawa, M., Hatakeyama, K., Yajima, T., Minami, N., Kodama, H. (1982). *Endocrinology* **111,** 1810–1816.

Hynes, R. O. (1985). *Annu. Rev. Cell Biol.* **1,** 67–90.
Hynes, R. O. (1987). *Cell (Cambridge, Mass.)* **51,** 549–554.
Ignotz, R. A., and Massagué, J. (1986). *J. Biol. Chem.* **261,** 4337–4345.
Ignotz, R. A. and Massagué, J. (1987). *Cell (Cambridge, Mass.)* **51,** 189–197.
Ignotz, R. A., Endo, T., and Massagué, J. (1987). *J. Biol. Chem.* **262,** 6443–6446.
Jang, Y.-J., Mubaidin, A. M. D., and Nilsen-Hamilton, M. (1987). *J. Cell Biol.* **105,** 256a.
Joseph, L. J., Chang, L. C., Stamenkovich, D., and Sukhatme, V. P. (1988). *J. Clin. Invest.* **81,** 1621–1629.
Kerr, L. D., Holt, J. T., and Matrisian, L. M. (1988). *Science* **242,** 1424–1427.
Kimelman, D., and Kirschner, M. (1987). *Cell (Cambridge, Mass.)* **51,** 869–877.
Kirby, D. R. S. (1965). *In* "Early Conceptus, Normal and Abnormal" (W. W. Park, ed.), pp. 68–73. Univ. of St. Andrews Press, Edinburgh.
Kirschke, H., Langner, J., Wiederanders, B., Ansorge, S., and Bohley, P. (1977). *Eur. J. Biochem.* **74,** 293–301.
Kirschke, H., Kembhavi, A. A., Bohely, P., and Barrett, A. J. (1982). *Biochem. J.* **201,** 367–372.
Kleinman, H. K., Klebe, R. J., and Martin, G. M. (1981). *J. Cell Biol.* **88,** 473–485.
Kleinman, H. K., McGarvey, M. L., Hassell, J. R., Martin, G. R., Baron-van Evercooren, A., and Dubois-Dalcq, M. (1984). *In* "The Role of Extracellular Matrix in Development" (R. L. Trelstad, ed.), pp. 123–143. Liss, New York.
Kornblihtt, A. R., Vibe-Pedersen, K., and Baralle, F. E. (1984). *EMBO J.* **3,** 221–228.
Kornblihtt, A. R., Umezawa, K., Vibe-Pedersen, K., and Baralle, E. (1985). *EMBO J.* **4,** 1755–1759.
Kumegawa, M., Hiramatsu, M., Yajima, T., Hatakeyama, K., Hosoda, S., and Namba, M. (1982). *Endocrinology* **110,** 607–612.
Lai, W. H., and Guyda, H. J. (1984). *J. Clin. Endocrinol Metab.* **58,** 344–351.
Lawler, J., and Hynes, R. O. (1986). *J. Cell Biol.* **103,** 1635–1648.
Lee, S.-J., and Nathans, D. (1987). *Endocrinology (Baltimore)* **120,** 208–213.
Lee, S.-J., and Nathans, D. (1988). *J. Biol. Chem.* **263,** 3521–3527.
Lee, S.-J., Talamantes, F., Wilder, E., Linzer, D. I. H., and Nathans, D. (1988). *Endocrinology (Baltimore)* **122,** 1761–1768.
LeRoy, E. C., Mercurio, S., and Sherer, G. K. (1982). *Proc. Natl. Acad. Sci. U.S.A.* **79,** 1286–1290.
Linzer, D. I. H., and Mordacq, J. C. (1987). *EMBO J.* **6,** 2281–2287.
Linzer, D. I. H., and Nathans, D. (1983). *Proc. Natl. Acad. Sci. U.S.A.* **80,** 4271–4275.
Linzer, D. I. H., and Nathans, D. (1984). *Proc. Natl. Acad. Sci. U.S.A.* **81,** 4255–4259.
Linzer, D. I. H., and Nathans, D. (1985). *EMBO J.* **4,** 1419–1423
Linzer, D. I. H., and Wilder, E. L. (1987). *Mol. Cell. Biol.* **7,** 2080–2086
Linzer, D. I. H., Lee, S.-J., Ogren, L., Talamantes, F., and Nathans, D. (1985). *Proc. Natl. Acad. Sci. U.S.A.* **82,** 4356–4359.
McKeown-Longo, P. J., and Mosher, D. F. (1985). *J. Cell Biol.* **100,** 364–374.
Madri, J. A., Pratt, B. M., and Tucker, A. M. (1988). *J. Cell Biol.* **106,** 1375–1384.
Majack, R. A. (1987). *J. Cell Biol.* **105,** 465–471.
Majack, R. A., Cook, S. C., and Bornstein, P. (1986). *Proc. Natl. Acad. Sci. U.S.A.* **83,** 9050–9054.
Martin, G. R., and Timpl, R. (1987). *Annu. Rev. Cell Biol.* **3,** 57–85.
Mason, R. W., Taylor, M. A. J., and Etherington, D. J. (1984). *Biochem. J.* **217,** 209–217.
Mason, R. W., Johnson, D. A., Barrett, A. J., and Chapman, H. A. (1986). *Biochem. J.* **233,** 925–927.
Mason, R. W., Gal, S., and Gottesman, M. M. (1987). *Biochem. J.* **248,** 449–454.
Massagué, J., Cheifetz, S., Endo, T., and Nadal-Ginard, B. (1986). *Proc. Natl. Acad. Sci. U.S.A.* **83,** 8206–8210.

Matrisian, L. M., Leroy, P., Ruhlman, C., Gesnel, M.-C., and Brethnach, R. (1986). *Mol. Cell. Biol.* **6,** 1679–1750.

Millis, A. J. T., and Hoyle, M. (1988). *J. Cell Physiol.* **134,** 200–210.

Millis, A. J. T., Hoyle, M., Mann, D. M., and Brennan, M. J. (1985). *Proc. Natl. Acad. Sci. U.S.A.* **82,** 2746–2750.

Millis, A. J. T., Sottile, J., Hoyle, M., Mann, D. M., and Diemer, V. (1989). *Exp. Gerontol.* (in press).

Morales, T. I., and Roberts, A. B. (1988). *J. Biol. Chem.* **263,** 12828–12831.

Murdoch, G. H., Potter, E., Nicolaisen, A. K., Evans, R. M., and Rosenfeld, M. G. (1982). *Nature* (*London*) **300,** 192–194.

Muller, G., Behrens, J., Nussbaumer, U., Bohlen, P., and Birchmeier, W. (1987). *Proc. Natl. Acad. Sci. U.S.A.* **84,** 5600–5604.

Naidet, C., Semeriva, M., Yamada, K. M., and Thiery, J. P. (1987). *Nature* (*London*) **325,** 348–350.

Narayanan, A. S., and Page, R. C. (1983). *J. Biol. Chem.* **258,** 11694–11699.

Newman, S. A. (1988). *Trends Genet.* **4,** 329–332.

Newman, S. A., Frenz, D. A., Tomasek, J. J., and Rabuzzi, D. D. (1985). *Science* **228,** 885–889.

Nexø, E., Hollenberg, A., Figueroa, A., and Pratt, R. M. (1980). *Proc. Natl. Acad. Sci. U.S.A.* **77,** 2782–2785.

Nilsen-Hamilton, M. (1989). *In* "Growth Factors in Mammalian Development," CRC Press, Boca Raton, Florida. pp. 135–166.

Nilsen-Hamilton, M., and Hamilton, R. T. (1982). *Cell Biol. Int. Rep.* **6,** 815–836.

Nilsen-Hamilton, M., and Holley, R. W. (1983). *Proc. Natl. Acad. Sci. U.S.A.* **80,** 5636–5640.

Nilsen-Hamilton, M., Shapiro, J. M., Massoglia, S. L., and Hamilton, R. T. (1980). *Cell* **20,** 19–28.

Nilsen-Hamilton, M., Hamilton, R. T., Allen, W. R., and Massoglia, S. L. (1981). *Biochem. Biophys. Res. Commun.* **101,** 411–417.

Nilsen-Hamilton, M., Hamilton, R. T., and Adams, G. A. (1982). *Biochem. Biophys. Res. Commun.* **108,** 158–166.

Nilsen-Hamilton, M., Hamilton, R. T., and Alvarez-Azaustre, E. A. (1987). *Gene* **51,** 163–170.

Nilsen-Hamilton, M., Jang, Y.-J., Alvarez-Azaustre, E., and Hamilton, R. T. (1988). *Mol. Cell. Endocrinol.* **56,** 179–190.

Noda, M., Yoon, K., Prince, C. W., Butler, W. T., and Rodan, G. A. (1988). *J. Biol. Chem.* **263,** 13916–13921.

Ogren, L., and Talamantes, F. (1988). *Int. Rev. Cytol.* **112,** 1–65.

Osaki, Y., Tsunoi, M., Hakeda, Y., Kurisu, K., and Kumegawa, M. (1984). *J. Histochem. Cytochem.* **32,** 1231–1233.

Panayotou, G., End, P., Aumailley, M., Timpl, R., and Engel, J. (1989). *Cell* (*Cambridge, Mass.*) **56,** 93–101.

Parfett, C. L. J., Hamilton, R. T., Howell, B. W., Edwards, D. R., Nilsen-Hamilton, M., and Denhardt, D. T. (1985).*Mol. Cell. Biol.* **5,** 3289–3292.

Paul, J. I., and Hynes, R. O. (1984). *J. Biol. Chem.* **259,** 13477–13487.

Pennypacker, J. P., Hassell, J. R., Yamada, K. M., and Pratt, R. M. (1979). *Exp. Cell Res.* **121,** 411–415.

Pfeilschifter, J., D'Sousa, S. M., and Mundy, G. R. (1987). *Endocrinology* **121,** 212–218.

Penttinen, R. P., Kobayshi, S., and Bornstein, P. (1988). *Proc. Natl. Acad. Sci. U.S.A.* **85,** 1105–1108.

Portnoy, D. A., Erickson, A. H., Kochan, J., Ravetch, J. V., and Unkeless, J. C. (1986). *J. Biol. Chem.* **261,** 14697–14703.

Rabin, M. S., Doherty, P. J., and Gottesman, M. M. (1986). *Proc. Natl. Acad. Sci. U.S.A.* **83,** 357–360.
Raghow, R., Postlethwaite, A. E., Keski-Oja, J., Moses, H. L., and Kang, A. H. (1987). *J. Clin. Invest.* **79,** 1285–1288.
Recklies, A. D., and Mort, J. S. (1985). *Biochem. Biophys. Res. Commun.* **131,** 402–407.
Reddi, A. H., and Anderson, W. A. (1976). *J. Cell Biol.* **69,** 557–572.
Roberts, A. B., Sporn, M. B., Assoian, R. K., Smith, J. M., Roche, N. S., Wakefield, L. M., Heine, U. I., Liotta, L. A., Falanga, V., Kehl, J. H., and Fauci, A. A. (1986). *Proc. Natl. Acad. Sci. U.S.A.* **83,** 4167–4171.
Roberts, C. J., Birkenmeier, T. M., McQuillan, J. J., Akiyama, S. K., Yamada, S. S., Chen, W.-T., Yamada, K. M., and McDonald, J. A. (1988). *J. Biol. Chem.* **263,** 4586–4592.
Rossi, P., Karsenty, G., Roberts, A. B., Roche, N. S., Sporn, M. B., and De Crombrugghe, B. (1988). *Cell (Cambridge, Mass.)* **52,** 405–414.
Ruoslahti, E. (1988). *Annu. Rev. Biochem.* **57,** 375–413.
Ruoslahti, E., and Pierschbacher, M. D. (1987). *Science* **238,** 491–497.
Ruoslahti, E., Hayman, E., and Pierschbacher, M. D. (1985). *Arteriosclerosis* **5,** 581–594.
Sahagian, G. G., and Gottesman, M. M. (1982). *J. Biol. Chem.* **257,** 11145–11150.
Salomon, D. S., Liotta, L. A., and Kidwell, W. R. (1981). *Proc. Natl. Acad. Sci. U.S.A.* **78,** 382–386.
Scher, C. D., Dick, R. L., Whipple, A. P., and Locatell, K. L. (1983). *Mol. Cell. Biol.* **3,** 70–81.
Schmid, T. M., and Linsenmayer, T. F. (1985). *J. Cell Biol.* **100,** 598–605.
Schwartzbauer, J. E., Patel, R. S., Fonda, D., and Hynes, R. O. (1987). *EMBO J.* **6,** 2573–2580.
Silver, M. H., Murray, J. C., and Pratt, R. M. (1984). *Differentiation (Berlin)* **27,** 205–208.
Slack, J. M. W., Darlington, B. G., Heath, J. K., and Godsave, S. F. (1987). *Nature (London)* **326,** 197–200.
Smith, R. E., and Farquhar, M. G. (1966). *J. Cell Biol.* **31,** 319–333.
Soares, M. J., and Talamantes, F. (1982). *Endocrinology (Baltimore)* **95,** 29–34.
Sporn, M. B., Roberts, A. B., Shull, J. H., Smith, J. M., and Ward, J. M. (1983). *Science* **219,** 1329–1330.
Steinman, B. U., Abe, S., and Martin, G. R. (1982). *Collagen Relat. Res.: Clin. Exp.* **2,** 185–195.
Thalacker, F. W., and Nilsen-Hamilton, M. (1987). *J. Biol. Chem.* **262,** 2283–2290.
Thiery, J. P., Duband, J. L., and Tucker, G. C. (1985). *Annu. Rev. Cell Biol.* **1,** 91–113.
Timpl, R., Rohde, H., Gehron-Robey, P., Rennard, S. I., Foidart, J. M., and Martin, G. R. (1979). *J. Biol. Chem.* **254,** 9933–9937.
Tseng, S. C., Savion, N., Stern, R., and Gospodarowicz, D. (1982). *Eur. J. Biochem.* **122,** 355–360.
Vaheri, A., and Mosher, D. (1978). *Biochim. Biophys. Acta* **516,** 1–25.
van der Rest, M., Mayne, R., Ninomiya, Y., Seidah, N. G., Chretien, M., and Olsen, B. R. (1985). *J. Biol. Chem.* **260,** 220–225.
Varga, J., Rosenbloom, J., and Jimenez, S. A. (1987). *Biochem. J.* **247,** 597–604.
West, C. M., Lanza, R., Rosenbloom, J., Lowe, M., Holtzer, H., and Adalovic, N. (1979). *Cell (Cambridge, Mass.)* **17,** 491–501.
Wilcox, J. N., and Derynck, R. (1988). *Mol. Cell. Biol.* **8,** 3415–3422.
Wilder, E. L., and Linzer, D. I. H. (1986). *Mol. Cell. Biol.* **6,** 3283–3286.
Wilder, E. L., and Linzer, D. I. H. (1989). *Mol. Cell. Biol.* **9,** 430–441.
Wrana, J. L., Sodek, J., Ber, R. L., and Bellows, C. G. (1986). *Eur. J. Biochem.* **159,** 69–76.

Yamada, K. M. (1983). *Annu. Rev. Biochem.* **52,** 761–799.
Yamada, K. M., and Olden, K. (1978). *Nature (London)* **275,** 179–184.
Yang, J., Richards, J., Guzman, R., Imagawa, W., and Nandi, S. (1980). *Proc. Natl. Acad. Sci. U.S.A.* **77,** 2088–2092.
Yang, J., Larson, L., and Nandi, S. (1982). *Exp. Cell Res.* **137,** 481–485.
Zardi, L., Carnemolla, B., Siri, A., Petersen, T. E., Paolella, G., Sebastio, G., and Baralle, F. E. (1987). *EMBO J.* **6,** 2337–2344.

8

Growth Factor-Regulated Proteases and Extracellular Matrix Remodeling during Mammalian Development

Lynn M. Matrisian and Brigid L. M. Hogan
Department of Cell Biology
Vanderbilt University
Nashville, Tennessee 37232

I. Growth Factors and Extracellular Matrix in Development

Studies examining the role of specific growth factors in mammalian development must inevitably impinge on many exciting and rapidly changing areas of cell and molecular biologies, as evidenced by the diverse contents of this book. The thesis of this chapter is that one way in which growth factors may influence embryonic development and tissue morphogenesis is by altering the expression or activity of a specific set of proteases that, directly or indirectly, modify the extracellular matrix (ECM). Other discussions of the regulation of the expression of proteases and their inhibitors can be found in Chapters 4 and 7 of this volume.

Current Topics in Developmental Biology, Vol. 24

A. ECM and Development

The ECM is a complex and dynamic meshwork that is assembled outside cells from the specialized glycoproteins and proteoglycans secreted by them. As well as providing structural support in the form of bone, cartilage, and tendon, the ECM influences many cell biological processes. These include cell adhesion and migration and tissue morphogenesis, as well as cell proliferation and differentiation. For the purposes of this chapter, the ECM can be divided into two categories: the basement membrane and the interstitial connective tissue.

Basement membranes are extracellular structures that usually separate cells from underlying connective tissue. They are found, for example, between endothelial and epithelial cells and the underlying connective tissue and around muscle cells, adipose cells, and Schwann cells. The major components of basement membranes are types IV and V collagens, laminin, entactin, and several proteoglycans. These interact noncovalently to form a dense network. In the adult the basement membrane usually forms a barrier to most cell types and thus compartmentalize tissues and organs. However, in specific cases (e.g., white blood cell diapedesis into surrounding tissue) the basement membrane can be selectively penetrated. The glomerular basement membrane of the kidney plays a critical role in filtering blood plasma and selectively retaining plasma proteins. This selectivity may depend on "pore size" and on electrostatic forces within the matrix, due to the presence of charged molecules such as sulfated proteoglycans.

During embryonic development, the basement membrane, which separates epithelial cells from the underlying connective tissue, plays a role in maintaining tissue architecture and establishing epithelial cell polarity. This latter function is important not only in glandular and secretory epithelia, where cells have a distinct, specialized apical surface, but also in tissues such as skin, where the epidermis is organized so that daughter cells are directed from the basal proliferating layer into a spatially distinct suprabasal layer. Basement membranes also play a role in separating the maternal and fetal environments in extraembryonic tissues such as the placenta, yolk sac, and amnion. In rodent embryos Reichert's membrane produced by the extraembryonic parietal endoderm cells excludes large molecules and acts as a major barrier between maternal blood and the parietal yolk sac cavity (Hogan *et al.*, 1983, 1986; Kurkinen *et al.*, 1983). Reichert's membrane has been widely used as a model for studying the biosynthesis, assembly, and turnover of basement membranes.

Included among the interstitial connective tissues are heterogeneous regions such as the dermis and stroma, as well as more specialized tissues such as bone and cartilage. These tissues contain several cell types in addition to those responsible for producing the bulk of the ECM (i.e., fibroblasts in connective tissue and osteoblasts and chondroblasts in bone and cartilage). These additional cell types include macrophages, lymphocytes, granulocytes, melanocytes, and fat, endothelial, muscle, and nerve cells.

The major protein of connective tissue matrix is collagen. Collagens types I and III are found in most connective tissues, while types II and IX collagens are present in cartilage (for reviews of collagens, see Mayne and Burgeson, 1987; Burgeson, 1988). Collagens types VI, VII, VIII, IX, X, and XII have also been described in specific tissues. In addition to the collagens, interstitial connective tissue contains fibronectin, elastin, chondroitin sulfate proteoglycans, heparan sulfate proteoglycans, tenascin, and hyaluronic acid. Laminin and entactin are also found in certain interstitial connective tissues and are not exclusively basement membrane components. The recently described ECM components merosin (related to the A chain of laminin) (Ehrig *et al.*, 1990) and S-laminin (related to the B1 chain of laminin) have very restricted tissue distribution (Hunter *et al.*, 1989).

From the description above, it is clear that both basement membranes and interstitial connective tissue are important structural features of embryonic and adult tissues. It is not hard to imagine that defects in their synthesis and assembly can have profound effects on normal development. Indirect evidence for specific roles of the ECM in development come mostly from *in vitro* culture systems in which cells are grown on matrices of different composition. For example, primary mammary epithelial cells cultured on a complex matrix of basement membrane components show a more normal morphology and a much higher level of casein gene expression than cells grown on type I collagen or plastic (Li *et al.*, 1987). In a few studies the composition of the ECM has been altered experimentally *in vivo* and shown to affect development. This is illustrated by work on the *white* mutant of the Mexican axolotl (*Ambystoma mexicanum*), in which pigment cell precursors fail to migrate from the neural crest through the subepidermal ECM. This subepidermal matrix was adsorbed onto nucleopore carrier membranes, which were then grafted under the skin. Carriers containing matrix made by the epidermis of normal animals promoted the migration of pigment cell precursors from mutants if they were reimplanted at an early stage of development, before the outgrowth of cells from the neural crest. This result suggests that the subepidermal matrix is defective in the mutant, rather than in the neural crest cells themselves (Perris *et al.*, 1988). Finally, studies on the normal development and regeneration of structures such as the neuromuscular junction have led to the identification of specific ECM proteins with specialized functions (e.g., S-laminin) (Hunter *et al.*, 1989).

Some of the most direct evidence for the importance of the ECM in normal mammalian development comes from the study of mutants in which ECM components are altered as a result of changes at the DNA level. There are many examples of skeletal and skin defects caused by specific mutations in collagen genes in humans (see, e.g., Byers *et al.*, 1988; Maroteaux *et al.*, 1988; Lee *et al.*, 1989). One well-known example of an altered gene for an ECM component that affects development is the Mov-13 mouse line, in which a murine retrovirus has been inserted into the first intron of the $\alpha 1$ type I collagen gene (Harbers *et al.*, 1984). As a result of this insertion, type I collagen synthesis and secretion are reduced to negligible levels in most cells of homozygous embryos. These embryos die at around 13.5 days of gestation as a result of disruption of weakened blood vessel walls. Surprisingly, most organ systems, such as lung, salivary gland, and mammary gland, develop normally in spite of the complete absence of type I collagen in the surrounding connective tissue (Kratochwil *et al.*, 1986). Teeth and bone develop normally in culture due to use of an alternative cell type-specific promoter for $\alpha 1$ type I collagen, which escapes inactivation by the viral insertion (Kratochwil *et al.*, 1989).

Many spontaneous mouse mutants have been reported which have defects in ECM deposition and maturation (Green, 1981). For example, mice homozygous for the recessive mutation *short ears* (*se*) have defective cartilage formation not only in the ears but throughout the skeleton. This can be traced to the earliest condensation of precartilagenous mesenchyme in the embryo. Homozygous *congenital hydrocephaly* (*ch*) embryos are also defective in cartilage formation and maturation. Mice which are homozygous for the mutation *microphthalmia* (*mi*) show abnormal bone resorption due to an abnormality in the osteoclasts which degrade mineralized bone matrix. In all of these mutants, the molecular basis of the defects is not yet known.

When considering the possible ways in which defects in the ECM may be generated, it is important to remember that the quality and quantity of the matrix depends not only on structural components such as collagen, laminin, and proteoglycan, but also on the regulated expression of matrix-degrading proteases and their inhibitors. These proteases and inhibitors have, for the most part, been studied in the context of their possible role in tumor cell invasion and metastasis. However, it is likely that the abnormal expression of proteases by tumor cells reflects some normally transient and well-regulated expression by a subpopulation of precursor cells in the same tissue during embryonic development.

Several secreted proteinases, including plasmin, plasminogen activators, elastase, stromelysin, interstitial and type IV collagenases, as well as lysosomal cathepsins, participate in the degradation of the ECM (Mullins and Rohrlich, 1983; Thorgeirsson *et al.*, 1985; Tryggvason *et al.*, 1987). Genes for many of these enzymes have been cloned within the last few years, and more information is becoming available on the factors that regulate their expression. The activities of the enzymes can also be regulated at several levels. For example, many of the matrix-degrading enzymes are expressed in a latent form and require activation (e.g., by proteolytic cleavage). Some of the enzymes require specific environmental conditions (e.g., acid pH) for activity. In addition, there are specific inhibitors for most of these enzymes. Thus, the final expression of proteolytic activity is dependent on the presence of enzyme and activator and on the balance between active enzyme and inhibitor.

The condition of the ECM at any time and place is influenced by the balance between the levels of structural proteins and matrix-degrading proteinases and, as stated above, inhibitors and activators of the proteinases. It is the premise of this chapter that this balance may be readily modulated by growth and differentiation factors acting indirectly through target cells. Thus, matrix remodeling and tissue morphogenesis during embryonic development represent situations in which growth factor modulation of the ECM could profoundly affect the outcome.

B. Model Systems to Study the Role of Growth Factor-Regulated Proteases and ECM in Development

Studies examining the role of growth factors in development have expanded in recent years due to technological advances in methods for their detection in tissues and localization to cells of origin. Early studies relied on biochemical techniques to identify growth factor activities in embryonic tissues (e.g., Nexø *et al.*, 1980; Twardzik, 1985; Proper *et al.*, 1982). Immunohistochemical studies have, in most cases, confirmed and extended these studies (e.g., Heine *et al.*, 1987; Thompson *et al.*, 1989). Moreover, using specific anti-sense RNA probes, it has recently become possible to identify the tissue and, in some cases, the specific cell type responsible for growth factor production. Thus, transforming growth factor-α (TGF-α) mRNA has been localized in rodent embryos and maternal decidual cells using Northern blot analysis and *in situ* hybridization (Lee *et al.*, 1985; Han *et al.*, 1987; Wilcox and Derynck, 1988). Similar studies have been performed with TGF-β- and TGF-β2-specific probes and are particularly informative because of the ability to differentiate between the various members of the TGF-β family (Sandberg *et al.*, 1988a,b;

Lehnert and Akhurst, 1988; Wilcox and Derynck, 1988; Pelton *et al.*, 1989).

The technique of single-cell mRNA phenotyping, which takes advantage of the polymerase chain reaction for amplification of reverse-transcribed cDNA, has allowed the detection of the presence in single blastocysts of transcripts encoding growth factors; platelet-derived growth factor (PDGF)-A, TGF-α, and TGF-β were found, while those encoding epidermal growth factor (EGF), basic fibroblast growth factor (bFGF), nerve growth factor (NGF), and granulocyte colony-stimulating factor were absent (Rappolee *et al.*, 1988). In addition, RNA from unfertilized oocytes, two-, four-, and eight-cell zygotes, and 16-cell morulae were also analyzed for growth factor-encoding transcripts (Rappolee *et al.*, 1988). This technique is sensitive enough to detect transcripts from single cells and should prove extremely valuable in future studies of the source of embryonic growth factors. Transgenic animal technology, in which a growth factor gene can be misregulated or mutated, has also provided information on the role of growth factors in development. Expression of granulocyte–macrophage colony-stimulating factor (Lang *et al.*, 1987; Metcalf and Moore, 1988) and insulinlike growth factor (Mathews *et al.*, 1988) in transgenic mice has been accomplished. Continued application of these techniques should greatly expand our knowledge of developing systems in which growth factors play a regulatory role.

Unfortunately, the expression of matrix-degrading proteases during development is much less studied than expression of the growth factors. At this time, no studies exist that specifically define a cause-and-effect relationship between growth factors and matrix-degrading proteases during embryonic development.

We can, however, extrapolate possible roles for growth factor and protease involvement in matrix modeling during development from information available from cell and organ culture model systems, or from normal or pathological processes in the adult—such as tissue repair, angiogenesis, and tumor invasion—that mimic events that occur during embryogenesis. Information regarding the effects of oncogenes on protease production may also be relevant to understanding normal development, because many oncogenes are modified components of normal growth factor signaling pathways. In this chapter each class of matrix-degrading proteases is discussed separately with regard to hormonal and growth factor regulation and the possible involvement of its members in developing systems. In light of this information, we attempt to reconstruct possible scenarios for growth factor involvement in developmental remodeling via the action of matrix-degrading proteases.

II. Growth Factor-Regulated Proteases and Their Inhibitors

A. Serine Proteases: Plasmin, Plasminogen Activators, and Plasminogen Activator Inhibitors

1. Properties

Plasmin is a neutral serine protease which is most commonly thought of in association with the proteolytic breakdown of fibrin clots (Astrup, 1975). Plasmin is formed by the action of another serine protease, plasminogen activator (PA), on the inactive plasma zymogen, plasminogen. Both of these enzymes, plasmin and PA, degrade ECM proteins (see below) and may thus play a role in processes such as tumor invasion, ovulation, and matrix remodeling during development.

Two different PAs have been identified: a tissue type (t-PA, molecular weight 70,000) and a urokinase type (u-PA, molecular weight 50,000). They are so named because of their original identification in tissue extracts and urine. Both enzymes convert plasminogen to plasmin, although the enzymatic activity of t-PA largely depends on its binding to fibrin, while u-PA does not directly associate with fibrin (Camiolo *et al.*, 1971). The two PAs are molecularly and functionally distinct and are products of two separate genes, although their amino acid sequences reveal 40% amino acid identity (Pennica *et al.*, 1983; Verde *et al.*, 1984; Belin *et al.*, 1985). Each enzymes is secreted as a single-chain proenzyme which is proteolytically converted to a two-chain form (Danø *et al.*, 1985). Proteolysis is generally thought to activate the zymogens. However, single-chain t-PA is also an active enzyme (Rijken *et al.*, 1982), and the u-PA zymogen has been reported to have limited activity for plasminogen, but not for low-molecular-weight substrates (see Ellis *et al.*, 1987, and references therein). Full activation of u-PA apparently requires proteolysis by plasmin, thus suggesting an autocatalytic loop (Verde *et al.*, 1984).

The activities of plasmin and PAs are controlled not only at the level of activation, but also through the action of serine protease inhibitors, or serpins (see Carrell *et al.*, 1987, for review). To date, four immunologically distinct inhibitors specific for PA (PAIs) (Sprengers and Kluft, 1987) have been identified: the endothelial-type PAI-1, the placental PAI-2, the urinary inhibitor of urokinase (PAI-3), and protease nexin (Collen, 1986). PAI-1 inhibits both u-PA and t-PA (Colucci *et al.*, 1986; Hekman and Loskutoff, 1988), while PAI-2 is primarily an inhibitor of u-PA (Colucci *et al.*, 1986). These inhibitors act by forming 1 : 1 complexes with the enzyme. The circulating serpin α_2 antiplasmin also inhibits plasmin activity, and the plasma protein α_2-macroglobulin is a nonspecific inhibitor of many proteases, including plasmin (Travis and Salveson, 1983).

2. Plasmin, PA, PAI, and the ECM

PA is secreted immediately after its synthesis by many cells, so that the active forms of the enzymes are found to be extracellular (Unkeless *et al.*, 1974; Chou *et al.*, 1979). However, active PA can also be located intracellularly or found attached to the cell surface, where it can exert a more local control of cellular response (Quigley, 1976; Vassalli *et al.*, 1985). The interaction of plasminogen, plasmin, PAs, and PAIs with the ECM therefore contributes to the localization and extent of the proteolysis.

Plasmin can degrade most of the matrix components (i.e., laminin, fibronectin, and possibly type V collagen) (Balian *et al.*, 1979; Liotta *et al.*, 1981), but not types I, II, and III collagens. However, several reports demonstrate that plasmin can activate latent collagenase and may thereby participate in the complete degradation of ECM (Werb *et al.*, 1977; Stricklin *et al.*, 1977; Danø *et al.*, 1977; O'Grady *et al.*, 1981).

The breakdown of ECM by u-PA can occur in the absence of plasminogen, when cells are in close contact with the ECM. This result suggests that PA can itself degrade ECM components (Fairbairn *et al.*, 1985). PA produced by tumor cells and u-PA degrade native fibronectin (Quigley *et al.*, 1987). u-PA can bind to specific high-affinity binding sites on cell surfaces and in the ECM and, in this configuration, retains catalytic activity (Stoppelli *et al.*, 1986). Plasminogen also binds to the plasma membrane and the ECM (Salonen *et al.*, 1984; Plow *et al.*, 1986; Knudsen *et al.*, 1986). Thus, by binding to cell surfaces or the ECM, PA may mediate very local proteolytic activity through the activation of plasminogen.

The presence of PA inhibitors in the ECM may influence the extent of local PA- and plasmin-mediated proteolysis. Immunohistochemical studies have demonstrated that PAI-1 is homogeneously distributed under fibroblast and fibrosarcoma cells grown in culture dishes (Pollanen *et al.*, 1987; Rheinwald *et al.*, 1987) and closely associated with the pericellular space of endothelial cells (Mimuro *et al.*, 1987; Knudsen *et al.*, 1987; Levin and Santell, 1987). PAI-1 does not seem to be receptor bound. Protease nexin-1 is also associated with the ECM and codistributes with fibronectin (Pollanen *et al.*, 1987). α_2-Macroglobulin, in contrast, is unable to inhibit u-PA-mediated ECM destruction, possibly because of its large size (Fairbairn *et al.*, 1985).

3. Growth Factor Regulation of Plasmin, PAs, and PAIs

Regulation of plasmin activity probably occurs mainly at the level of control of PAs and PAIs, because the circulating level of plasminogen remains relatively constant over a range of physiological states. PA and PAI levels are influenced by many hormones, growth factors, oncogenes, and biologically active compounds, such as phorbol esters. Steroid hormones, glucocorticoids, retinoic acid, vasopressin, calcitonin, and prostaglandins either increase or decrease PA production, depending on the cell or organ type (Mira-y-Lopez *et al.*, 1983; Danø *et al.*, 1985; Saksela *et al.*, 1987). Follicle-stimulating hormone and luteinizing hormone increase PA production in granulosa cells (Ny *et al.*, 1985; Reich *et al.*, 1986; Wang and Leung, 1987). EGF increases secretion of PA in many human and rodent cell types (Lee and Weinstein, 1978; Eaton and Baker, 1983; Jetten and Goldfarb, 1983; Hamilton *et al.*, 1984; Stoppelli *et al.*, 1986), and in some cases it increased stimulation of both u-PA and t-PA (Laiho *et al.*, 1986a). bFGF is also an effective stimulator of u-PA in cultured capillary endothelial cells (Moscatelli *et al.*, 1986; Presta *et al.*, 1986). TGF-β inhibits u-PA secretion by several cell lines (Laiho *et al.*, 1986a,b, 1987), although increases in u-PA secretion and u-PA mRNA synthesis have been observed in certain human tumor cell lines (Keski-Oja *et al.*, 1988).

Growth factors also affect the secretion of PAIs. EGF induces both PA and protease nexin-1 in fibroblasts (Eaton and Baker, 1983). bFGF increases both u-PA and PAI-1 production by cultured endothelial cells (Saksela *et al.*, 1987). TGF-β is a potent inducer of PAI-1 in fibroblasts and epithelial cells from several species (Laiho *et al.*, 1986a,b, 1987; Chiang and Nilsen-Hamilton, 1986; Thalacker and Nilsen-Hamilton, 1987). The 48-kDa protein referred to as mesosecrin is also regulated by TGF-β and seems identical to PAI-1 (Rheinwald *et al.*, 1987). Various agents, including interleukin-1, dexamethasone, and the phorbol ester tumor promoter 12-*O*-tetradecanoyl phorbol-13-acetate (TPA), selectively influence the production of one PAI without altering the production of another. This result suggests that the PAIs are not necessarily coordinately regulated (Schleef *et al.*, 1988).

B. Matrix-Degrading Metalloproteinases

1. Properties

The family of ECM-degrading neutral metalloproteinases contains at least three well-characterized members: type I interstitial collagenase [matrix metalloproteinase 1 (MMP1)], type IV collagenase (gelatinase, MMP2), and stromelysin (transin, proteoglycanase, collagenase activator MMP3). Several other enzymes, including a 75-kDa collagenase produced by granulocytes (Hasty *et al.*, 1986) and a 92-kDa gelatinase from macrophages and neutrophils (Hibbs *et al.*, 1985), have also been reported, although the genes for these enzymes have not been cloned and are therefore less well characterized. In addition, other, perhaps more distant, relatives have been isolated: MMP4 telopeptidase (Nakano and Scott, 1987) from human gingival tissue, MMP6 from human cartilage (Azzo and Woessner, 1986), and MMP7 from rat uterus (Woessner and Taplin, 1988). The major ECM-degrading metalloproteinases possess several common characteristics that allow their classification as a family: (1) they are all secreted in a latent form and require activation for proteolytic activity, (2) they contain a heavy metal ion, preferably Zn^{2+}, and require Ca^{2+} for proteolytic activity, (3) they degrade ECM components, (4) they are inhibited by the tissue-specific inhibitor of metalloproteinases (TIMP), and (5) primary sequence data obtained from molecular cloning of these family members demonstrate sequence similarities between them.

Interstitial collagenase is the best characterized of the matrix-degrading metalloproteinases. It is produced by human skin fibroblasts in culture, as well as fibroblasts from human colon, cornea, gingiva, and lung (Wilhelm *et al.,* 1986), synovial fibroblasts (Brinckerhoff *et al.,* 1987), alveolar macrophages (Welgus *et al.,* 1985), and endothelial cells (Moscatelli *et al.,* 1980). Human skin collagenase is synthesized as a 54,092-Da preproenzyme and secreted as a 53-kDa proenzyme and as a glycosylated species of 57 kDa (Goldberg *et al.,* 1986; Wilhelm *et al.,* 1986). Activation of procollagenase can occur by several mechanisms, including proteolysis by trypsin and plasmin, incubation with chaotropic ions, and exposure to organomercurial compounds (see Grant *et al.,* 1987, and references therein). By any of these mechanisms, the final active form of collagenase is a stable 42-kDa protein that is probably the result of an intramolecular autoproteolytic cleavage (Grant *et al.,* 1987). The activated collagenase specifically degrades the native, triple helix of type I collagen, as well as types II and III, by making a single, sequence-specific cleavage (Miller *et al.,* 1976). The action of the collagenase on collagen results in "unwinding" of the helical structure to produce a molecule that is now susceptible to proteolytic cleavage by other proteinases and gelatinases.

Stromelysin was identified by Werb and colleagues (Chin *et al.,* 1985) as a secreted metalloproteinase capable of degrading proteoglycans, laminin, and fibronectin and with limited proteolytic activity against type IV collagen and elastin, but with no proteolytic activity for native type I collagen. Similar activities were identified in rabbit bone culture medium (Galloway *et al.,* 1983) and in human cartilage (Woessner and Selzer, 1984), and the enzyme was purified from human rheumatoid synovial fibroblasts (Okada *et al.,* 1986). The molecule was first cloned by virtue of its inducibility by oncogenes and growth factors and was referred to as transin (Matrisian *et al.,* 1985, 1986). Transin was later shown to be the rat homolog of human stromelysin (Whitham *et al.,* 1986; Muller *et al.,* 1988). In addition, a rabbit collagenase activator cDNA was cloned and sequenced and found to be homologous with stromelysin (Fini *et al.,* 1987).

Human stromelysin is synthesized as a 54-kDa preproenzyme and is secreted as a proenzyme of two sizes, 57 and 60 kDa, which are the unglycosylated and glycosylated species, respectively (Wilhelm *et al.,* 1987). Stromelysin, like collagenase, is also activated by serine proteases and organic mercurides and undergoes autoproteolysis to produce a stable 45-kDa species (Wilhelm *et al.,* 1987). Studies with rat stromelysin (transin) have demonstrated a region of ten amino acids which constitutes a highly conserved region in the metalloproteinase family and which seems to be involved in autoactivation (Sanchez-Lopez *et al.,* 1988).

Several other members of the stromelysin subfamily have been identified in addition to stromelysin (transin). Stromelysin-2 has been identified both in the rat (Breathnach *et al.,* 1987) and in humans (Muller *et al.,* 1988; Sirum and Brinckerhoff, 1988) and has similar amino acid sequence (75–80% identity) and substrate specificity to stromelysin (Nicholson *et al.,* 1989). The two genes are regulated differently by growth factors, however, and rat stromelysin (transin)-1 but not -2 is inducible by EGF (Breathnach *et al.,* 1987). A third, truncated member of the stromelysin subfamily has been cloned and is referred to as putative metalloproteinase (pUMP) (Muller *et al.,* 1988). The characteristics of pUMP suggest that it may be identical to MMP7, isolated by Woessner and Taplin (1988) from rat uterus (Quantin *et al.,* 1989).

Human gelatinase/type IV collagenase has recently been cloned in Goldberg's laboratory (Collier *et al.,* 1988). It is a 72-kDa proenzyme and degrades the following substrates in order of preference: gelatin, type IV collagen, type V collagen, fibronectin, and type VII collagen. It does not, however, cleave type I collagen or laminin. The primary amino acid sequence of gelatinase/type IV collagenase is similar to that of type I collagenase and stromelysin in amino- and carboxy-terminal domains, but contains an additional middle domain of 175 residues with a repeat that is homologous to the type II motif of the collagen binding domain of fibronectin. It is speculated that this inserted middle domain may be involved in binding gelatinase to the ECM. Type IV collagenase is activated by organomercurials in a manner identical to that of stromelysin and type I collagenase (Stetler-Stevenson *et al.,* 1989).

A 92-kDa type IV collagenase/gelatinase has also been cloned from transformed tissue culture cells (Wilhelm *et al.,* 1989) and may be similar to the enzyme from phagocytes (Hibbs *et al.,* 1985). The 92-kDa enzyme contains, in addition to the domains found in the 72-kDa gelatinase, an additional domain that has sequence similarities to $\alpha2$ (type V) collagen.

2. Inhibitors of Metalloproteinases

The activity of metalloproteinases is modulated not only by the levels of the proenzyme and the presence of activators, but also by the presence of specific inhibitors. In serum, α_2-macroglobulin is a potent inhibitor of collagenase (Eisen *et al.,* 1970). Tissue-derived inhibitors of collagenase are, however, more likely to be of biological significance in the control of collagen degradation in the extracellular environment. A specific inhibitor, now referred to as TIMP, is a 28.5-kDa glycoprotein produced by fibroblasts from skin, lung, cornea, gingiva, and uterine smooth muscle cells, osteoblasts, tendon, and cartilage cells in culture (Welgus and Stricklin, 1983; Murphy and Reynolds, 1985). TIMP inhibits metalloproteinases on a 1 : 1 stoichiometric basis by binding tightly to the activated form of collagenase and stromelysin (Welgus *et al.,* 1979; Cawston *et al.,* 1983; Herron *et al.,* 1986b). TIMP has been cloned and is identical to erythroid potentiating factor (Docherty *et al.,* 1985).

Other specific inhibitors of metalloproteinases have also been identified, but are thus far less well characterized than TIMP (Herron *et al.,* 1986b; Goldberg *et al.,* 1989; Stetler-Stevenson *et al.,* 1989). These factors are regulated independently of TIMP and, with TIMP, constitute a family of metalloproteinase inhibitors.

3. Regulation of Metalloproteinases and TIMP by Growth Factors

The expression of the metalloproteinases and TIMP is regulated by a diverse range of extracellular stimuli, including growth factors, phorbol esters, hormones, steroids, and lymphokines. Their expression is also regulated by oncogenes and protooncogenes. Interstitial collagenase and stromelysin have been reported to be coordinately regulated, for example, by phorbol ester tumor promoters and by shape change induced by cytochalasin B treatment in rabbit alveolar macrophages and rabbit brain capillary endothelial cells (Frisch *et al.,* 1987). Many factors induce both stromelysin and type I collagenase in cultured fibroblasts, for example, PDGF and EGF (Chua *et al.,* 1985; Kerr *et al.,* 1988a), interleukin-1 (Murphy and Reynolds, 1985; Frisch and Ruley, 1987), tumor promoters (Wilhelm *et al.,* 1986; Kerr *et al.,* 1988a), and oncogenes (Matrisian *et al.,* 1985; Wilhelm *et al.,* 1987; Schönthal *et al.,* 1988). The effect of the growth factors, tumor promoters, and oncogenes seems to be influenced by the cell type, species of origin, and conditions of cell growth, because not all cells respond to these stimuli by production of collagenase and stromelysin (see, e.g., Wilhelm *et al.,* 1987). In addition, bFGF and serum induce type I collagenase expression in human fetal lung fibroblasts (Edwards *et al.,* 1985, 1987), but do not induce stromelysin in either rat embryo (Matrisian *et al.*, 1985, 1986) or human foreskin fibroblasts (L. D. Kerr and L. M. Matrisian, unpublished observations).

Growth factor and oncogene induction of rat stromelysin (transin-1) is mediated at the transcriptional level and requires new protein synthesis. These results suggest that the induction of stromelysin-1 is mediated through an indirect signal transduction pathway (Matrisian *et al.*, 1985). In some cases the protooncogene c-*fos* has been implicated in the regulation of stromelysin and collagenase (Schonthal *et al.*, 1988; Kerr *et al.*, 1988a). Both collagenase and stromelysin genes contain an activator protein-1 binding site consensus sequence in their promoter regions, and this seems to be involved in growth factor (Kerr *et al.*, 1988a) and oncogene (Imler *et al.*, 1988; Schönthal *et al.*, 1988) induction of transcription. Differences in other sequences within the promoter regions of these two genes could account for the differences observed in their response to external stimuli. Variations in constitutive and inducible levels of specific *trans*-acting transcription factors could also account for the species and cell type variability observed in the regulation of metalloproteinase gene expression.

Negative regulators of metalloproteinase gene expression have also been described. TGF-β has an inhibitory effect on growth factor- and oncogene-induced rat stromelysin, which is mediated at the transcriptional level (Matrisian *et al.*, 1986; Machida *et al.*, 1988; Kerr *et al.*, 1988b). TGF-β also represses procollagenase levels (Overall *et al.*, 1989) and growth factor-induced collagenase and stromelysin mRNA (Edwards *et al.*, 1987) in human gingival and fetal lung fibroblasts, respectively, although Chua *et al.* (1985) reported that TGF-β induced increases in collagenase secreted by human foreskin fibroblasts. Dexamethasone has been reported to inhibit interleukin-1-induced rabbit stromelysin transcription (Frisch and Ruley, 1987), and agents that increase intracellular cAMP also inhibit growth factor- and oncogene-induced rat stromelysin gene expression (Kerr *et al.*, 1988b).

The production of type IV collagenase has long been associated with malignancy and metastasis and is believed to play a causal role in tumor invasion through the basement membrane (see Goldfarb and Liotta, 1986, for a review). Type IV collagenase was cloned from Ha-*ras*-transformed human bronchial epithelial cells, and its expression in these cells depends on the expression of the Ha-*ras* oncogene (Collier *et al.*, 1988). The type IV collagenase gene, however, does not seem to respond to phorbol ester tumor promoter stimulation, even in cell lines that respond to tumor promoters with increased production of interstitial collagenase and stromelysin (Collier *et al.*, 1988).

TIMP expression is also regulated in tissue culture systems by agents such as serum, growth factors, and phorbol esters (Edwards *et al.*, 1985,

1986; Murphy *et al.*, 1985). In some cases TIMP, collagenase, and stromelysin mRNAs are induced by the same agents (see, e.g., Edwards *et al.*, 1987). Although this seems paradoxical, spatial and/or temporal differences in protein production or localization may play a role in determining the net effect of enzyme and inhibitor on local matrix degradation. TGF-β, in contrast, seems to have opposing effects on metalloproteinase and TIMP expression and may shift the balance toward ECM synthesis and away from ECM degradation (see Section III,C for a discussion of TGF-β effects on matrix production). Treatment of human fibroblasts with TGF-β results in an elevation in TIMP mRNA and protein and a selective reduction in procollagenase protein (Overall *et al.*, 1989). TGF-β also interacts cooperatively with EGF and bFGF to superinduce TIMP expression, while in the same cells it represses growth factor induction of collagenase and stromelysin (Edwards *et al.*, 1987). The combined effect of TGF-β on the repression of protease production and stimulation of inhibitor production most likely results in an effective means to rapidly arrest ECM degradation.

C. Lysosomal Proteinases

1. Major Excreted Protein (MEP)/Cathepsin L

MEP is a 39-kDa secreted glycoprotein with acid proteinase activity. Originally identified in malignantly transformed mouse fibroblasts (Gottesman, 1978), this protein is also induced in fibroblasts by treatment with the tumor promoter TPA (Gottesman and Sobel, 1980) and growth factors such as PDGF and EGF (Scher *et al.*, 1982) and FGF (Nilsen-Hamilton *et al.*, 1980). Increases in MEP protein are the result of increases in mRNA transcription (Rabin *et al.*, 1986). TGF-β-1 and TGF-β-2 suppress the constitutive and EGF-stimulated synthesis of cathepsin L (Chiang and Nilsen-Hamilton, 1986).

It has recently been confirmed that human MEP is identical to human procathepsin L (Gal and Gottesman, 1988). The 39-kDa species is processed to two lower-molecular-weight forms of 29 and 21 kDa, which contain the lysosomal recognition marker mannose-6-phosphate (Gal *et al.*, 1985; Sahagian and Gottesman, 1982). Inhibitors of cathepsin L include α_2-macroglobulin and members of the cystatin family.

MEP is an acid-activatable protease with a broad substrate specificity (Gal and Gottesman, 1986a,b). In human tissues cathepsin L is the cysteine protease with the greatest activity against collagen and proteoglycans (Werb, 1988) and can cleave the amino-terminal peptides of collagen (Kirschke *et al.*, 1982).

The role of cathepsin L in ECM remodeling is not clear. Although macrophages and tumor cells actively secrete both the proenzyme and active forms, it is unclear whether the microenvironment is sufficiently acidic to allow proteolytic degradation by this enzyme, whose optimum pH is below 6. It is conceivable that an acidic microenvironment exists close to the ECM or that inflammatory cells generate an environment of sufficiently low pH to allow proteolytic activity. Specialized cells (e.g., osteoclasts) are believed to create sealed microenvironments of low pH (see Section III,C). An extensive discussion of cathepsin L and its role in development is found in Chapter 7 of this volume.

2. Cathepsin B

Cathepsin B is a lysosomal thiol proteinase active at acidic pH. The 40-kDa proenzyme is secreted by cancer cells and requires a pepsinlike enzyme for activation to a 25-kDa form. Cathepsin B activity is inhibited by α_2-macroglobulin and by inhibitors of the cystatin family.

Cathepsin B can degrade matrix proteins such as type I collagen (Burleigh *et al.*, 1974) and laminin and proteoglycans (Morrison *et al.*, 1973; Roughley and Barrett, 1977). Although most active at acidic pH, cathepsin B has slight degradative activity at neutral pH, and thus a role for cathepsin B in ECM degradation cannot be ruled out. The enzyme also activates latent type I collagenase (Eeckhout and Vaes, 1977). Therefore, any activity of this proteinase on the ECM may be amplified by its activation of metalloproteinases.

Cathepsin B production is stimulated by estrogens in the rat uterus (Pietras and Szego, 1979). Higher levels of cathepsin B are seen in cultures of malignant human breast tumors as compared to benign tumors (Recklies *et al.*, 1982), and its production correlates with the metastatic potential of mouse melanoma cells (Sloane *et al.*, 1982). It has therefore been proposed that cathepsin B is involved in the proteolytic enhancement of tumor invasion (Sloane *et al.*, 1982).

3. Cathepsin D

Cathepsin D is an aspartyl protease found in the lysosomes of most cells and in particularly high levels in phagocytic cells (see Werb, 1988; Rochefort *et al.*, 1987, for reviews). The enzyme is secreted as a 52-kDa procathepsin and can be autoactivated at acidic pH. Cathepsin D is processed in the cell to a 48-kDa form and eventually to 34-kDa and 14-kDa forms. The enzyme contains two N-linked oligosaccharide chains that contain the lysosomal marker mannose-6-phosphate. Cathepsin D is specifically inhibited by pepstatin, a pentapeptide from fungi. In mammalian tissue α_2-macroglobulin binds the enzyme, but probably does not inhibit its activity, since the inhibitor is unstable at acid pH (Barrett and Starkey, 1973).

A culture medium containing the 52-kDa protein can degrade ECM from bovine corneal endothelial cells and human proteoglycans, and inhibitor studies suggest that this activity is due to the cathepsin D (Capony *et al.*, 1987). Cartilage proteoglycans are cleaved by cathepsin D in both the hyaluronic acid-binding and the polysaccharide-rich regions (Morrison *et al.*, 1973; Roughley and Barrett, 1977). During periods of rapid ECM destruction, such as inflammation, cathepsin D is secreted extracellularly by macrophages and connective tissue cells (Erickson *et al.*, 1981). It is not clear that the secreted enzyme is active, however, because its optimum pH is between 5 and 6.

Cathepsin D is secreted by estrogen-treated MCF7 human breast cancer cells and other estrogen receptor-positive breast tumor cells and is constitutively produced by estrogen receptor-negative breast carcinoma cell lines (reviewed by Rochefort *et al.*, 1987). The cathepsin D mRNA and protein are induced in estrogen receptor-positive cells by treatment with estrogens and high doses of androgens, but not by glucocorticoids or progestins. Antiestrogens inhibit DNA synthesis and block induction of the protein. It is therefore proposed that cathepsin D may be a mitogen for MCF7 human breast cancer cells. Possible mechanisms proposed for the protease-mediated mitogenesis include the release of active growth factors from precursors, that is, TGF-α release from the plasma membrane-attached precursor and TGF-β release from the secreted precursor. It is also possible that cathepsin D releases growth factors from their ECM storage sites (e.g., FGF). Proteases may also act on cells directly via specific receptors, as in the case of thrombin, although there is no evidence for cathepsin D receptors other than the mannose-6-phosphate receptor.

III. Regulation of ECM, Proteases, and Inhibitors in Specific Developmental Systems by Growth Factors

A. Embryo Implantation

Implantation involves cell–cell interaction and tissue invasion, whereby the blastocyst associates first with the luminal surface of the uterus, traverses the epithelial layer, and then anchors in the connective tissue of the endometrium. Proper implantation seems to be governed by synchronous changes in the uterus and the developing embryo, so that the uterus is primed to respond to the presence of the blastocyst or to any inert body, such as oil, air, or hair, as a result of changes elicited by the steroid hormones estrogen and progesterone. The precise mode of action of these hormones is unknown, but they cause changes in the uterine epithelium and stroma to allow attachment of the embryo and subsequent formation of the decidua that is necessary for proper implantation.

The first phase of implantation involves attachment of the blastocyst to the uterine epithelium. This is followed by migration of the blastocyst through the epithelial layer and association with the underlying stroma. Little is known about the mechanism of initial blastocyst–epithelial cell interaction (Welsh and Enders, 1987), and studies have focused on the subsequent stage of blastocyst–ECM association. Many investigators have used cell culture models to study blastocyst attachment to the ECM, and isolated blastocysts have been cultured on glass, plastic, and collagen (Mintz, 1964; Cole and Paul, 1965; Gwatkin, 1966; Nilsson, 1974). More complex substrates, such as ECMs consisting of collagen, elastin, and glycoproteins, have also been used as models of implantation (Glass *et al.*, 1983). On these substrates, trophoblasts associate with and locally degrade the ECM components. Purified molecules, such as fibronectin, laminin, and collagen type IV, also support trophoblast outgrowth (Armant *et al.*, 1986; Farach *et al.*, 1987; Sutherland *et al.*, 1988).

The ability of embryos to associate with these defined ligands suggests the presence of receptors for each ligand on the surface of the developing embryo. It has been shown that implantation stage embryos can be inhibited from binding to these specific ECM components by using antibodies that specifically recognize the ligand or receptor. These antibodies were used to reveal surface receptors for fibronectin and laminin in the implantation stage embryo by immunolocalization and to show that these receptors, which belong to the integrin family of molecules, were not present in embryos of earlier developmental stages (Sutherland *et al.*, 1988; Fisher *et al.*, 1989). Together, these data suggest that the integrin family of cell–matrix receptors plays a significant role in the interactions of the implanting embryo with the uterine stroma and the basement membrane. Whether other classes of receptors are also involved in earlier trophoblast–uterine epithelium interactions has not been investigated.

Migration of the blastocyst through the uterine stroma is assumed to depend on the actions of proteolytic enzymes and, in particular, on metalloproteinases. Recent evidence suggests that most embryonic proteolytic enzymes are metalloproteinases (Brenner *et al.*, 1989). A 68-kDa gelatinase is secreted by the unfertilized egg and the one-cell embryo, but is not produced subsequently until the embryo reaches the blastocyst stage, when the enzyme is again secreted. By using the polymerase chain reaction to identify small quantities of specific mRNAs, transcripts for collagenase and stromelysin were identified as maternal transcripts in unfertilized eggs (Brenner *et al.*, 1989). These transcripts remain present throughout preimplantation development, and their levels increase at the blastocyst stage. The time of this increase corresponds to the time at which the embryo prepares to implant in the uterine wall. u-PA has also been detected as a product of the blastocyst and trophoblast at this stage of development (Strickland *et al.,* 1976). Interestingly, transcripts for the protease inhibitor TIMP have been detected in the decidua (Nomura *et al.,* 1989) as well as in the developing embryo (Brenner *et al.,* 1989). TIMP levels increase in parallel with those of the metalloproteases. Together, these data suggest that the embryo's ability to invade the uterine epithelium and the stroma is due, at least in part, to the presence of ECM-degrading enzymes and is held in check locally by the production of protease inhibitors both by the embryo and the decidua. Growth factors such as PDGF-A, TGF-α, and TGF-β are also expressed by the embryo at these early stages of development (Rappolee *et al.,* 1988). As with the proteases and the inhibitor described above, their levels of expression increase from early cleavage stages through the blastocyst stage. This correlation could have significant implications for the control of the production of ECM-degrading enzymes and, ultimately, embryonic implantation.

It has been shown that growth-regulatory factors can modulate the expression of proteases and TIMP, as described earlier in this chapter. One can envision a system whereby one or more growth factors might initially stimulate an increase in protease production and enhance degradation of the ECM, facilitating the invasion of the uterus by the embryo. At the same time, the blastocyst could become associated with the uterine connective tissue matrix via the integrin family of receptors on the trophoblast, as described above. Once this initial implantation stage is completed, proteases and inhibitors may be further involved in the breakdown of maternal blood vessels and endothelium, as occurs in the mouse (Welsh and Enders, 1987), and the continued proliferation and expansion of the trophoblasts. It will be interesting to see whether future experimentation provides evidence for the regulation of protease and inhibitors through the expression of growth factors in the implanting embryo.

B. Angiogenesis

Development of the vascular system in the embryo involves two processes. First, there is *de novo* differentiation of the endothelial cells from pluripotent mesodermal precursors, known as vasculogenesis. Vasculogenesis occurs in the extraembryonic mesoderm of the yolk sac, in both avian and mammalian embryos, and in select organ systems (Risau and Lemmon, 1988, and references therein; Pardanaud *et al.,* 1989, and references therein). Following the initial generation of endothelial cells from mesodermal precursors, they proliferate and migrate throughout the embryo, forming a complex network of blood vessels. This process is known as angiogenesis and is focused on here. Angiogenesis is important not only in embryonic development, but in a variety of normal and pathological conditions in the adult as well, including ovulation (see Section III,D), bone formation (see Section III,C), inflammation, wound repair, and tumor growth (for a review, see Folkman, 1985; Furcht, 1986).

The composition of the ECM affects the angiogenic response. In order to form a new capillary sprout in response to an angiogenic stimulus, endothelial cells must first degrade the basement membrane that surrounds the preexisting capillary. The cells then migrate from the vascular wall toward the angiogenic stimulus. This is a process that necessitates the cells' penetrating barriers imposed by the ECM. The subsequent events of proliferation of the cells behind the leading front, formation of a vascular lumen, and further capillary maturation are also effected by ECM composition. Capillary endothelial cells that have been plated onto interstitial collagens (types I and III) proliferate and migrate, whereas those plated onto basement membrane collagens (types IV and V) seem to differentiate and assemble into capillarylike tubes (Madri *et al.,* 1983). During embryonic vasculogenesis and angiogenesis, immature capillaries of the yolk sac blood islands initially migrate and proliferate in a fibronectin-rich ECM, and then subsequently express laminin, which is associated with vascular maturation (Risau and Lemmon, 1988). The composition of the ECM may therefore play a key role in guiding the newly forming vessels; the leading cells must elaborate appropriate proteases to allow the degradation and penetration of existing ECM components, and the following cells must be supported by appropriate ECM components to allow proliferation, migration, and differentiation into vascular tubes.

Angiogenesis is regulated by the presence of angiogenic factors. There are two related classes of heparin-binding angiogenic molecules, acidic and basic FGFs (aFGF and bFGF, also known as class 1 and 2 heparin-binding growth factors, respectively; Lobb *et al.,* 1986; Gospodarowicz *et al.,* 1986; Folkman and Klagsbrun, 1987). There seems to be a differential distribution of these two factors among tissues: aFGF is found primarily in neural tissue (see Risau *et al.,* 1988, and references therein) and in vascular smooth muscle cells (Winkles *et al.,* 1987), while bFGF has a very wide tissue distribution (Lobb *et al.,* 1986). aFGF and bFGF do not have a leader sequence and seem mainly to be sequestered within cells of both neoplastic and normal tissue. In addition, bFGF is associated with ECM components—in particular, heparan sulfate proteoglycans—and is believed to be stored in this form (Folkman *et al.,* 1988). An extensive review of the FGFs, including several new members of the family, and further discussion of the role of the FGFs in angiogenesis and other developmental activities can be found in Chapter 3 of this volume.

It has been hypothesized that poor perfusion in tumors may result in ischemia, acidosis, and tissue damage, which may release FGF from cells and ECM stores and thus stimulate neovascularization (D'Amore, 1988). Other angiogenic factors identified in model systems *in vivo* and which most likely act indirectly include angiotropin (Hockel *et al.*, 1987), angiogenin (Fett *et al.*, 1985), TNF-α (Leibovich *et al.*, 1987), EGF and TGF-α (Schreiber *et al.*, 1986), and TGF-β (Roberts *et al.*, 1986).

The penetration of local ECM barriers by endothelial cells requires the spatially and temporally controlled elaboration of an array of proteolytic activities (see Moscatelli and Rifkin, 1988, for a review). Cultured capillary endothelial cells synthesize increased amounts of interstitial collagenase and u-PA in response to preparations known to contain bFGF-like angiogenic activities (Gross *et al.*, 1983; Moscatelli *et al.*, 1986; Presta *et al.*, 1986). TPA, which has effects similar to those of bFGF in inducing bovine capillary endothelial cells to invade type I collagen and fibrin gels and form blood vessel-like tubes (Montesano and Orci, 1985; Montesano *et al.*, 1987), also induces type I collagenase, PA activity, and stromelysin in cultured endothelial cells (Gross *et al.*, 1982; Moscatelli and Rifkin, 1988; Herron *et al.*, 1986a; see also Section II,B). Type IV collagenase has also been identified in endothelial cells (Kalebic *et al.*, 1983). Although the metalloproteinases are secreted in a latent form, they are likely to be activated locally by plasmin produced by the action of u-PA which is coordinately released (see Section II,B).

Self-limitation of protease-mediated angiogenic events may be achieved by the elaboration of several protease inhibitors. PAI-1 is a major secreted product of cultured bovine aortic endothelial cells (van Mourik *et al.*, 1984) and is produced by virtually all endothelial cell types (Moscatelli and Rifkin, 1988; see also Section II,A). Rabbit brain capillary endothelial cells synthesize TIMP, an inhibitor of stromelysin and collagenase, and two other protease-inhibiting activities (Herron *et al.*, 1986b). The opposing effects of the proteases and protease inhibitors may be controlled by differential localization; the proteases are frequently cell surface associated, while PAI-1 is ECM associated and TIMP may be secreted into interstitial fluids.

Parallels between endothelial cell invasion and tumor cell invasion, the most thoroughly characterized invasive process, suggest that the proteolytic activities of endothelial cells may be cell associated (reviewed by Moscatelli and Rifkin, 1988). In support of this idea, u-PA (Moscatelli, 1986), plasminogen (Hajjar *et al.*, 1986), and plasmin (Bauer *et al.*, 1984) bind to cultured endothelial cells. Other components of the proteolytic cascade are localized to the endothelial cell ECM. For example, PAI-1 is associated with the substratum and stabilized in its active form in such a way that it can complex with t-PA and thus inhibit activity (Levin and Santell, 1987). The PAI-1 deposited near endothelial cells may protect the capillary basement membrane and other matrix proteins from proteolysis by plasmin-generating enzymes. It is proposed that the localization of proteases to cell surfaces may provide several advantages for increased invasive neovascularization, which include concentration of proenzyme and activator enzymes, with a resulting enhanced rate of enzyme activation, protection from inactivation by secreted or ECM-associated inhibitors, and localization of enzymatic activity to discrete regions so that proteolysis and angiogenesis can proceed in a specific direction (Moscatelli and Rifkin, 1988).

The effects of TGF-β on protease production and angiogenesis are paradoxical. TGF-β is angiogenic *in vivo* (Roberts *et al.*, 1986), yet it inhibits endothelial cell proliferation (Fräter-Schröder *et al.*, 1986) and migration (Heimark *et al.*, 1986) in cell cultures. However, TGF-β elicits the formation of tubelike vessels when microvascular endothelial cells are placed in three-dimensional collagen gels (Madri *et al.*, 1988). In cultured bovine capillary endothelial cells TGF-β decreases the amount of cell-associated and secreted PA and stimulates secretion of PAI-1, and decreases cell invasion into collagen matrices and through amniotic membranes (see Section II,A; Müller *et al.*, 1987; Mignatti *et al.*, 1989). Although controversial, these results suggest that *in vivo* TGF-β induces angiogenesis indirectly, perhaps by eliciting the release of angiogenic factors from nearby monocytes or from a noninflammatory cell type (Wahl *et al.*, 1987). A review of TGF-β and its role in regulating angiogenesis and other developmental events is found in Chapter 4 of this volume.

The role of bFGF-induced proteases in the invasion of cultured bovine capillary endothelial cells through a human amnion basement membrane was recently described (Mignatti *et al.*, 1989). Endothelial cell invasion depended on bFGF and was inhibited by anti-bFGF antibody. FGF-induced invasion was also inhibited by inhibitors of both plasmin and metalloproteinases activity, as well as by antibodies to t-PA and types I and IV collagenase. These results demonstrate that both the PA–plasmin system and specific metalloproteinases are involved in the bFGF-induced invasion associated with angiogenesis. Further investigations to answer questions as to which factors constitute an angiogenic signal, how matrix components influence the angiogenic response, and how proteases and their inhibitors modulate the ECM such that angiogenesis can occur in a precisely regulated fashion will continue to clarify the specifics of the angiogenic process.

C. Osteogenesis and Bone Remodeling

Bone development is a prime candidate for a system in which the regulation of ECM components and matrix-degrading proteases by growth factors may play a key role. Both intramembranous and endochondral bone formation, which occur during embryogenesis, and subsequent remodeling in response to use, stress, or injury involve complex processes that require matrix deposition and resorption. Recent evidence suggests that growth factors, in particular, members of the TGF-β family, may play a key role in regulating and coordinating the synthesis and degradation of matrix components to allow new bone formation and the remodeling of existing bone. Clearly, however, the process of bone development is extremely complex. Although progress has been made in isolating primary cell cultures from bone, unambiguous identification of the cell types is not always possible. Interpretation of data relating to bone formation and remodeling derived from *in vivo* studies may be complicated by the concomitant processes of angiogenesis and hematopoiesis which occur in developing bone. Therefore, although the hypotheses relating to the role of growth factors such as TGF-β and the bone morphogenic proteins (BMPs) are provocative, further experimentation with simpler models and better-defined cell culture systems is required.

1. The TGF-β Family in Bone Matrix Synthesis

Synthesis of the ECM components of bone is performed by osteoblasts. The availability of osteoblastlike osteosarcoma cell lines and primary bone cell cultures has strengthened *in vivo* studies by demonstrating the production of organic components of the bone matrix, such as types I and X collagen (Leboy *et al.*, 1988), proteoglycans, and sialoglycoproteins by osteoblasts (see Huffer, 1988, for review). The results of several studies indicate that the synthesis of matrix components by osteoblasts can be modulated by soluble factors *in vivo*. Skeletal growth factor (Farley and Baylink, 1984) and bone-derived growth factor (β_2-microglobulin) (Canalis *et al.*, 1987) stimulate matrix accumulation in bone organ cultures and primary osteoblast cultures. Bone is one of the most abundant sources of TGF-β and -2 *in vivo* (Seyedin *et al.*, 1985, 1986; Ellingsworth *et al.*, 1986). TGF-β activity has been found in mediums conditioned by rat and mouse calvarial cultures (Centrella and Canalis, 1985; Pfeilschifter and Mundy, 1987). These observations have been supported by immunostaining of TGF-β in the developing bones of mouse embryos (Heine *et al.*, 1987) and by Northern blot analysis and *in situ* hybridization of rat, mouse, and human bone and calvaria (Robey *et al.*, 1987; Lehnert and Akhurst, 1988; Sandberg *et al.*, 1988a,b). TGF-β_2 has also been identified by *in situ* hybridization in both the periosteum and the osteoblasts of developing limbs in mouse embryos (Pelton *et al.*, 1989) (Fig. 1C and D).

The cartilage-inducing factors A and B isolated from bovine demineralized bone have been identified as TGF-β1 and -2, respectively (Seyedin *et al.*, 1986, 1987; Madisen *et al.*, 1988). The recently cloned bone-morphogenetic proteins BMP-2A and BMP-3 are also members of the

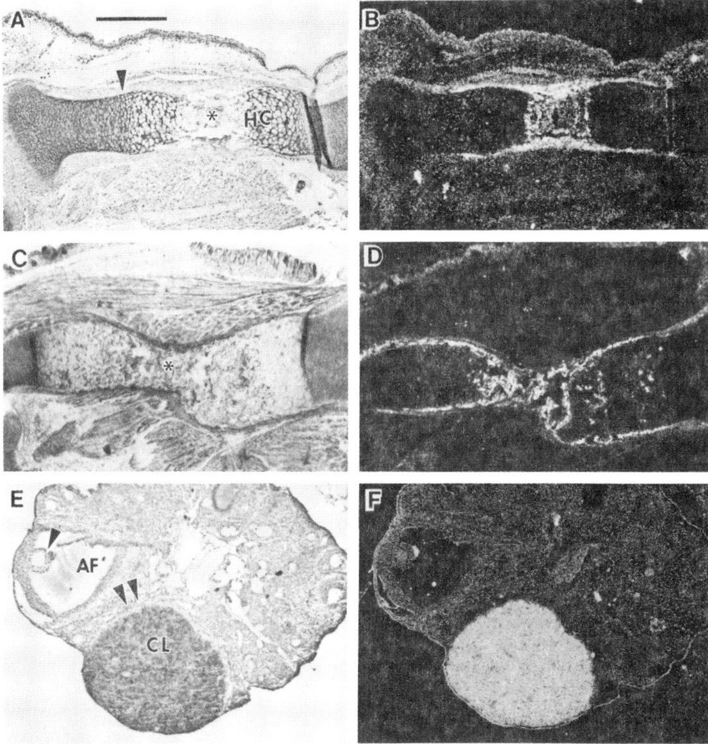

Fig. 1 Expression of TGF-β2 and TIMP transcripts in developing bone and adult ovary. (A and B) Section through a limb of a 16.5-day post coitum mouse embryo hybridized with a [^{35}S]-UTP, single-stranded, anti-sense mouse TIMP RNA probe (Nomura *et al.*, 1989). Bright-field (A) and dark-ground (B) illumination. Note the localization of transcripts to the periosteum (arrowhead), the central region of endochondral bone formation (asterisk), and the absence of hypertrophic cartilage (HC). (C and D) Section through a limb of 15.5-day post coitum mouse embryo hybridized with a [^{35}S]-UTP, single-stranded, anti-sense human TGF-β2 RNA probe (Pelton *et al.*, 1989). Bright-field (C) and dark-ground (D) illumination. Note the similar pattern of distribution to that seen with the TIMP probe. (E and F) Section through the ovary of an adult mouse hybridized with a [^{35}S]-UTP, anti-sense TIMP RNA probe (Nomura *et al.*, 1989). Bright-field (E) and dark-ground (F) illumination. Note the localization of TIMP transcripts to the corpus luteum (CL) and the absence of TIMP transcripts in cells of the antral follicle (AF), thecal layers (double arrowheads), or oocyte (arrowhead). Bar, 100 μm.

TGF-β superfamily (Wozney *et al.*, 1988). BMPs were first isolated as factors from demineralized bone that induce bone formation at extraskeletal ectopic sites. Purification of this activity revealed three distinct polypeptides, designated BMP-1, BMP-2A, and BMP-3. Isolation of cDNA clones for BMP-3 and two cDNA clones that hybridized to BMP-2, namely, BMP-2A and BMP-2B, revealed that these two proteins are members of the TGF-β family of growth and differentiation factors. Interestingly, the primary sequence of BMP-1 resembles a protease isolated from crayfish and has an EGF-like domain. Recombinant BMPs induce cartilage formation in ectopic sites from mesenchymal cells, but the production of bone apparently requires an additional factor (Wozney *et al.*, 1988). Clearly, further investigations into the activities of these interesting proteins, as well as characterization of other members of the rapidly expanding family of TGF-β-like molecules (see Chapter 4 of this volume), will provide further evidence for the role of growth factors and proteases in bone development.

TGF-β may play a key role in bone remodeling via its stimulatory effects on the synthesis of matrix components. TGF-β increases the expression of type I collagen in fetal rat bone cells, and, in particular, in cultures rich in osteoblastlike cells (Centrella *et al.*, 1987; Wrana *et al.*, 1988), as well as in a variety of fibroblasts (Ignotz and Massagué, 1986; Roberts *et al.*, 1986; Fine and Goldstein, 1987). TGF-β seems to regulate type I collagen expression at several levels, depending on the target cells. Regulation by TGF-β has been reported to involve altered rates of transcription (Ignotz *et al.*, 1987; Rossi *et al.*, 1988) and posttranscriptional mechanisms that can include, but are not exclusively, changes in mRNA stability (Raghow *et al.*, 1987; Penttinen *et al.*, 1988). TGF-β also stimulates fibronectin, SPARC (secreted protein, acidic and rich in cysteine)/osteonectin, and osteopontin production by fetal rat bone cultures and rat osteosarcoma cells (Wrana *et al.*, 1988; Noda *et al.*, 1988). The effect of TGF-β on collagen synthesis in osteoblast cells is complex, however, and inhibitory responses have been reported (Guenther *et al.*, 1988; Ibbotson *et al.*, 1989). Reasons for the reported differences in the response of osteoblasts to TGF-β could include differences in species, culture conditions, TGF-β concentration, and length of time of TGF-β exposure. It is also necessary to bear in mind the difficulties in obtaining pure, well-characterized cultured bone cells and the multiplicity of TGF-β-like proteins, for which biological characterization has just begun (see Chapter 4 of this volume). As stated above, further experimentation with well-defined culture systems and pure growth factors is required to fully understand the role of TGF-β and TGF-β-like factors in bone development and remodeling.

Osteotropic agents stimulate TGF-β production by cultured bone cells. Parathyroid hormone (PTH), 1,25-dihydroxyvitamin D_3, and interleukin-1 all stimulate TGF-β levels in cultured rodent calvariae, while calcitonin treatment results in a decrease in TGF-β levels (Pfeilschifter and Mundy, 1987; Centrella *et al.*, 1988). Estrogen, which has been shown to retard the loss of bone mass in postmenopausal women suffering from osteoporosis, also stimulates an increase in the TGF-β mRNA level in osterosarcoma cell lines (Komm *et al.*, 1988).

The TGF-β and -2 produced during endochondral bone development are preferentially compartmentalized in the mineralized matrix of cartilage and bone (Carrington *et al.*, 1988). This observation suggested the interesting possibility that TGF-β is produced and sequestered in mineralized matrix to either aid in the process of *de novo* bone formation or to coordinate resorptive and synthetic activities during subsequent bone growth and remodeling (Carrington *et al.*, 1988) (Fig. 2). During remodeling, the osteoclast degradation of existing bone matrix by osteoclasts involves the action of lysosomal enzymes (see Vaes, 1988, for a review). This degrada-

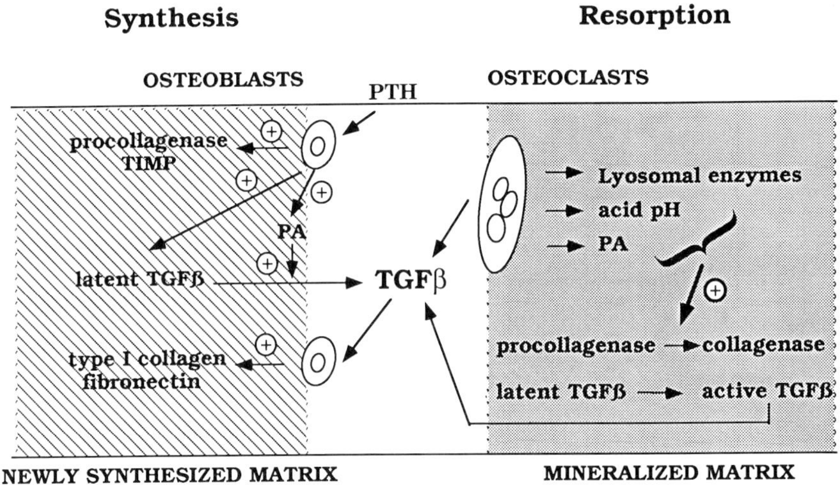

Fig. 2 TGF-β and matrix-degrading proteases in bone remodeling. As discussed in the text, osteotrophic hormones such as parathyroid hormone stimulate osteoblasts to produce procollagenase, PA, and TIMP. The presence of TIMP may prevent the degradation of newly synthesized matrix components by PA–plasmin-activated collagenase, and inactive procollagenase may be deposited in the bone matrix. Parathyroid hormone also stimulates osteoblasts to produce TGF-β, some of which may be activated by PA-activated plasmin and stimulate the osteoblasts to produce matrix components such as type I collagen and fibronectin. Some of the TGF-β may remain latent and be incorporated into matrix. In subsequent remodeling cycles active osteoclasts produce TGF-β, as well as lysosomal enzymes, PA, and an acid environment which may activate and release collagenase and TGF-β from the mineralized matrix. The collagenase aids the bone-resorptive process, and active TGF-β may feed back and stimulate matrix synthesis by osteoblasts, thus coupling bone resorption and synthesis.

tion occurs within a membrane seal (Jones *et al.*, 1986), and H^+-ATPases localized to the surface of the osteoclast seem to maintain the proper pH for proteolytic degradation within the sealed-off external compartment (Baron *et al.*, 1985; Ghiselli *et al.*, 1987). Both acid pH and proteases have been shown to convert latent TGF-β to its active form (Lawrence *et al.*, 1984; Lyons *et al.*, 1988). In addition, osteoclasts produce PA, and plasmin, its enzymatic product, is an activator of TGF-β *in vivo* and in cell culture (Lyons *et al.*, 1988; Sato and Rifkin, 1989). It is therefore possible that the process of bone resorption results in the release of activated TGF-β from the mineralized bone matrix stores, and that this TGF-β stimulates new matrix production by osteoblasts.

2. Metalloproteinases and Inhibitors in Bone Resorption

That osteoblasts are the major source of bone collagenase has been established by biochemical and immunohistochemical studies of bone cultures and cultured osteogenic cells (see Huffer, 1988, for a review). PTH, which stimulates bone resorption *in vivo* and in cell culture, also stimulates collagenase synthesis and release by cultured osteoblasts (Heath *et al.*, 1984). Collagenase is usually secreted in latent form into cell or organ culture supernatants (Sakamoto and Sakamoto, 1986) and therefore requires activation which could involve other proteases, as discussed above. PTH, which also stimulates PA accumulation in cultured osteoblasts (Hamilton *et al.*, 1984), may provide the means of activating collagenase in resorbing bone.

TIMP accumulation is also increased in PTH-treated osteoblasts (Partridge *et al.*, 1987). TIMP mRNA has been identified by *in situ* hybridization in developing osteogenic calvariae and limbs of late gestational and neonatal mice (Nomura *et al.*, 1989) (Fig. 1A and B). The expression of the genes encoding the enzyme, its activator, and inhibitor in the same tissue is somewhat puzzling. It is interesting to note, however, that TIMP is found in the culture medium of PTH-stimulated calvariae, but not in the ECM, while latent collagenase is extracted from mineralized bone and is not found in the culture medium (Eeckhout *et al.*, 1986). Mechanic *et al.* (1982) have suggested that the collagenase produced by osteoblasts in response to PTH may be deposited in bone, to be released and activated during a subsequent cycle of remodeling. The simultaneous production of TIMP and collagenase may therefore prevent the degradation of newly synthesized matrix components, while allowing collagenase deposition into bone.

Procollagenase requires activation by proteases such as trypsin or plasmin or by organic mercurides *in vitro* (see Section II,B). The release of procollagenase from mineralized bone matrix and its conversion to an active form may therefore also be mediated by PA and other proteases produced by osteoclasts during active bone resorption. Thus, in a manner similar to that observed for TGF-β, metalloproteinases may be deposited and stored in a mineralized matrix during bone synthesis and become activated in subsequent cycles of bone remodeling (Fig. 2).

Growth factors, including TGF-β, may also regulate the synthesis of metalloproteinases and their inhibitors, and this regulation may affect bone remodeling. EGF, TGF-α, and PDGF stimulate bone resorption, as measured by Ca^{2+} release in fetal long bone and neonatal calvarial systems (Stern *et al.*, 1985; Ibbotson *et al.*, 1986). In some cases this effect may be mediated via a prostaglandin intermediary (Tashjian *et al.*, 1985). However, these growth factors also stimulate the production of mRNA for matrix-degrading metalloproteinases, such as stromelysin/transin (Matrisian *et al.*, 1985; Kerr *et al.*, 1988a) and type I collagenase (Chua *et al.*, 1985; Sirum and Brinckeroff, 1988) in fibroblast cells. In contrast, TGF-β inhibits growth factor-induced procollagenase (Edwards *et al.*, 1987) and transin/stromelysin (Matrisian *et al.*, 1986) mRNA production in cultured fibroblasts. TIMP mRNA levels are stimulated coordinately with a decrease in procollagenase synthesis by TGF-β1, thus allowing for both a reduction in the levels of protease and an increase in its inhibitor (Edwards *et al.*, 1987; Overall *et al.*, 1989). In developing bone the spatial distribution of TGF-β2 transcripts is similar to that observed for TIMP; both are localized to the periosteum and the osteoblasts of the developing limb, but not in the hypertrophic cartilage (Fig. 1A–D). TGF-β is also localized to the periosteum and the osteoblasts of developing bone (Sandberg *et al.*, 1988b; Lehnert and Akhurst, 1988). This spatial coincidence supports the hypothesis that TGF-β has a similar effect of stimulating TIMP mRNA levels *in vivo,* as it does with cultured cells. Production of PAI is also stimulated by TGF-β1 in human fibroblasts (Overall *et al.*, 1989) and rodent epithelial and endothelial cells (Laiho *et al.*, 1987; Thalacker and Nilsen-Hamilton, 1987), which may further reduce the activity of any collagenase present by inhibiting its activation. If similar growth factor regulation of metalloproteinases and inhibitors occurs in osteoblasts and/or their precursors, EGF, PDGF, and TGF-α may promote bone resorption, in part, by stimulating metalloproteinase and PA production. TGF-β may exert negative effects on ECM-degrading metalloproteinases and positive effects on protease inhibitors, and shift the balance toward bone synthesis by decreasing proteolytic degradation of ECM components and stimulating their production (see above).

TGF-β may also stimulate proliferation and differentiation of osteoblastic cells (Centrella *et al.*, 1986, 1987; Robey *et al.*, 1987), although bifunctional responses have been observed, depending on experimental conditions (Centrella *et al.*, 1987, 1988). TGF-β inhibits the formation of osteoclastlike cells in human bone marrow cultures (Chenu *et al.*, 1988). Osteoblasts also contain TGF-β mRNA (Sandberg *et al.*, 1988a,b) which suggests that, in addition to activating latent TGF-β stored in matrix (see above), resorbing osteoclasts may also produce TGF-β protein that stimulates the osteoblastic production of matrix (Fig. 2). Thus, TGF-β may play a key role in coordinating the processes of bone synthesis and bone resorption, both during embryonic development and in the adult animal.

D. Ovulation

The ovary of an adult mammal contains oocytes at different stages of maturation, each contained within a follicle with cumulus and granulosa cells (Blandau, 1983; Hogan *et al.*, 1986). The most mature oocytes are found in antral follicles, where, surrounded by a layer of cumulus cells, they are suspended in a fluid-filled cavity lined by granulosa cells. The whole follicle is about 8–10 mm in diameter (in the mouse) and is surrounded by a dense thecal layer of fibroblasts and blood vessels. In order for ovulation to take place, the antral follicle must first move through the ovarian stroma toward the perimeter. The oocyte and its surrounding cumulus cells then break through both the thecal layer and the ovarian wall, whereupon they are discharged into the oviduct. Following ovulation, the granulosa cells remaining in the follicle and differentiate into steroid-producing luteal cells. At the same time, the follicle is invaded by numerous blood vessels from the thecal layer and becomes highly vascularized by a process involving angiogenesis (see Section III,B). The resulting steroidogenic corpus luteum will be maintained until the end of pregnancy, when it undergoes luteolysis, involving programmed cell death and degeneration of its vascular supply.

The expression of PA has been particularly well studied during the process of ovulation, by using a variety of techniques to follow mRNA levels and secreted protein and enzyme activities. Both follicle cells and oocytes express PA, but the regulation of its expression is complicated. The mouse oocyte contains stable mRNA for t-PA that accumulates during the growth phase, but which is not translated into protein until meiotic maturation and ovulation. The t-PA mRNA then decays and cannot be detected in the fertilized egg (Huarte *et al.*, 1987). The activation of maternal oocyte t-PA mRNA is accompanied by 3′ polyadenylation, and its activation and translation can be blocked by injecting anti-sense oligonucleotides into the oocyte (Huarte *et al.*, 1987; Strickland *et al.*, 1988). Granulosa cells also contain mRNA for PA. In the mouse this is t-PA, but in the rat it is u-PA (Liu *et al.*, 1986); the reason for this species difference is not known. The function of the oocyte and the follicular PA is presumably to generate local plasmin activity to aid in the migration of the antral follicle through the matrix of the ovarian stroma, to loosen the association of the oocyte–cumulus complex from the rest of the follicle, and to facilitate its passage through the thecal layer and the wall of the ovary. Secreted PA is found in the follicular fluid of the antral follicle, and the production of active PA by granulosa cells is stimulated by follicle stimulating hormone (Liu *et al.*, 1987; Huarte *et al.*, 1985; Beers, 1975; Beers *et al.*, 1975; Strickland and Beers, 1976).

Northern analysis and *in situ* hybridization studies have revealed that high levels of mRNA for TIMP are specifically located in the cells of the corpus luteum of the mouse ovary (Nomura *et al.*, 1989) (Fig. 1E and F). It is not yet known whether this mRNA is translated into protein. If so, the TIMP may play a role in regulating the process of angiogenesis and/or preventing premature luteolysis of the corpus luteum. The expression of metalloproteinases during the process of ovulation has not been examined in detail. However, perfusing the rat ovary with chemical inhibitors of collagenase and metalloproteinases suppresses ovulation (Brannstrom *et al.*, 1988).

E. Neurogenesis

Proteases have recently been implicated in neurite outgrowth (reviewed by Monard, 1988). Neurite outgrowth is a key step in the maturation of the nervous system, as it influences subsequent synapse formation. The growth cone of the developing neurite probes surrounding tissues in a back-and-forth motion, making transitory contacts with ECM components in a manner similar to that observed for invading tumor cells. Also, as for invading tumor cells, proteases seem to be involved in this process. In cultured dorsal root ganglion neurons approximately 50% of individual neurons showed PA secretion, especially at some growth cones (Krystosek and Seeds, 1981a,b). A Ca^{2+}-dependent protease activity has also been localized to the growth cone (Pittman, 1985). Plasmin, PA, and metalloproteinases activated by plasmin could cause local degradation of matrix components and facilitate the penetration of surrounding tissues by the cone.

A neurite-promoting activity from cultured glioma and glial cells was purified and shown to be identical to the potent serine protease inhibitor, protease nexin-1 (Monard, 1988; McGrogan *et al.*, 1988). This activity, now referred to as glia-derived nexin (GDN), inactivates PA and thrombin (Guenther *et al.*, 1985). The apparent paradox between the presence of proteases at the growth cone and the observation that protease inhibitors promote neurite outgrowth may be resolved when one considers that extensive degradation of ECM would destroy adhesion zones and could retard or prohibit neurite extension. Monard (1988) speculates that glial release of glia-derived nexin could stabilize the interaction of the growth cone with the ECM and allow a net increase in neurite length.

Growth factors such as NGF and FGF stimulate neurite extension in primary adrenal medulla cells (Claude *et al.*, 1988, and references therein; Doupe *et al.*, 1985, and references therein) and in cell culture lines (e.g., the frequently studied pheochromocytoma cell line, PC12). (Greene and Tischler, 1976; Togari *et al.*, 1985; Rydel and Greene, 1987). Further discussion of the effects of NGF and other growth factors on the proliferation of neuronal cells and neurite extension can be found in Chapter 6 of this volume.

Machida *et al.* (1989) have recently demonstrated that FGF and NGF stimulate mRNA synthesis for the metalloproteinase transin/stromelysin in PC12 cells. Stromelysin mRNA was detectable as early as 2 hours following NGF treatment and peaked at approximately 48 hours. Neurites were detectable at 10 hours, and the proportion of cells possessing neurites increased steadily thereafter. Induction of stromelysin by NGF thus preceded and closely correlated with neurite outgrowth in these cells. Although PA levels are frequently modulated by growth factors in many cell types (see Section II,A), it is unclear whether PA levels are altered by growth factors in nervous tissue. NGF did not increase cultured mouse neuron expression of PA activity in one study (Krystosek and Seeds, 1984). However, regulation of metalloproteinases, and possibly PAs, by neurogenic factors may play a role in axon extension in the developing nervous system.

IV. Summary and Conclusions

Although specific details may vary from system to system, some general concepts have emerged from studies of the regulation of ECM components, proteases, and protease inhibitors by growth factors. Growth factors may be divided into those that enhance matrix synthesis and inhibit matrix degradation and those that stimulate protease production and result in a general degradation of ECM. These relationships are illustrated in Fig. 3. In general, growth factors such as EGF, PDGF, bFGF, and IL-1 induce genes for ECM-degrading proteinases and their activators (e.g., metalloproteinases and PAs). This concerted release of proteases results in the degradation of the many components of basement membranes or ECM. Other growth factors (e.g., the TGF-β family) stimulate the synthesis of ECM structural proteins (e.g., collagens and fibronectin), elevate levels of inhibitors of proteases (e.g., TIMP and PAI-1), and repress expression of the matrix-degrading metalloproteinases and PA. The overall result is

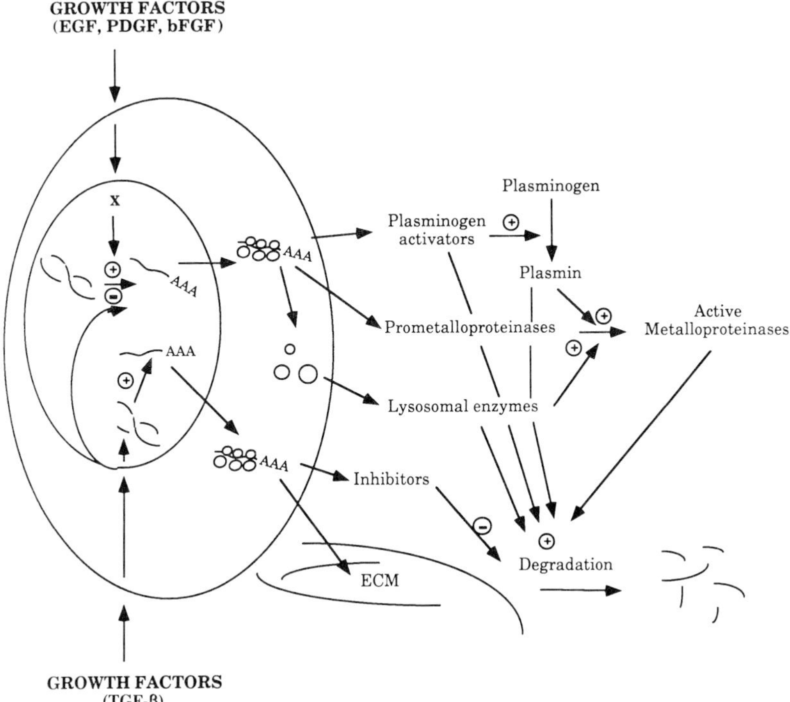

Fig. 3 Growth factors such as EGF, PDGF, and bFGF may promote ECM degradation by stimulating the transcription of genes encoding proteinases. These growth factors often work indirectly and activate a transcription factor (x, in some cases c-*fos*), which then activates protease gene transcription. A cascade of proteolytic activation occurs, which results in the production of a number of active proteases that degrade ECM components. Other growth factors (e.g., TGF-β) stimulate the production of matrix components and inhibit protease degradation of the ECM by repressing the transcription of proteases and stimulating the transcription of inhibitors of matrix-degrading proteases. Thus, growth factors can modulate both the synthesis and the degradation of the ECM through their action on structural components, matrix-degrading proteases, and protease inhibitors.

therefore an increase in matrix accumulation and a decrease in matrix degradation. Studies such as those illustrated in Fig. 1, in which TGF-β2 and TIMP transcripts are localized to the same regions of developing bone, suggest that these relationships that were demonstrated in cultured cells may also be maintained *in vivo* and may play a role in embryonic development and morphogenesis.

A causal effect of growth factor regulation of levels of ECM components, matrix-degrading proteases, or protease inhibitors on a specific developmental process has yet to be unequivocally demonstrated. The examples presented in this chapter, which are by no means exhaustive, are systems in which such a relationship seems very likely. Direct evidence should become available within the next few years now that the technology exists to correlate spatial and temporal expression of growth factors with expression of ECM-associated proteases and inhibitors and to misregulate this expression in specific ways, for example, in transgenic mice. Future studies involving the use of model systems in which complex tissue interactions and organogenesis can be followed in culture should also provide the opportunity to examine cause-and-effect relationships between growth factors and ECM-modulating proteins.

Acknowledgments

The authors wish to thank Gail Ganser, Michael Jones, and Susan McDonnell for their contributions, and Zena Werb, Marc Schapira, Edmund Yang, and Herbert Schwartz for their useful comments. We also thank the investigators who forwarded information and manuscripts before publication. Work in the authors' laboratories has been supported by grants from the National Institutes of Health (CA 46843 to L.M.M., EY 08000 to B.L.M.H., and HD 25580 to B.L.M.H. and L.M.M.) and from the American Cancer Society (JFRA-192 to L.M.M.).

References

Armant, D. R., Kaplan, H. A., and Lennarz, W. I. (1986). *Dev. Biol.* **113,** 228–237.

Astrup, T. (1975). *In* "Proteases and Biological Control" (E. Reich, D. B. Rifkin, and E. Shaw, eds.), pp. 343–355. Cold Spring Harbor Laboratory, Cold Spring Harbor, New York.

Azzo, W., and Woessner, J. F., Jr. (1986). *J. Biol. Chem.* **261,** 5434–5441.

Balian, G., Click, E. M., Crouch, E., Davidson, J. M., and Bornstein, P. (1979). *J. Biol. Chem.* **254,** 1429–1432.

Baron, R., Neff, L., Louvard, D., and Courtoy, P. (1985). *J. Cell Biol.* **101,** 2210–2222.

Barrett, A. J., and Starkey, P. M. (1973). *Biochem. J.* **133,** 709–724.

Bauer, P. I., Machovich, R., Buki, K. G., Csonka, E., Koch, S. A., and Horvath, I. (1984). *Biochem. J.* **218,** 119–124.

Beers, W. H. (1975). *Cell (Cambridge, Mass.)* **6,** 379–386.

Beers, W. H., Strickland, S., and Reich, E. (1975). *Cell (Cambridge, Mass.)* **6,** 387–394.

Belin, D., Vassalli, J.-D., Combepine, C., Godeau, F., Nagamine, Y., Reich, E., Kocher, H. P., and Duvoisin, R. M. (1985). *Eur. J. Biochem.* **148,** 225–232.

Blandau, R. J. (1983). *In* "Histology Cell and Tissue Biology" (L. Weiss, ed.), 5th Ed., pp. 914–943. Elsevier, New York.

Brannstrom, M., Woessner, J. F., Jr., Koos, R. D., Sear, C. H., and LeMaire, W.J. (1988). *Endocrinology (Baltimore)* **122,** 1715–1721.

Breathnach, R., Matrisian, L. M., Gesnel, M. C., Staub, A., and Leroy, P. (1987). *Nucleic Acids Res.* **15,** 1139–1151.

Brenner, C. A., Adler, R. R., Rappolee, D. A., Pedersen, R. A., and Werb, Z. (1989). *Genes Devl.* **3,** 848–859.

Brinckerhoff, C. E., Ruby, P. L., Austin, S. D., Fini, M. E., and White, H. D. (1987). *J. Clin. Invest.* **79,** 542–546.

Burgeson, R. E. (1988). *Annu. Rev. Cell Biol.* **4,** 551–579.

Burleigh, M. C., Barrett, A. J., and Lazarus, G. S. (1974). *Biochem. J.* **137,** 387–398.

Byers, P. H., Bonadio, J. F., Cohn, D. H., Starman, B. J., Wenstrup, R. J., and Willing, M. C. (1988). *Ann. N.Y. Acad. Sci.* **543,** 117–128.

Camiolo, S. M., Thorsen, S., and Astrup, T. (1971). *Proc. Soc. Exp. Biol. Med.* **138,** 277–280.

Canalis, E., McCarty, T., and Centrella, M. (1987). *Endocrinology (Baltimore)* **121,** 1198–1200.

Capony, F., Morisset, M., Barrett, A. J., Capony, J. P., Broquet, P., Vignon, F., Chambon, M., Louisot, P., and Rochefort, H. (1987). *J. Cell Biol.* **104,** 253–262.

Carrell, R. W., Pemberton, P. A., and Boswell, D. R. (1987). *Cold Spring Harbor Symp. Quant. Biol.* **52,** 527–535.

Carrington, J. L., Roberts, A. B., Flanders, K. C., Roche, N. S., and Reddi, A. H. (1988). *J. Cell Biol.* **107,** 1969–1975.

Cawston, T. E., Murphy, G., Mercer, E., Galloway, W. A., Hazleman, B. L., and Reynolds, J. J. (1983). *Biochem. J.* **211,** 313–318.

Centrella, M., and Canalis, E. (1985). *Proc. Natl. Acad. Sci. U.S.A.* **82,** 7333–7339.

Centrella, M., Massagué, J., and Canalis, E. (1986). *Endocrinology (Baltimore)* **119,** 2306–2312.

Centrella, M., McCarthy, T. L., and Canalis, E. (1987). *J. Biol. Chem.* **262,** 2869–2874.

Centrella, M., McCarthy, T. L., and Canalis, E. (1988). *Proc. Natl. Acad. Sci. U.S.A.* **85,** 5889–5893.

Chenu, C., Pfeilschifter, J., Mundy, G. R., and Roodman, G. D. (1988). *Proc. Natl. Acad. Sci. U.S.A.* **85,** 5683–5687.

Chiang, C.-P., and Nilsen-Hamilton, M. (1986). *J. Biol. Chem.* **261,** 10478–10481.

Chin, J. R., Murphy, G., and Werb, Z. (1985). *J. Biol. Chem.* **260,** 12367–12376.

Chou, I.-N., Cox, R., and Black, P. H. (1979). *J. Cell. Physiol.* **100,** 457–466.

Chua, C. C., Geiman, D. E., Keller, G. H., and Ladda, R. L. (1985). *J. Biol. Chem.* **260,** 5213–5216.

Claude, P., Parada, I. M., Gordon, K. A., D'Amore, P. A., and Wagner, J. A. (1988). *Neuron* **1,** 783–790.

Cole, R. J., and Paul, J. (1965). *In* "Properties of Preimplantation Stages of Pregnancy" (G. E. W. Wolstenholme and M. O'Conner, eds.), pp. 82–122. Academic Press, New York.

Collen, D. (1986). *Thromb. Haemostasis* **56,** 415–416.

Collier, I. E., Wilhelm, S. M., Eisen, A. Z., Marmer, B. L., Grant, G. A., Seltzer, J. L., Kronberger, A., He, C., Bauer, E. A., and Goldberg, G. I. (1988). *J. Biol. Chem.* **263,** 6579–6587.

Colucci, M., Paramo, J. A., and Collen, D. (1986). *J. Lab. Clin. Med.* **108,** 53–59.

D'Amore, P. A. (1988). *Semin. Thromb. Hemostasis* **14,** 73–78.

Danø, K., Oronsky, A., and Gjedde, S. (1977). *In* "Regulatory Proteolytic Enzymes and Their Inhibitors" (S. Magnusson, M. Ottesen, B. Foltmann, K. Danø, and H. Neurath, eds.), pp. 113–125. Pergamon, Oxford.

Danø, K., Andreasen, P. A., Grondahl-Hansen, J., Kristensen, P., Nielsen, L. S., and Skriver, L. (1985). *Adv. Cancer Res.* **44,** 139–266.

Docherty, A. J. P., Lyons, A., Smith, B. J., Wright, E. M., Stephens, P. E., Harris, T. J. R., Murphy, J., and Reynolds, J. J. (1985). *Nature (London)* **318,** 66–69.

Doupe, A. J., Landis, S. C., and Patternson, P. H. (1985). *J. Neurosci.* **5,** 2119–2142.

Eeckhout, Y., and Vaes, G. (1977). *Biochem. J.* **166,** 21–31.

Eeckhout, Y., Delaisse, J. M., and Vaes, G. (1986). *Biochem. J.* **239,** 793–796.
Eaton, D. L., and Baker, J. B. (1983). *J. Cell Biol.* **97,** 323–328.
Edwards, D. R., Parfett, C. L. J., and Denhardt, D. T. (1985). *Mol. Cell. Biol.* **5,** 3280–3288.
Edwards, D. R., Waterhouse, P., Holman, M. L., and Denhardt, D. T. (1986). *Nucleic Acids Res.* **14,** 8863–8878.
Edwards, D. R., Murphy, G., Reynolds, J. J., Whitham, S. E., Docherty, A. J. P., Angel, P., and Heath, J. K. (1987). *EMBO J.* **6,** 1899–1904.
Ehrig, K., Leivo, I., Argraves, W. S., Ruoslahti, E., and Engvall, E. (1990). *Proc. Natl. Acad. Sci. U.S.A.* (in press).
Eisen, A. Z., Bloch, K. J., and Sakai, T. (1970). *J. Lab. Clin. Med.* **75,** 258–263.
Ellingsworth, L. R., Brennan, J. E., Fok, K., Rosen, D. M., Bentz, H., Piez, K. A., and Seyedin, S. M. (1986). *J. Biol. Chem.* **261,** 12362–12367.
Ellis, V., Schully, M. F., and Kakkar, V. V. (1987). *J. Biol. Chem.* **262,** 14998–15003.
Erickson, A. H., Conner, G. E., and Blobel, G. (1981). *J. Biol. Chem.* **256,** 11224–11231.
Fairbairn, S., Gilbert, R., Ojakian, G., Schwimmer, R., and Quigley, J. P. (1985). *J. Cell Biol.* **101,** 1790–1798.
Farach, M. C., Tang, J. P., Decker, G. L., and Carson, D. D. (1987). *Dev. Biol.* **123,** 401–410.
Farley, J. R., and Baylink, D. J. (1984). *In* "Osteoporosis" (C. Christiansen, C. D. Arnaud, B. E. C. Norden, A. M. Parfit, W. A. Peck, and B. C. Riggs, eds.), Vol. 1, p. 423. Excerpta Med. Found., Amsterdam.
Fett, J. W., Strydom, D. J., Lobb, R. R., Alderman, E. M., Bethune, J. L., Riordan, J. F., and Vallee, B. L. (1985). *Biochemistry* **24,** 5480–5486.
Fine, A., and Goldstein, R. H. (1987). *J. Biol. Chem.* **262,** 3897–3902.
Fini, M. E., Karmilowicz, M. J., Ruby, P. L., Beeman, A. M., Borges, K. A., and Brinckerhoff, C. E. (1987). *Arthritis Rheum.* **30,** 1254–1264.
Fisher, S. J., Sutherland, A., Moss, L., Hartman, L., Crowley, E., Bernfield, M., Calarco, P., and Damsky, C. (1989). *Trophoblast Res.* (in press).
Folkman, J. (1985). *Adv. Cancer Res.* **43,** 175–203.
Folkman, J., and Klagsbrun, M. (1987). *Science* **235,** 442–447.
Folkman, J., Klagsbrun, M., Sasse, J., Wadzinski, M., Ingber, D., and Vlodavsky, I. (1988). *Am. J. Pathol.* **130,** 393–400.
Fräter-Schröder, M., Müller, G., Birchmeier, W., and Böhlen, P. (1986). *Biochem. Biophys. Res. Commun.* **137,** 295–302.
Frisch, S. M., and Ruley, H. E. (1987). *J. Biol. Chem.* **262,** 16300–16304.
Frisch, S. M., Clark, E. J., and Werb, Z. (1987). *Proc. Natl. Acad. Sci. U.S.A.* 2600–2604.
Furcht, L. T., (1986). *Lab. Invest.* **55,** 505–509.
Gal, S., and Gottesman, M. M. (1986a). *Biochem. Biophys. Res. Commun.* **139,** 156–162.
Gal, S., and Gottesman, M. M. (1986b). *J. Biol. Chem.* **261,** 1760–1765.
Gal, S., and Gottesman, M. M. (1988). *Biochem. J.* **253,** 303–306.
Gal, S., Willingham, M. C., and Gottesman, M. M. (1985). *J. Cell Biol.* **100,** 535–544.
Galloway, W. A., Murphy, G., Sandy, J. D., Gavrilovic, J., Cawston, T. E., and Reynolds, J. J. (1983). *Biochem. J.* **209,** 741–752.
Ghiselli, R., Blair, H., Teitelbaum, S. L., and Gluck, S. (1987). *J. Bone Miner. Res.* **2,** 275.
Glass, R. H., Aggeler, J., Spindle, A., Pedersen, R. A., and Werb, Z. (1983). *J. Cell Biol.* **96,** 1108–1116.
Goldberg, G. I., Wilhelm, S. M., Kronberger, A. M., Bauer, E. A., Grant, G. A., and Eisen, A. Z. (1986). *J. Biol. Chem.* **261,** 6600–6605.

Goldberg, G. I., Marmer, B. L., Grant, G. A., Eisen, A. Z., Wilhelm, S., and He, C. S. (1989). *Proc. Natl. Acad. Sci. U.S.A.* **86,** 8207–8212.
Goldfarb, R. H., and Liotta, L. A. (1986). *Semin. Thromb. Hemostasis* **12,** 294–307.
Gospodarowicz, D., Neufeld, G., and Schweigerer, L. (1986). *Cell Differ.* **19,** 1–17.
Gottesman, M. M. (1978). *Proc. Natl. Acad. Sci. U.S.A.* **75,** 2767–2771.
Gottesman, M. M., and Sobel, M. E. (1980). *Cell (Cambridge, Mass.)* **19,** 449–455.
Grant, G. A., Eisen, A. Z., Marmer, B. L., Roswit, W. T., and Goldberg, G. I. (1987). *J. Biol. Chem.* **262,** 5886–5889.
Green, M. C. (1981). "Genetic Variants and Strains of the Laboratory Mouse." Fischer, Jena.
Greene, L. A., and Tischler, A. S. (1976). *Proc. Natl. Acad. Sci. U.S.A.* **73,** 2424–2428.
Gross, J. L., Moscatelli, D., Jaffe, E. A., and Rifkin, D. B. (1982). *J. Cell Biol.* **95,** 974–981.
Gross, J. L., Moscatelli, D., and Rifkin, D. B. (1983). *Proc. Natl. Acad. Sci. U.S.A.* **80,** 2623–2627.
Guenther, H. L., Cecchini, M. G., Elford, P. R., and Fleisch, H. (1988). *J. Bone Miner. Res.* **3,** 269–278.
Guenther, J., Nick, H., and Monard, D. (1985). *EMBO J.* **4,** 1963–1966.
Gwatkin, R. B. L. (1966). *J. Cell. Physiol.* **68,** 335–344.
Hajjar, K. A., Harpel, P. C., Jaffe, E. A., and Nachman, R. L. (1986). *J. Biol. Chem.* **261,** 11656–11662.
Hamilton, J. A., Lingelbach, S., Partridge, N. C., and Martin, T. J. (1984). *Biochem. Biophys. Res. Commun.* **122,** 230–236.
Han, V. K. M., Hunter, E. S., III, Pratt, R. M., Zendegui, J. G., and Lee, D. C. (1987). *Mol. Cell. Biol.* **7,** 2335–2343.
Harbers, K., Kuehn, M., Delius, H., and Jaenisch, R. (1984). *Proc. Natl. Acad. Sci. U.S.A.* **81,** 1504–1508.
Hasty, K. A., Hibbs, M. S., Kang, A. H., and Mainardi, C. L. (1986). *J. Biol. Chem.* **261,** 5645–5650.
Heath, J. K., Atkinson, S. J., Meikle, M. C., and Reynolds, J. J. (1984). *Biochim. Biophys. Acta* **802,** 151–154.
Heimark, R. L., Twardzik, D. R., and Schwartz, S. M. (1986). *Science* **233,** 1078–1080.
Heine, U. I., Munoz, E. F., Flanders, K. C., Ellingsworth, L. R., Lam, H. Y. P., Thompson, N. L., Roberts, A. B., and Sporn, M. B. (1987). *J. Cell Biol.* **105,** 2861–2876.
Hekman, C. M., and Loskutoff, D. J. (1988). *Arch. Biochem. Biophys.* **262,** 199–210.
Herron, G. S., Werb, Z., Dwyer, K., and Banda, M. J. (1986a). *J. Biol. Chem.* **261,** 2810–2813.
Herron, G. S., Banda, M.J., Clark, E. J., Gavrilovic, J., and Werb, Z. (1986b). *J. Biol. Chem.* **261,** 2814–2818.
Hibbs, M. S., Hasty, K. A., Seyer, J. M., Kang, A. H., and Mainardi, C. L. (1985). *J. Biol. Chem.* **260,** 2493–2500.
Hockel, M., Sasse, J., and Wissler, J.H. (1987). *J. Cell. Physiol.* **133,** 1–13.
Hogan, B. L. M., Barlow, D. P., and Tilly, R. (1983). *Cancer Surv.* **2,** 115–140.
Hogan, B., Constantini, F., and Lacy, E. (1986). "Manipulating the Mouse Embryo, A Laboratory Manual." Cold Spring Harbor Laboratory, Cold Spring Harbor, New York.
Huarte, J., Belin, D., and Vassalli, J.-D. (1985). *Cell (Cambridge, Mass.)* **43,** 551–558.
Huarte, J., Belin, D., Vassalli, A., Strickland, S., and Vassalli, J.-D. (1987). *Genes Dev.* **1,** 1201–1211.
Huffer, W. E. (1988). *Lab. Invest.* **59,** 418–441.

Hunter, D. D., Shah, V., Merlie, J. P., and Sanes, F. R. (1989). *Nature (London)* **338,** 229–234.

Ibbotson, K. J., Harrod, J., Gowen, M., D'Souza, S., Smith, D. D., Winkler, M. E., Derynck, R., and Mundy, G. R. (1986). *Proc. Natl. Acad. Sci. U.S.A.* **83,** 2228–2232.

Ibbotson, K. J., Orcutt, C. M., Anglin, A. M., and D'Souza, S. M. (1989). *J. Bone Miner. Res.* **4,** 37–45.

Ignotz, R. A., and Massagué, J. (1986). *J. Biol. Chem.* **261,** 4337–4345.

Ignotz, R. A., Endo, T., and Massagué, J. (1987). *J. Biol. Chem.* **262,** 6443–6446.

Imler, J. L., Schatz, C., Wasylyk, C., Chatton, B., and Wasylyk, B. (1988). *Nature (London)* **332,** 275–278.

Jetten, A. M., and Goldfarb, R. H. (1983). *Cancer Res.* **43,** 2094–2099.

Jones, S. J., Boyde, A., and Ali, N. N. (1986). *Scanning Electron Microsc.* **4,** 1555–1569.

Kalebic, T., Garbisa, S., Glaser, B., and Liotta, L. A. (1983). *Science* **221,** 281–283.

Kerr, L. D., Holt, J. T., and Matrisian, L. M. (1988a). *Science* **242,** 1424–1427.

Kerr, L. D., Olashaw, N. E., and Matrisian, L. M. (1988b). *J. Biol. Chem.* **263,** 16999–17005.

Keski-Oja, J., Raghow, R., Sawdey, M., Loskutoff, D. J., Postlethwaite, A. E., Kang, A. H., and Moses, H. L. (1988). *J. Biol. Chem.* **263,** 3111–3115.

Kirschke, H., Kembhavi, A. A., Bohley, P., and Barrett, A. J. (1982). *Biochem. J.* **201,** 367–672.

Knudsen, B. S., Silverstein, R. L., Leung, L. L. K., Harpel, P. C., and Nachman, R. L. (1986). *J. Biol. Chem.* **261,** 10765–10771.

Knudsen, B. S. Harpel, P. C., and Nachman, R. L. (1987). *J. Clin. Invest.* **80,** 1082–1089.

Komm, B. S., Terpening, C. M., Benz, D. J., Graeme, K. A., Gallegos, A., Korc, M., Greene, G. L., O'Malley, B. W., and Haussler, M. R. (1988). *Science* **241,** 81–84.

Kratochwil, K., Dziadek, M., Lohler, J., Harbers, K., and Jaenisch, R. (1986). *Dev. Biol.* **117,** 596–606.

Kratochwil, K., von der Mark, K., Kollar, E. J., Jaenisch, R., Mooslehner, K., Schwarz, M., Haase, K., Gmachl, I., and Harbers, K. (1989). *Cell (Cambridge, Mass.)* **57,** 807–816.

Krystosek, A., and Seeds, N. W. (1981a). *Proc. Natl. Acad. Sci. U.S.A.* **78,** 7810–7814.

Krystosek, A., and Seeds, N. W. (1981b). *Science* **213,** 1532–1534.

Krystosek, A., and Seeds, N. W. (1984). *J. Cell Biol.* **98,** 773–776.

Kurkinen, M., Barlow, D. P., Helfman, D. M., Williams, J. G., and Hogan, B. L. M. (1983). *Nucleic Acids Res.* **11,** 6199–6209.

Laiho, M., Saksela, O., Andreasen, P. A., and Keski-Oja, J. (1986a). *J. Cell Biol.* **103,** 2403–2410.

Laiho, M., Saksela, O., and Keski-Oja, J. (1986b). *Exp. Cell Res.* **164,** 399–407.

Laiho, M., Saksela, O., and Keski-Oja, J. (1987). *J. Biol. Chem.* **262,** 17467–17474.

Lang, R. A., Metcalf, D., Cuthbertson, R. A., Lyons, I., Stanley, E., Kelso, A., Kannourakis, G., Williamson, D. J., Klintworth, G. K., Gonda, T. J., and Dunn, A. R. (1987). *Cell (Cambridge, Mass.)* **51,** 675–686.

Lawrence, D. A., Pircher, R., Kryceve-Martinerie, C., and Jullien, P. (1984). *J. Cell. Physiol.* **121,** 184–188.

Leboy, P. S., Shapiro, I. M., Uschmann, B. D., Oshima, O., and Lin, D. (1988). *J. Biol. Chem.* **263,** 8515–8520.

Lee, B., Vissing, H., Ramirez, F., Rogers, D., and Rimion, D. (1989). *Science* **244,** 978–980.

Lee, D. C., Rochford, R., Todaro, G. J., and Villarreal, L. P. (1985). *Mol. Cell. Biol.* **5,** 3644–3646.

Lee, L. S., and Weinstein, I. B. (1978). *Nature (London)* **274,** 696–697.

Lehnert, S. A., and Akhurst, R. J. (1988). *Development* **104,** 263–273.

Leibovich, S. J., Polverini, P. J., Shepard, H. M., Wiseman, D. M., Shively, V., and Nuseir, N. (1987). *Nature (London)* **329,** 630–632.

Levin, E. G., and Santell, L. (1987). *J. Cell Biol.* **105,** 2543–2549.

Li, M. L., Aggeler, J., Farson, D. A., Hatier, C., Hassell, J., and Bissell, M. J. (1987). *Proc. Natl. Acad. Sci. U.S.A.* **84,** 136–140.

Liotta, L. A., Goldfarb, R. H., Brundage, R., Siegal, G. P., Terranova, V., and Garbisa, S. (1981). *Cancer Res.* **41,** 4629–4636.

Liu, Y.-X., Ny, T., Sarkar, D., Loskutoff, D., and Hsueh, A. J. W. (1986). *Endocrinology (Baltimore)* **119,** 1578–1587.

Liu, Y.-X., Cajander, S. B., Ny, T., Kristensen, P., and Hsueh, A. J. (1987). *Mol. Cell. Endocrinol.* **54,** 221–229.

Lobb, R., Sasse, J., Sullivan, R., Shing, Y., D'Amore, P., Jacobs, J., and Klagsburn, M. (1986). *J. Biol. Chem.* **261,** 1924–1928.

Lyons, R. M., Keski-Oja, J., and Moses, H. L. (1988). *J. Cell Biol.* **106,** 1659–1665.

McGrogan, M., Kennedy, J., Li, M. P., Hsu, C., Scott, R. W., Simonsen, C. C., and Baker, J. B. (1988). *Bio/Technology* **6,** 172–177.

Machida, C. M., Muldoon, L. L., Rodland, K. D., and Magun, B. E. (1988). *Mol. Cell. Biol.* **8,** 2479–2483.

Machida, C. M., Rodland, K. D., Matrisian, L., Magun, B. E., and Ciment, G. (1989). *Neuron* **2,** 1587–1596.

Madisen, L., Webb, N. R., Rose, T. M., Marquardt, H., Ikeda, T., Twardzik, D., Seyedin, S., and Purchio, A. F. (1988). *DNA* **7,** 1–8.

Madri, J. A., Williams, S. K., Wyatt, T., and Mezzio, C. (1983). *J. Cell Biol.* **97,** 153–165.

Madri, J. A., Pratt, B. M., and Tucker, A. M. (1988). *J. Cell Biol.* **106,** 1375–1384.

Maroteaux, P., Cohen-Solal, L., and Bonadventure, J. (1988). *Ann. N.Y. Acad. Sci.* **543,** 16–29.

Mathews, L. S., Hammer, R. E., Behringer, R. R., Dercole, A. J., Bell, G. I., Brinster, R. L., and Palmiter, R. D. (1988). *Endocrinology (Baltimore)* **123,** 2827–2833.

Matrisian, L. M., Glaichenhaus, N., Gesnel, M.-C., and Breathnach, R. (1985). *EMBO J.* **4,** 1435–1440.

Matrisian, L. M., Leroy, P., Ruhlmann, C., Gesnel, M.-C., and Breathnach, R. (1986). *Mol. Cell. Biol.* **6,** 1679–1686.

Mayne, R., and Burgeson, R. (1987). "Structure and Function of Collagen Types." Academic Press, Orlando, Florida.

Mechanic, G. L., Binderman, I., and Harrell, A. (1982). *In* "Current Advances in Skeletogenesis" (M. Silbermann and H. C. Slavkin, eds.), p. 322. Excerpta Med. Found., Amsterdam.

Metcalf, D., and Moore, J. G. (1988). *Proc. Natl. Acad. Sci. U.S.A.* **85,** 7767–7771.

Mignatti, P., Tsuboi, R., Robbins, E., and Rifkin, D. B. (1989). *J. Cell Biol.* **108,** 671–682.

Miller, E. J., Harris, E. D., Jr., Chung, E., Finch, J. E., Jr., McCroskery, P. A., and Butler, W. T. (1976). *Biochemistry* **15,** 787–792.

Mimuro, J., Schleef, R. R., and Loskutoff, D. J. (1987). *Blood* **70,** 721–728.

Mintz, B. (1964). *J. Exp. Zool.* **157,** 273–292.

Mira-y-Lopez, R., Reich, E., and Ossowski, L. (1983). *Cancer Res.* **43,** 5467–5477.

Monard, D. (1988). *Trends Neurosci.* **11,** 541–544.

Montesano, R., and Orci, L. (1985). *Cell (Cambridge, Mass.)* **42,** 469–477.

Montesano, R., Pepper, M. S., Vassalli, J.-D., and Orci, L. (1987). *J. Cell. Physiol.* **132,** 509–516.

Morrison, R. I. G., Barrett, A. J., Dingle, J. T., and Prior, D. (1973). *Biochim. Biophys. Acta* **302,** 411–419.

Moscatelli, D. (1986). *J. Cell. Biochem.* **30,** 19–29.
Moscatelli, D., and Rifkin, D. B. (1988). *Biocim. Biophys. Acta* **948,** 67–85.
Moscatelli, D., Jaffe, E., and Rifkin, D. B. (1980). *Cell (Cambridge, Mass.)* **20,** 343–351.
Moscatelli, D., Presta, M., and Rifkin, D. B. (1986). *Proc. Natl. Acad. Sci. U.S.A.* **83,** 2091–2095.
Müller, G., Behrens, J., Nussbaumer, U., Böhlen, P., and Birchmeier, W. (1987). *Proc. Natl. Acad. Sci. U.S.A.* **84,** 5600–5604.
Muller, D., Quantin, B., Gesnel, M.-C., Millon-Collard, R., Abecassis, J., and Breathnach, R. (1988). *Biochem. J.* **253,** 187–192.
Mullins, D. E., and Rohrlich, S. T. (1983). *Biochim. Biophys. Acta* **695,** 177–214.
Murphy, G., and Reynolds, J. J. (1985). *BioEssays* **2,** 55–60.
Murphy, G., Reynolds, J. J., and Werb, Z. (1985). *J. Biol. Chem.* **260,** 3079–3083.
Nakano, T., and Scott, P. G. (1987). *Biochem. Cell. Biol.* **65,** 286–292.
Nexø, E., Hollenberg, M. D., Figueroa, A., and Pratt, R. M. (1980). *Proc. Natl. Acad. Sci. U.S.A.* **77,** 2782–2785.
Nicholson, R., Murphy, G., and Breathnach, R. (1989). *Biochemistry* **28,** 5195–5203.
Nilsen-Hamilton, M., Shapiro, J. M., Massoglia, S. L., and Hamilton, R. T. (1980). *Cell (Cambridge, Mass.)* **20,** 19–28.
Nilsson, O. (1974). *J. Reprod. Fertil.* **39,** 187–194.
Noda, M., Yoon, K., Prince, C. W., Butler, W. T., and Rodan, G. A. (1988). *J. Biol. Chem.* **263,** 13916–13921.
Nomura, S., Hogan, B. L. M., Wills, A. J., Heath, J. K., and Edwards, D. R. (1989). *Development* **105,** 575–583.
Ny, T., Bjersing, L., Hsueh, A. J. W., and Loskutoff, D. J. (1985). *Endocrinology (Baltimore)* **116,** 1666–1668.
O'Grady, R. L., Upfold, L. I., and Stephens, R. W. (1981). *Int. J. Cancer* **28,** 509–515.
Okada, Y., Nagase, H., and Harris, E. D., Jr. (1986). *J. Biol. Chem.* **261,** 14245–14255.
Overall, C. M., Wrana, J. L., and Sodek, J. (1989). *J. Biol. Chem.* **264,** 1860–1869.
Pardanaud, L., Yassine, F., and Dieterlen-Lievre, ■. (1989). *Development* **105,** 473–485.
Partridge, N. C., Jeffrey, J. J., Ehlich, L. S., Teitelbaum, S. L., Fliszar, C., Welgus, H. G., and Kahn, A. J. (1987). *Endocrinology (Baltimore)* **120,** 1956–1962.
Pelton, R., Nomura, S., Moses, H. L., and Hogan, B. L. M. (1989). *Development* **106,** 759–767.
Pennica, D., Holmes, W. E., Kohr, W. J., Harkins, R. N., Vehar, G. A., Ward, C. A., Bennett, W. R., Yelverton, E., Seeburg, P. H., Heyneker, H. L., Goeddel, D. V., and Collen, D. (1983). *Nature (London)* **301,** 214–221.
Penttinen, R. P., Kobayashi, S., and Bornstein, P. (1988). *Proc. Natl. Acad. Sci. U.S.A.* **85,** 1105–1108.
Perris, R., von Boxberg, Y., and Lofberg, J. (1988). *Science* **241,** 86–89.
Pfeilschifter, J., and Mundy, G. R. (1987). *Proc. Natl. Acad. Sci. U.S.A.* **84,** 2024–2028.
Pietras, R. J., and Szego, C. M. (1979). *J. Cell Biol.* **81,** 649–663.
Pittman, R. N., (1985). *Dev. Biol.* **110,** 91–101.
Plow, E. F., Freaney, D. E., Plescia, J., and Miles, L. A. (1986). *J. Cell Biol.* **103,** 2411–2420.
Pollanen, J., Saksela, O., Salonen, E.-M., Andreasen, P., Nielsen, L., Danø, K., Vaheri, A. (1987). *J. Cell Biol.* **104,** 1085–1096.
Presta, M., Moscatelli, D., Joseph-Silverstein, J., and Rifkin, D. B. (1986). *Mol. Cell. Biol.* **6,** 4060–4066.
Proper, J. A., Bjornson, C. L., and Moses, H. L. (1982). *J. Cell. Physiol.* **110,** 169–174.
Quantin, B., Murphy, G., and Breathnach, R. (1989). *Biochemistry* **28,** 5327–5334.
Quigley, J. P. (1976). *J. Cell Biol.* **71,** 472–486.

Quigley, J. P., Gold, L. I., Schwimmer, R., and Sullivan, L. M. (1987). *Proc. Natl. Acad. Sci. U.S.A.* **84,** 2776–2780.

Rabin, M. S., Doherty, P. J., and Gottesman, M. M. (1986). *Proc. Natl. Acad. Sci. U.S.A.* **83,** 357–360.

Raghow, R., Postlethwaite, A. E., Keski-Oja, J., Moses, H. L., and Kang, A. H. (1987). *J. Clin. Invest.* **79,** 1285–1288.

Rappolee, D. A., Brenner, C. A., Schultz, R., Mark, D., and Werb, Z. (1988). *Science* **241,** 1823–1825.

Recklies, A. D., Mort, J. S., and Poole, A. R. (1982). *Cancer Res.* **42,** 1026–1032.

Reich, R., Miskin, R., and Tsafriri, A. (1986). *Endocrinology (Baltimore)* **119,** 1588–1593.

Rheinwald, J. G., Jorgensen, J. L., Hahn, W. C., Terpstra, A. J., O'Connell, T. M., and Plummer, K. K. (1987). *J. Cell Biol.* **104,** 263–275.

Rijken, D. C., Hoylaerts, M., and Collen, D. (1982). *J. Biol. Chem.* **257,** 2920–2925.

Risau, W., and Lemmon, V. (1988). *Dev. Biol.* **125,** 441–450.

Risau, W., Gautschi-Sova, P., and Böhlen, P. (1988). *EMBO J.* **7,** 959–962.

Roberts, A. B., Sporn, M. B., Assoian, R. K., Smith, J. M., Roche, N. S., Wakefield, L. M., Heine, U. I., Liotta, L. A., Falanga, V., Kehrl, J. H., and Fauci, A. S. (1986). *Proc. Natl. Acad. Sci. U.S.A.* **83,** 4167–4171.

Robey, P. G., Young, M. F., Flanders, K. C., Roche, N. S., Kondaiah, P., Reddi, A. H., Termine, J. D., Sporn, M. B., and Roberts, A. B. (1987). *J. Cell Biol.* **105,** 457–463.

Rochefort, H., Capony, F., Garcia, M., Cavailles, V., Freiss, G., Chambon, M., Morisset, M., and Vignon, F. (1987). *J. Cell. Biochem.* **35,** 17–29.

Rossi, P., Karsenty, G., Roberts, A. B., Roche, N. S., Sporn, M. B., and de Crombrugghe, B. (1988). *Cell (Cambridge, Mass.)* **52,** 405–414.

Roughley, P. J., and Barrett, A. J. (1977). *Biochem. J.* **167,** 629–637.

Rydel, R. E., and Greene, L. A. (1987). *J. Neurosci.* **7,** 3639–3653.

Sahagian, G. G., and Gottesman, M. M. (1982). *J. Biol. Chem.* **257,** 11145–11150.

Sakamoto, S., and Sakamoto, M. (1986). *In* "Bone and Mineral Research" (W. A. Peck, ed.), Chap. 2. Elsevier, New York.

Saksela, O., Moscatelli, D., and Rifkin, D. B. (1987). *J. Cell Biol.* **105,** 957–963.

Salonen, E. M., Zitting, A., and Vahri, A. (1984). *FEBS Lett.* **172,** 29–32.

Sanchez-Lopez, R., Nicholson, R., Gesnel, M.-C., Matrisian, L. M., and Breathnach, R. (1988). *J. Biol. Chem.* **263,** 11892–11899.

Sandberg, M. A., Hirvonen, H., and Vuorio, E. (1988a). *Dev. Biol.* **130,** 324–334.

Sandberg, M., Vuorio, T., Hirvonen, H., Alitalo, K., and Vuorio, E. (1988b). *Development* **102,** 461–470.

Sato, Y., and Rifkin, D. B. (1989). *J. Cell Biol.* **109,** 309–315.

Scher, C. D., Hendrickson, S. L., Whipple, A. P., Gottesman, M. M., and Pledger, W. J. (1982). *Cold Spring Harbor Conf. Cell Proliferation* **9,** 289–303.

Schleef, R. R., Wagner, N. V., and Loskutoff, D. J. (1988). *J. Cell. Physiol.* **134,** 269–274.

Schönthal, A., Herrlich, P., Rahmsdorf, H. J., and Ponta, H. (1988). *Cell (Cambridge, Mass.)* **54,** 325–334.

Schreiber, A. B., Winkler, M. E., and Derynck, R. (1986). *Science* **232,** 1250–1253.

Seyedin, S. M., Thomas, T. C., Thompson, A. Y., Rosen, D. M., and Piez, K. A. (1985). *Proc. Natl. Acad. Sci. U.S.A.* **82,** 2267–2271.

Seyedin, S. M., Thompson, A. Y., Bentz, H., Rosen, D. M., McPherson, J. M., Conti, A., Siegel, N. R., Galluppi, G. R., and Piez, K. A. (1986). *J. Biol. Chem.* **261,** 5693–5695.

Seyedin, S. M., Segarini, P. R., Rosen, D. M., Thompson, A. Y., Bentz, H., and Graycar, J. (1987). *J. Biol. Chem.* **262,** 1946–1949.

Sirum, K. L., and Brinckerhoff, C. E. (1988). *J. Cell Biol.* **107,** 376a.

Sloane, B. F., Honn, K. V., Sadler, J. G., Turner, W. A., Kimpson, J. J., and Taylor, J. D. (1982). *Cancer Res.* **42,** 980–986.

Sprengers, E. D., and Kluft, C. (1987). *Blood* **69,** 381–387.

Stern, P. H., Krieger, N. S., Nissenson, R. A., Williams, R. D., Winkler, M. E., Derynck, R., and Strewler, G. J. (1985). *J. Clin. Invest.* **76,** 2016–2019.

Stetler-Stevenson, W. G., Krutzsch, H. C., and Liotta, L. (1989). *J. Biol. Chem.* **264,** 17374–17378.

Stetler-Stevenson, W. G., Krutzsch, H. C., Wacher, M. P., Margulies, I. M. K., and Liotta, L. A. (1989). *J. Biol. Chem.* **264,** 1353–1356.

Stoppelli, M. P., Verde, P., Grimaldi, G., Locatelli, E. K., and Blasi, F. (1986). *J. Cell Biol.* **102,** 1235–1241.

Strickland, S., and Beers, W. H. (1976). *J. Biol. Chem.* **251,** 5694–5702.

Strickland, S. E., Reich, E., and Sherman, M. E. (1976). *Cell (Cambridge, Mass.)* **9,** 231–240.

Strickland, S., Huarte, J., Belin, D., Vassalli, A., Rickles, R. J., and Vassalli, J.-D. (1988). *Science* **241,** 680–684.

Stricklin, G. P., Bauer, E. A., Jeffrey, J. J., and Eisen, A. Z. (1977). *Biochemistry* **16,** 1607–1615.

Sutherland, A. E., Calarco, P. G., and Damsky, C. H. (1988). *J. Cell Biol.* **106,** 1331–1348.

Tashjian, A. H., Jr., Voelkel, E. F., Lazzaro, M., Singer, F. R., Roberts, A. B., Derynck, R., Winkler, M. E., and Levine, L. (1985). *Proc. Natl. Acad. Sci. U.S.A.* **82,** 4535–4538.

Thalacker, F. N., and Nilsen-Hamilton, M. (1987). *J. Biol. Chem.* **262,** 2283–2290.

Thompson, N. L., Flanders, K. C., Smith, J. M., Ellingsworth, L. R., Roberts, A. B., and Sporn, M. B. (1989). *J. Cell Biol.* **108,** 661–669.

Thorgeirsson, U. P., Turpeenniemi-Juhanen, T., and Liotta, L. A. (1985). *Int. Rev. Exp. Pathol.* **27,** 203–234.

Togari, A., Dickens, G., Kuzuya, H., and Guroff, G. (1985). *J. Neurosci.* **5,** 307–316.

Travis, J., and Salveson, G. S. (1983). *Annu. Rev. Biochem.* **52,** 655–709.

Tryggvason, K., Hoyhtya, M., and Salo, T. (1987). *Biochim. Biophys. Acta* **907,** 191–217.

Twardzik, D. R. (1985). *Cancer Res.* **45,** 5413–5416.

Unkeless, J. C., Gordon, S., and Reich, E. (1974). *J. Exp. Med.* **139,** 834–850.

Vaes, G. (1988). *Clin. Orthop.* **231,** 239–71.

van Mourik, J. A., Lawrence, D. A., and Loskutoff, D. J. (1984). *J. Biol. Chem.* **259,** 14914–14921.

Vassalli, J.-D., Baccino, D., and Belin, D. (1985). *J. Cell Biol.* **100,** 86–92.

Verde, P., Stoppelli, M. P., Galeffi, P., Nocera, P. D., and Blasi, F. (1984). *Proc. Natl. Acad. Sci. U.S.A.* **81,** 4727–4731.

Wahl, S. M., Hunt, D. A., Wakefield, L. M., McCartney-Francis, N., Wahl, L. M., Roberts, A. B., and Sporn, M. B. (1987). *Proc. Natl. Acad. Sci. U.S.A.* **84,** 5788–5792.

Wang, C., and Leung, A. (1987). *Endocrinology (Baltimore)* **120,** 2131–2136.

Welgus, H. G., and Stricklin, G. P. (1983). *J. Biol. Chem.* **258,** 12259–12264.

Welgus, H. G., Stricklin, G. P., Eisen, A. Z., Bauer, E. A., Cooney, R. V., and Jeffrey, J. J. (1979). *J. Biol. Chem.* **254,** 1938–1943.

Welgus, H. G., Campbell, E. J., Bar-Shavit, Z., Senior, R. M., and Tietelbaum, S. L. (1985). *J. Clin. Invest.* **76,** 219–224.

Welsh, A. O., and Enders, A. C. (1987). *Anat. Rec.* **217,** 203–219.

Werb, Z. (1988). *In* "Textbook of Rheumatology" (W. N. Kelly, E. D. Harris, Jr., S. Ruddy, and C. B. Sledge, eds.), Chap. 18. Saunders, Philadelphia, Pennsylvania.

Werb, Z., Mainardi, C. L., Vater, C. A., and Harris, E. D. (1977). *N. Engl. J. Med.* **296,** 1017–1023.

Whitham, S. E., Murphy, G., Angel, P., Rahmsdorf, H. J., Smith, B. J., Lyons, A., Harris, T. J., Reynolds, J. J., Herrlich, P., and Docherty, A. J. (1986). *Biochem. J.* **240,** 913–916.

Wilcox, J. N., and Derynck, R. (1988). *Mol. Cell. Biol.* **8,** 3415–3422.

Wilhelm, S. M., Eisen, A. Z., Teter, M., Clark, S. D., Kronberger, A., and Goldberg, G. (1986). *Proc. Natl. Acad. Sci. U.S.A.* **83,** 3756–3760.

Wilhelm, S. M., Collier, I. E., Kronberger, A., Eisen, A. Z., Marmer, B. L., Grant, G. A., Bauer, E. A., and Goldberg, G. I. (1987). *Proc. Natl. Acad. Sci. U.S.A.* **84,** 6725–6729.

Wilhelm, S. M., Collier, I. E., Marmer, B. L., Eisen, A. Z., Grant, G. A., and Goldberg, G. I. (1989). *J. Biol. Chem.* **264,** 17213–17221.

Winkles, J. A., Friesel, R., Burgess, W. H., Howk, R., Mehlman, T., Weinstein, R., and Maciag, T. (1987). *Proc. Natl. Acad. Sci. U.S.A.* **84,** 7124–7128.

Woessner, J. F., Jr., and Selzer, M. G. (1984). *J. Biol. Chem.* **259,** 3633–3638.

Woessner, J. F., Jr., and Taplin, C. J. (1988). *J. Biol. Chem.* **263,** 16918–16925.

Wozney, J. M., Rosen, V., Celeste, A. J., Mitsock, L. M., Whitters, M. J., Kriz, R. W., Hewick, R. M., and Wang, E. A. (1988). *Science* **242,** 1528–1534.

Wun, T.-C., Palmier, M. O., Siegel, N. R., and Smith, C. E. (1989). *J. Biol. Chem.* **264,** 7862–7868,

Wrana, J. L., Maeno, M., Hawrylyshyn, B., Yao, K. L., Domenicucci, C., and Sodek, J. (1988). *J. Cell Biol.* **106,** 915–924.

9

The Role of Growth Factors in Embryonic Induction in Amphibians

Igor B. Dawid, Thomas D. Sargent, and Frédéric Rosa
Laboratory of Molecular Genetics
National Institute of Child Health and Human Development
National Institutes of Health
Bethesda, Maryland 20892

I. Introduction

A. Growth Factors and the Study of Embryogenesis

Two fields with very different histories have recently been brought together, to the benefit of both. The younger partner, the study of growth factors, is nevertheless the much larger field, whether measured by the number of investigators engaged in it or the rate of progress in the past decade. The rapid increase in the variety of factors that have been identified, the characterization of their biological effects, and the studies of their modes of action are documented in the various chapters of this volume and elsewhere. One outcome of many studies of growth factors that provides part of the conceptual foundation for their joining with the field of embryology is the realization that the term "growth factor" is an incomplete and sometimes even misleading description of substances that, in many cases, inhibit growth or affect differentiation in complex ways (Sporn and Roberts, 1988). The response obtained frequently depends as much or more on the responding cell as on the growth factor that elicits the effect. This circumstance reminds the embryologist of the concept of *competence*, an important concept in induction, as we discuss later.

Embryonic induction is a much older subject than growth factor biology, having been discovered in amphibians by Spemann and Mangold (1924), who used grafting experiments as a tool. By 1986 much progress had been made, but altogether it is fair to say that the field was not very active, with relatively few laboratories working directly on the mechanism of induction. There were, however, rumblings of an approaching change with the application of new techniques and concepts of molecular and cellular biology to questions of development in amphibians and other animals. The beginning of the recent period in the studies of embryonic induction may be dated by the appearance of the paper by Smith (1987) on the secretion of a mesoderm-inducing factor (MIF) by XTC cells. We still do not know how embryonic induction works, but there is intense activity and much progress, as summarized in this chapter.

B. Cytoplasmic Localization versus Embryonic Induction

All embryos depend on two general phenomena for their ordered differentiation that leads from the relatively simple single cell, the zygote, to the highly complex organism. Cytoplasmic localization of developmental information refers to the phenomenon in which certain regions of the egg contain determinants that direct cells developing from these regions to differentiate along specific and distinct paths. The other major mechanism depends on cell interactions in which one group of cells transmits a signal that elicits a certain developmental response in another group of cells; this is termed embryonic induction. Different animals depend on these two mechanisms to differing extents, as was recognized at least a century ago and excellently reviewed since then (Wilson, 1925; Davidson, 1986; Gilbert, 1988). Amphibian embryos are useful objects for the study of vertebrate embryogenesis for several reasons, not the least of which is the fact that both cytoplasmically localized information and embryonic induction play important and well-defined roles in their development.

II. Summary of Amphibian Embryogenesis

A. Outline of Main Events

In the context of this chapter, the period of primary interest covers early development, from fertilization through the gastrula stage. Induction has been studied extensively in newts, but recent work focused on the South African clawed frog *Xenopus laevis*. For more detailed descriptions of embryogenesis, see work by Nieuwkoop and Faber (1975) and Balinsky (1975). The amphibian egg is the product of a long period of oogenesis, during which many materials required for embryogenesis are accumulated; these include both storage substances and informational molecules that are important in directing subsequent differentiation (reviewed by Dawid *et al.*, 1983; Davidson, 1986).

After fertilization, a period of rapid cleavage follows which results in the blastula, a hollow ball of cells with only a limited degree of overt differentiation (Fig. 1A). The beginning of gastrulation is signaled by the formation of a dorsal lip, the external sign of the migration of cells into and along the roof of the blastocoel (Fig. 1B). Formation of the dorsal lip is an early manifestation of the establishment of the dorsoventral axis in the embryo; we return to the issue of this polarization in Section IV,B,2. At the same time, animal hemisphere cells realize their ectodermal fate by expanding around the embryo in a process called epiboly, eventually enclosing the entire embryo. The region of dorsal ectoderm overlying the dorsal mesoderm (chordamesoderm) differentiates into the neural plate, subsequently giving rise to the nervous system and the neural crest. At the same time, different regions of the mesoderm begin to differentiate into distinct tissue anlagen along the dorsoventral axis of the embryo. Some biochemical tissue-specific differentiation is already initiated by the late blastula stage, but much of the expression of differentiation markers takes place during gastrulation and neurulation, and the complexity of embryonic tissue types increases dramatically in the neurula stages (Dawid *et al.*, 1983; Dworkin

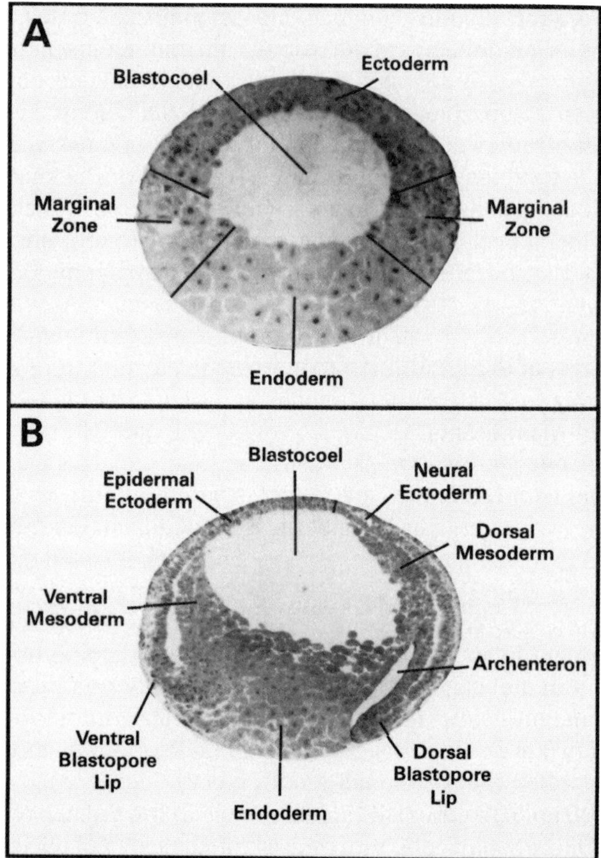

Fig. 1 Sections through blastula (A) and gastrula (B) embryos of *Xenopus laevis*. The animal pole is at the top. Approximate diameter, 1.4 mm.

et al., 1984). As we describe later (Section III), molecular markers for regional differentiation during the periods of embryogenesis just discussed have been particularly useful in the analysis of inductive interactions.

B. Some Terms and Definitions

In any discussion of development, clear definitions are desirable, but it is equally critical that terms be operationally defined and flexibility be maintained to prevent purely semantic debates. As generally understood and used in this chapter, the fate of a cell or region is defined by its products during normal development; fate can be studied by marking cell lineages. A cell's fate may be influenced by its environment, for example, through induction. If a cell or region follows a certain path of development without being exposed to such influences, it is said to be specified (i.e., reversibly committed) for this fate (Slack, 1983). In amphibian embryos such specification is often tested by culturing explants in simple media assumed to be neutral; one must remember that the neutrality of the environment is assumed here. A different and more stringent assay for specification is to disperse embryonic cells in the medium, preventing intercellular communication, and to test their differentiation after appropriate culture periods.

Cells specified for a certain fate may be directed to a different fate by exposure to inductive influences experimentally generated by the application of factors, culturing recombinates, or grafting into an ectopic site in the embryo. The ability to respond to induction is termed "competence." When such a diversion of fate is no longer possible, the cell or tissue is considered to be (irreversibly) determined. Dogmatism in such distinctions is ill advised, since the boundaries between these states are blurred. A tissue thought to be determined may be directed to a different path by a more effective inductive challenge, while a tissue thought to be unspecified may turn out to have an inherent bias toward its normal fate when tested in a more sensitive way.

III. Use of Molecular Markers in Induction Studies

One foundation for recent work in the field of embryonic induction was the realization of the distinctness of mesoderm and neural induction and the elaboration of well-defined biological assays, as described in Section IV,B. The other key development was the availability of molecular markers for early differentiation which supplement histology in determining the outcome of embryological experiments. The value of such markers is multiple. They can be used to quantitate inductive effects, the need for subjective judgments may be reduced, and they allow an assay of differentiation in single cells or scrambled cell populations that are histologically uninformative. This is an important point, because the requirements for generating a recognizable structure are likely to exceed the requirements for changing the pattern of gene expression of induced cells, and some interactions may be missed when morphology alone is used as the criterion for induction.

Another advantage in the use of such markers is that the time required to see an effect is often reduced: Classical induction experiments that involve lengthy culture periods before tissue differentiation is assessed introduce the possibility of secondary effects that could complicate interpretation of the results. In contrast, the expression of molecular markers can usually be assayed after culture periods of a few hours. Furthermore, the availability of cloned genes whose expression is subject to inductive influences allows a molecular approach to the study of mechanisms of induction; such studies have been initiated, as discussed below.

A. Mesoderm Markers

Notwithstanding their great value, the range of available cloned genes and monoclonal antibody markers for *Xenopus* mesoderm differentiation is still quite limited. Among the various mesodermal tissues, only muscle is represented by a good set of markers. The most widely used marker for muscle is α-actin mRNA, which accumulates exclusively in the myotome, beginning at the late gastrula stage (stage 13) (Mohun *et al.*, 1984). The mechanism of transcriptional regulation of the α-actin gene in embryogenesis has been studied after the injection of cloned DNA into the embryo, which allows the definition of DNA sequences required for developmental control (Wilson *et al.*, 1986; Mohun *et al.*, 1986). Other muscle-specific cDNA clones (Dworkin-Rastl *et al.*, 1986) and antibodies (Kintner and Brockes, 1984) are also used widely.

Unfortunately, no similarly effective markers are available for other mesodermal derivatives. Globin can be visualized easily, but differentiation of blood, a ventral mesodermal derivative, is a rather late event and the ability to detect globin has not been very useful in induction studies. An antibody characteristic for later notochord development (Smith and Watt, 1985) and a keratin preferentially, but not exclusively, expressed in the notochord (LaFlamme *et al.*, 1988) have been described, but neither fulfills the requirements for a specific, early-expressed marker.

B. Neural Markers

Markers for early neural differentiation have been generated recently which promise to be very helpful. The neural cell adhesion molecule (N-CAM) is expressed early and specifically in the *Xenopus* neural plate, as assayed by immunocytochemsitry and by *in situ* hybridization (Jacobson and Rutishauser, 1986; Kintner and Melton, 1987); at later stages this molecule is expressed in muscle as well (Kay *et al.*, 1988). Several genes specific for the nervous system that are expressed from the late gastrula stage on have been isolated (Richter *et al.*, 1988). One of these genes encodes a β-tubulin isoform that is an early-expressed and abundant neural marker. A neurofilament gene that is highly neurospecific, but is expressed in the late neurula stage (stage 22), has been reported by Sharpe (1988). The homeodomain encoding gene, *XlHbox6*, is especially interesting in this context, since it shows differential expression in the posterior neural plate (Sharpe *et al.*, 1987).

Induction turns genes off as well as on; this fact is exploited in useful marker systems. Several keratin genes have been characterized that are activated in the late blastula stage in a regionally specific way and are subsequently expressed in the ectoderm and eventually the epidermis of the developing tadpole (Jonas *et al.*, 1985; Winkles *et al.*, 1985; Miyatani *et al.*, 1986). These keratin genes are turned off in the developing neural plate during gastrulation, presumably as a result of neural induction (Jamrich *et al.*, 1987), and they can be turned off under experimental conditions in which ectoderm is exposed to mesodermal induction signals (Dawid *et al.*, 1988; Symes *et al.*, 1988). Detailed studies of the regulation of expression of one member (XK81A1) of this group of keratin genes (Jonas *et al.*, 1989) promise to shed light on the molecular mechanisms responsible for its activation and inductive inactivation. A different epidermal marker, Epi 1, identified by a monoclonal antibody, has been used effectively to study epidermal differentiation and neural induction (Akers *et al.*, 1986; London *et al.*, 1988; Savage and Phillips, 1989).

IV. Embryonic Induction

A. Early History

In their famed experiment Spemann and Mangold (1924) grafted a dorsal lip from one embryo to the ventral side of another, as diagrammed in Fig. 2. The result was the formation of a second dorsal axis, including duplicated neural tube, notochord, and somites. Since most of the secondary axis was derived from the host, the implanted dorsal lip was named the "organizer," having organized host tissue around itself into a dorsal axis. From the results obtained during the next three decades of research, we should mention two major conclusions. The first is that regional specificity was detected in the inducing tissue, suggesting the existence of distinct inducing substances, such as archencephalic and spinocaudal inducers (Mangold, 1933; see also Section VIII,A). The second important point was the realization that the organizer need not be living tissue to have its effect; fixed or heated tissue could induce as well (Bautzmann *et al.*, 1932; Holtfreter, 1934), suggesting that substances derived from the killed tissue could effect induction.

The latter finding ushered in a period in the study of embryonic induction that generated much frustration. Many substances were tried as inducers,

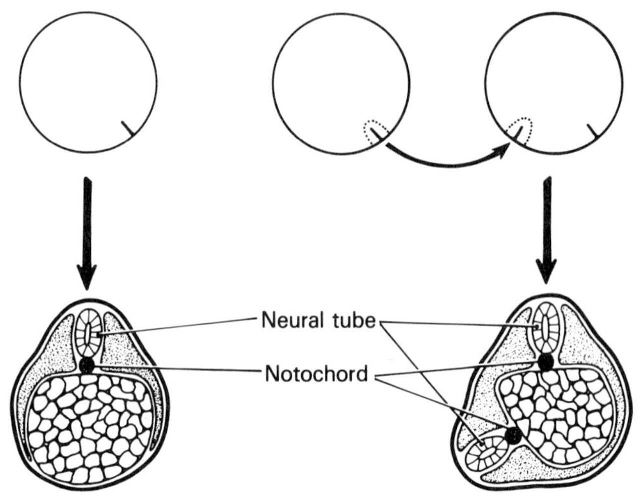

Fig. 2 The organizer experiment of Spemann and Mangold (1924). Implantation of a dorsal lip into the ventral vegetal region of a host gastrula led to the development of a secondary dorsal axis, mostly derived from host tissues.

and a bewildering variety appeared to work (Holtfreter, 1944, 1947; Waddington *et al.*, 1936; for reviews, see Witkowski, 1985; Brachet, 1986; Saxèn and Toivonen, 1986; Gurdon, 1987). The realization that all of these materials could not be natural inducers led to the hypothesis that certain substances are toxic and cytolyze some of the cells in the embryo, releasing otherwise sequestered natural inducers. In retrospect, it appears that a further development of biochemical technology and more clearly defined biological assay systems were required before additional progress toward the identification of inducers could be made.

B. A Modern View of Induction

1. Mesoderm and Neural Induction Are Distinct

a. Mesoderm Is Generated in the Earliest Inductive Interaction in Amphibian Embryogenesis. Several types of experiments during the past 25 years have shaped current thinking about inductive phenomena. Perhaps the most important of these is the work by Nieuwkoop and colleagues, who defined mesoderm induction as a distinct, early event in amphibian embryogenesis (Nieuwkoop, 1969, 1973; Sudarwati and Nieuwkoop, 1971). The basic experiment is illustrated in Fig. 3. The top, or animal, portion of a blastula embryo (an animal cap) forms only epider-

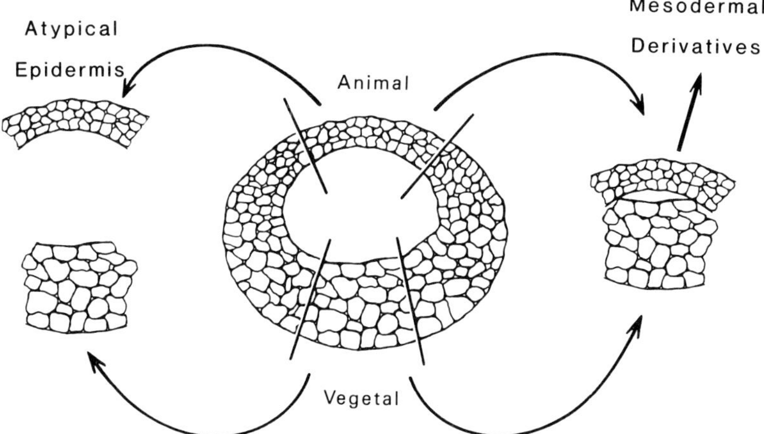

Fig. 3 The Nieuwkoop mesoderm induction experiment. Animal region explants (animal caps) from blastula stage embryos develop into epidermis when cultured in an amphibian salt solution, but when placed in contact with a vegetal explant, they give rise to a variety of mesodermal derivatives.

mis when cultured by itself, whether it is placed in an amphibian salt solution or a rich tissue culture medium; this explantation test is one version of the standard assay for specification, as discussed in Section II,B. However, when cultured in contact with a piece of vegetal tissue, the animal cap differentiates into a wide variety of mesodermal derivatives.

On the basis of this and similar experiments, Nieuwkoop concluded that mesoderm develops as a result of the induction of cells of an ectodermal character by a signal derived from the endodermal (vegetal) region of the embryo (Fig. 4). This conclusion does not follow directly from the type of experiment shown in Fig. 3, since in normal embryogenesis mesoderm derives mostly from the marginal zone, not the animal cap, and the ability of the cap to be induced under artificial conditions need not reflect events in the embryo. Explantation experiments have not provided a definitive answer to this issue, since it has not been possible to explant mesodermal precursor cells from early embryos that do not already possess the ability to differentiate into mesodermal derivatives after culture (see Section IV,B,3). One approach to test the conclusion that induction is normally required for mesoderm formation is represented by the experiment illustrated in Fig. 5. Cleavage stage embryos were dissociated into individual cells that were dispersed on a surface, preventing cell interactions; such dispersed cells survive and divide through blastula stages. Cells maintained under these conditions do not activate the α-actin gene or other muscle-specific markers, but do activate epidermal marker genes (Sargent

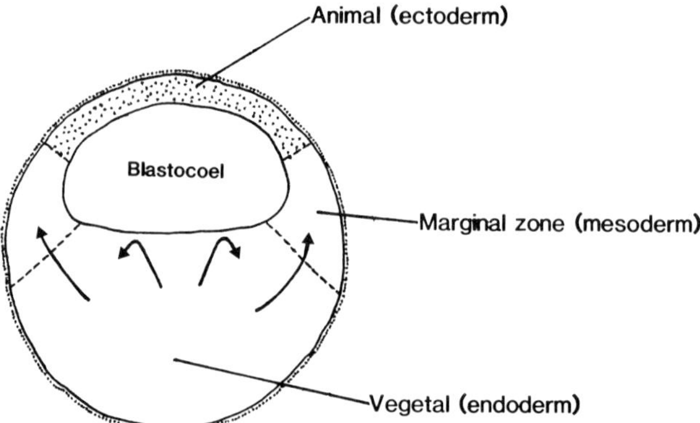

Fig. 4 The mesoderm induction hypothesis holds that the marginal zone is converted to a mesodermal fate as a result of a signal derived from the vegetal hemisphere. The signal does not reach the animal pole because it cannot be propagated through the blastocoel; thus, animal pole tissue will form ectoderm.

et al., 1986), indicating that cell interactions during the blastula stages are required for the differentiation of muscle, a major mesodermal tissue, but not for the initial steps of ectodermal differentiation.

Not every mesodermal character responds to the "dispersion test" in the same way as muscle-specific gene activation. When embryos were dispersed from the early cleavage stage through the early gastrula stage and then reaggregated, they expressed at least one neural-specific marker,

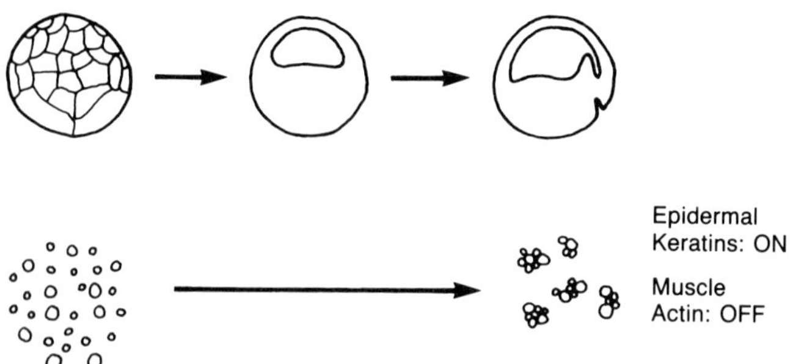

Fig. 5 Dispersion experiment testing the requirement for induction in muscle differentiation. Cells of 64- to 128-cell embryos were dissociated by removal of Ca^{2+} and Mg^{2+} from the medium, dispersed on an agarose surface, and cultured with repeated dispersion until the controls reached gastrulation. Cells were then reaggregated and, after further culture, tested for activation of epidermal keratin genes and muscle-specific actin genes. Muscle-specific gene activation was suppressed by the dispersion regimen, indicating that cell interactions during the blastula stage are required for subsequent muscle differentiation. The activation of the keratin genes is one control for the survival of the dispersed cells.

mRNA for the neural cell adhesion molecule, to a level comparable to that in controls (Sato and Sargent, 1989). As discussed in Sections IV,B,1,b and VIII, the nervous system is the product of an inductive interaction between dorsal mesoderm and overlying ectoderm; if dispersion had prevented the formation of all mesoderm, there should have been no source of neural inducer in the system. Interpretation of this finding is not straightforward, but it is reasonably clear that the ability of the *Xenopus* embryo to produce neural inducer(s) does not have the same requirement for blastula stage intercellular interactions as does muscle specification. Conceivably, the neural inducing function, which is an important characteristic of dorsal mesoderm, is acquired by a mechanism that is cell autonomous rather than inductive. The cortical/subcortical rotation that occurs before the first cleavage (see Section IV,B,2) might confer this trait upon the cytoplasm destined for inclusion in dorsal mesodermal derivatives.

b. Neural Induction Occurs during Gastrulation. The neural plate forms when dorsal ectoderm is diverted from epidermal to neural development by contact with the dorsal lip and migrating dorsal mesoderm (chordamesoderm), as illustrated in Fig. 6 (Gimlich and Cooke, 1983; Smith and Slack, 1983; Jacobson, 1984). What is the evidence that mesodermal and neural induction are distinct phenomena? Until the mechanisms of both types of interactions are fully understood, the distinction cannot be established beyond question, but different timing provides a basis for separating the two phenomena. Blastula ectoderm (animal caps) can be induced by vegetal tissue or by the mesoderm induction factor from XTC cells (XTC-MIF) (see Sections V,A and V,B) toward mesoderm and,

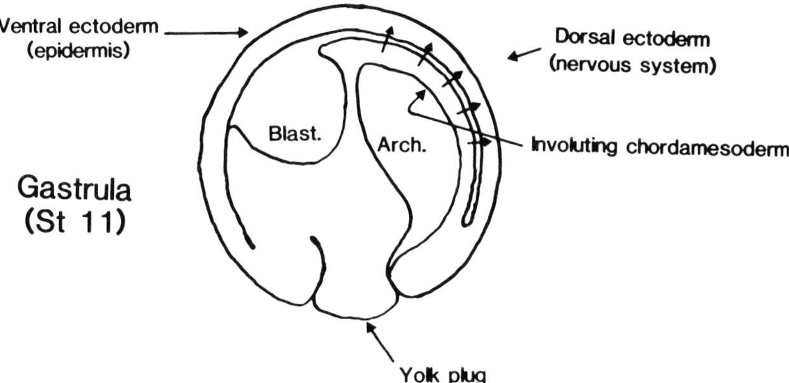

Fig. 6 Neural induction takes place during gastrulation, when a signal emanating from chordamesoderm influences the overlying dorsal ectoderm to form the neural plate. Blast., Blastula ectoderm; Arch., Archenteron.

under certain conditions, to neural tissue. In the latter case we may postulate that this is a secondary phenomenon in which the primarily induced mesoderm neuralizes remaining ectodermal cells (Nieuwkoop, 1973; Smith, 1987; Suzuki *et al.,* 1986; but see Smith *et al.,* 1988). In the early gastrula stage (at about stage 10.5) the ectoderm loses its competence to respond to mesodermalizing signals, including endodermal tissue (Gurdon *et al.,* 1985a; Jones and Woodland, 1987), and XTC-MIF (Symes *et al.,* 1988). At this time, however, the same tissue is still receptive to neuralizing signals (Sharpe *et al.,* 1987), although a detailed time course of ectodermal competence for neural induction in *Xenopus* is not available. While these observations are suggestive, we should keep in mind that the distinction between mesodermal and neural induction is somewhat tenuous: Neither the loss of mesodermal competence nor the maintenance of neural competence have been timed as precisely as is desirable, and the interval separating the two inductive events is short in any case.

Additional indications for the distinctness of mesodermal and neural induction come from a large volume of earlier literature, summarized by Gurdon (1987), showing that different materials have differential inducing capacity. However, these materials were quite uncharacterized mixtures, often whole killed tissues, not allowing definitive interpretations. Thus, we must keep an open mind about the relationship between mesodermal and neural induction in the present stage of knowledge.

2. Establishment of Dorsoventral Polarity and Mesoderm Induction

The fertilized frog egg is symmetrical around its animal/vegetal axis. The sperm entry point defines, under normal conditions, the future ventral side of the embryo. This is achieved through a rotational movement of the cortex relative to subcortical cytoplasm which is required for axis formation. The vector of this movement is the most precise predictor of the future dorsoventral axis (Ancel and Vintemberger, 1948; Scharf and Gerhart, 1980, 1983; Vincent *et al.,* 1986; Vincent and Gerhart, 1987; Gerhart *et al.,* 1987). It appears that this rotational movement displaces substances into the dorsal vegetal region of the embryo, which possibly accounts for special properties of this cytoplasm. It has been demonstrated that by the 32- to 64-cell stage the dorsal/vegetal blastomeres or their progeny are endowed with an inductive capacity to establish a dorsal axis (Gimlich and Gerhart, 1984). At a somewhat later stage the inductive capacity declines in vegetal cells and "moves" up into the dorsal marginal (equatorial) zone, the area that gives rise to much of the mesodermal tissues (Gimlich, 1986).

It is not entirely clear how the axis-inducing effects of dorsal/vegetal and equatorial cells in cleavage stages, as studied mostly by Gimlich, relate to the more general mesoderm-inducing properties of the vegetal region of blastula embryos, as defined originally by Nieuwkoop. A hypothetical unification of these experiments would postulate that inducers (or their precursors or activators) are moved to dorsal regions in the early cytoplasmic rotation, but that smaller amounts of the same factors, or qualitatively distinct factors, become located in ventral/lateral regions of the vegetal hemisphere. Subsequently, distinct mesoderm inductions could generate different tissues along the dorsoventral axis of the developing embryo, whether by the graded distribution of one factor (see Section VI,A), the presence of multiple factors (Slack, 1983), or both.

3. Timing of Mesoderm Induction

No simple answer to the question of timing is available, and there may not be one, because different tissues of the mesoderm may be induced at different but overlapping times. A resolution of this issue requires an experimental determination of the time at which cells become specified (reversibly) or determined (irreversibly) to particular mesodermal fates. As might be expected under such circumstances, different experimental protocols yield different answers. Nakamura *et al.* (1970) isolated regions from early embryos fated to give rise to mesoderm and cultured them in saline. These regions seldom formed mesoderm when isolated at the 32-cell stage, but differentiated more frequently when isolated at the 64-cell stage, and later. A conclusion from these experiments has been that mesoderm induction is complete by 64 cells, but not by 32 cells. However, Gimlich (1986) cites unpublished data showing that aggregates of two equatorial explants from 32-cell embryos are capable of generating mesoderm, casting doubt on the idea of a developmental boundary between the 32- and 64-cell stages. Further, the idea that mesoderm induction is terminated at the 64-cell stage is contradicted by considerable evidence discussed later in this section.

Studying even earlier stages, Gurdon *et al.* (1985b) found that subequatorial regions from the fertilized egg, and the corresponding sections of cleaving embryo, were capable of activating the α-actin gene (i.e., forming muscle) after being cultured to the equivalent of the neurula stage. These results were interpreted as being compatible with specification of the subequatorial region as muscle-forming without further cell interactions. Different conclusions emerged from dispersion experiments already mentioned in Section IV,B,1,a (see Fig. 5): When cells were kept separated from each other between cleavage (64- to 128-cell stage) and the early gastrula stage, no subsequent α-actin gene expression was seen (Sargent *et al.*, 1986; Symes *et al.*, 1988). An interesting aspect of these experiments is that reaggregation of the dispersed cells at a time equivalent to the late blastula stage or even the earliest gastrula stage (stage 10) allowed full activation of the α-actin gene (Symes *et al.*, 1988; Sato and Sargent, 1989). These experiments provide rather strong support for the view that induction of muscle-specific gene expression can occur up to the beginning of gastrulation.

Experiments with animal/vegetal recombinates give a more consistent picture. Vegetal cells provide an inducing signal at least from stage 5 (16 cells) on (Jones and Woodland, 1987). This capacity appears to move into the marginal zone during the later blastula stage (Boterenbrood and Nieuwkoop, 1973; Gurdon *et al.*, 1985a; Gimlich, 1986), a phenomenon that implies that an induced tissue can itself acquire inducing properties. Animal cells become competent to respond to mesodermal induction by about stage 6.5 (about 48 cells) and lose competence at about stage 10.5 (the early gastrula stage) (Gurdon *et al.*, 1985a; Jones and Woodland, 1987). The minimum contact time required for muscle induction is 1.5–2.5 hours (Gurdon *et al.*, 1985a). A third approach to the timing of determination events has been transplantation of individual marked cells to ectopic sites. Such cells develop according to their new position rather than their original lineage through the blastula period, eventually losing their regulative abilities in the late blastula to early gastrula stage (Heasman *et al.*, 1984, 1985; Snape *et al.*, 1987; M. Jacobson and P. Sheard, personal communication).

Taken together, these results suggest that mesoderm induction is unlikely to be completed in normal embryogenesis by the 64-cell stage. How, then, are the explant experiments of Nakamura *et al.* (1970) and Gurdon *et al.* (1985b) to be interpreted? A plausible explanation (Nieuwkoop, 1973)—mentioned, though not favored, by Gurdon *et al.* (1985b)—is that large blastomeres from the early marginal zone give rise to both inducing and inducible progeny, so that explants from early stages "induce themselves" toward mesoderm. The only apparent alternative interpretation would deny any requirement for cell interactions in muscle determination in the *Xenopus* embryo, a conclusion contradicted by much other data. Thus, it seems that there is no precise time point at which mesoderm induction takes place. The relevant interactions begin early, at the latest by the 32-cell stage, and are not irreversibly completed until the early gastrula stage (stage 10.5).

V. Mesoderm Induction Factors: Relationship to Growth Factors

A. Relationships between Earlier and Recent Work

The recent era in the study of induction dates from the discovery of the XTC-MIF (Smith, 1987) and the subsequent findings that mammalian fibroblast growth factor (FGF) (see Chapter 3 of this volume) and transforming growth factor-β (TGF-β) (see Chapter 4 of this volume) have mesoderm-inducing capacity (Slack *et al.*, 1987; Kimelman and Kirschner, 1987; Rosa *et al.*, 1988). Earlier work on induction factors was complicated by the problem of specificity of the response and the multiplicity of active materials, as discussed in Section II,A, although it could be shown that mesodermal and neural differentiations are induced by different substances (reviewed by Saxèn and Toivonen, 1986; Gurdon, 1987). Vegetalizing factor is probably the most extensively studied agent up to 1987. This factor has been obtained from chick embryos and it induces mesodermal differentiation, but has been called vegetalizing factor, since high concentrations induce apparent endodermal differentiation (Born *et al.*, 1985; Tiedemann, 1987). In retrospect, it appears that its heterologous derivation, a point that disturbed some observers, is not, in fact, a problem: FGF and TGF-β are likewise heterologous, and the significance of their effects has been accepted readily. More likely, a difficulty seems to have arisen from the fact that the molecular identity of the factor was not fully established. The molecular size of vegetalizing factor, its acid stability (Born *et al.*, 1985), and other properties (Grunz *et al.*, 1989) nevertheless invite the speculation that this factor, like XTC-MIF (see Section V,B), may be a member of the TGF-β family of factors.

B. Nature of MIFs

XTC-MIF is secreted by the XTC cell line, which was derived from a metamorphosing tadpole (Pudney *et al.*, 1973), and it is obscure why it should secrete such a factor. The factor is heat and acid stable (Smith, 1987; Smith *et al.*, 1988; Rosa *et al.*, 1988). Purified MIF has a molecular size of 27 kDa, is composed of two subunits, and is active in the nanogram-per-milliliter range (Smith *et al.*, 1988). Crude or purified XTC-MIF induces different mesodermal derivatives in blastula animal caps (fated as ectoderm) in a concentration-dependent manner, as described further in Section IV,A.

Both basic and acidic forms of FGF (bFGF and aFGF, respectively) induce animal cap explants toward mesoderm, yielding especially ventral derivatives such as mesenchyme, but also muscle (Slack *et al.*, 1987). As measured by the accumulation of α-actin mRNA, FGF is substantially less effective than XTC-MIF (Kimelman and Kirschner, 1987; Rosa *et al.*, 1988). Recently, Paterno *et al.* (1989) found that the *in vitro* synthesized product of the *kfgf* oncogene, kFGF, is a potent mesoderm inducer; the *kfgf* gene was isolated from Kaposi's sarcoma (Delli-Bovi *et al.*, 1988). Further, the product of the *int-2* oncogene, more distantly related to FGF (Dickson and Peters, 1987), exhibits lower, but easily measurable, inducing activity. Recombinant bFGF was, in fact, more potent than bFGF isolated from mammalian brain, being able to induce notochord, which "natural" bFGF does not do. The reason for this difference is not clear (Paterno *et al.,* 1989).

These interesting results show that the FGF family of factors is capable of acting in the system. The sequence of *Xenopus* FGF is highly homologous to mammalian FGF (Kimelman and Kirschner, 1987; Kimelman *et al.,* 1988). FGF mRNA and bFGF itself have been isolated from *Xenopus* eggs and embryos, and the FGF concentration in the embryo is such that it could exert an inductive effect (Kimelman and Kirschner, 1987; Kimelman *et al.,* 1988; Slack and Isaacs, 1989).

TGF-β1 has been found to act synergistically with FGF in inducing α-actin accumulation in animal caps (Kimelman and Kirschner, 1987). Rosa *et al.* (1988) found that TGF-β2 alone, as opposed to TGF-β1, can induce α-actin mRNA accumulation and morphological changes (e.g., elongation) in animal caps. Further, the inducing ability of XTC-MIF could be inhibited by an anti-TGF-β2 antibody (Rosa *et al.,* 1988). This result, and the physical properties of purified XTC-MIF (Smith *et al.,* 1988), suggest that this factor is a member of the TGF-β family (for reviews of FGF and TGF-β see Chapter 3 and 4 of this volume; see also Roberts and Sporn, 1989, for a review of TGF-β).

While more than one soluble factor may be involved in mesoderm induction, and additional interactions not mediated by diffusible molecules may occur (see Section IX,C), it is clear that a diffusible factor or combination of factors triggers mesodermalization. Which, if any, of the factors discussed above is the "natural mesoderm inducer"? XTC-MIF has the advantage of being a homologous, highly potent material that can elicit the differentiation of all tissue types in mesoderm. To date, however, its presence in the embryo has not been established. The gene *Vg1,* distantly related to the TGF-β family and thus presumably to XTC-MIF, is expressed in the oocyte specifically in the vegetal region which, in the embryo, is the source of the mesodermalizing signal (Melton, 1987; Weeks and Melton, 1987). Thus, *Vg1* is implicated in the mesoderm induction system, but the activity of its putative product has yet to be established. Thus, the XTC-MIF/TGF-β/*Vg1* family is strongly implicated, but not proven, to be involved in induction in the embryo. FGF, on the other hand, has been shown to be present in the early embryo at a concentration at which it is active (Kimelman *et al.,* 1988; Slack and Isaacs, 1989). However, FGF has not been localized to the vegetal region, and under experimental conditions it induces only part of the range of mesodermal derivatives that develop in the embryo. FGF almost certainly has a role in mesoderm induction, but it may not be the sole mediator of this process. Clearly, then, the issue is unresolved at present.

VI. Uses of XTC-MIF and FGF in Studying Mechanisms of Induction

A. Concentration-Dependent Differentiations

XTC-MIF has been used in important experiments on cellular responses to induction, even though it is not clear that this factor is a natural inducer. One important result is the observation that XTC-MIF induces different tissues in animal cap explants in a concentration-dependent manner, with ventral mesoderm elicited by low, and dorsal mesoderm by high, factor levels; the highest levels also generate neural differentiations, possibly as a secondary event (Smith *et al.*, 1988). A similar result was obtained earlier with vegetalizing factor, except that it induced apparent endodermal differentiation when present at high concentrations (Grunz, 1983). FGF also produced a concentration-dependent effect, albeit inducing a smaller range of tissue types (Slack and Isaacs, 1989). These results, especially the wide range of tissues elicited by purified XTC-MIF, are important in the longstanding debate over whether induction is instructive or permissive. If the question is translated to mean which partner—inducer or responding cell—provides more information for execution of a differentiation program, the answer is always that the cell is the much more complex partner. But the results summarized above make it clear that the inducer need not be a simple trigger that sets off a predetermined pathway: Different XTC-MIF concentrations send the same responding tissue in quite different directions. In reaching this conclusion, it must be considered, however, whether early animal embryos represent a homogeneous population or a mixture of cells of distinct potentialities. In the latter case the inducer could act by specifically selecting a subset of cells from this population that harbors the corresponding cell surface receptor. Evidence against induction through selection involving growth control comes from the following facts: (1) FGF does not change the overall rate of incorporation of [^{3}H]thymidine into the DNA of animal cap cells (Slack *et al.*, 1987), and XTC-MIF does not change the overall mitotic index of animal cap cells (Symes and Smith, 1987); and (2) cell division is not required for α-actin induction to take place in animal/vegetal recombinates (Gurdon and Fairman, 1986).

The concentration-dependent response to XTC-MIF suggests a simple model for generating the dorsoventral axis of the embryo: A strong source of inducer in the vegetal/dorsal region could, at first approximation, explain mesodermalization and dorsalization. It is clear, though, that current knowledge does not allow us to make any definite conclusions regarding the number of inducing factors and the spatial distribution of their activity in the embryo.

B. Effects of XTC-MIF *in Situ*

A set of interesting experiments tested the response of ectoderm *in situ* to the injection of XTC-MIF into the blastocoel (Cooke *et al.*, 1987; Cooke and Smith, 1989). Such irrigation transforms the entire inner layer of the ectoderm (blastocoel roof) into mesoderm. The result of this treatment is that the course of gastrulation is inhibited, apparently because the normal marginal zone mesoderm cannot migrate along the blastocoel roof, and because normal recruitment of inner ectodermal cells into the marginal zone is preempted. The clearest sign that the animal region of such XTC-MIF-injected embryos is mesodermalized is the finding that this tissue can act as a Spemann organizer; that is, it induces a secondary dorsal axis, including the central nervous system, when implanted into the ventral subequatorial region of an early gastrula stage host (Cooke *et al.*, 1987).

C. Early Molecular Responses to Induction

A very different approach that utilized the dramatic effect of XTC-MIF on animal cap explants was directed toward understanding early molecular responses to induction. RNA prepared from control animal caps and from caps treated with XTC-MIF during equivalent stages 7.5–9 was used in a differential screen of the DG cDNA library (Sargent and Dawid, 1983). Several rapidly induced genes were isolated (Rosa, 1989). These genes appear to represent the immediate transcriptional response to induction in that they are activated several hours before genes encoding terminal differentiation products, such as α-actin. One of the early induced genes, *Mix,* is of particular interest because it encodes a homeodomain-containing protein. The *Mix* mRNA is expressed transiently in the normal embryo, being detectable only between the late blastula (stage 9) and late gastrula (stage 13) stages, with a peak at stage 10. *Mix* is normally expressed mostly in the vegetal (endodermal) region. This raises questions about the reason that it should be activated by mesoderm induction, and reminds us of the apparent analogy between XTC-MIF and vegetalizing factor (see Section V,A). Because of the extensive evidence implicating homeodomain proteins as regulators of regional specification in development and as transcriptional control factors (Scott *et al.*, 1989; Herr *et al.*, 1988), the time course of expression and localization and inducibility of *Mix* mRNA implicate the *Mix* protein product as a regulatory molecule in gastrulation.

VII. Dorsalization versus Mesodermalization

We have described in Section IV,B,2 the establishment of the dorsoventral axis in the embryo as a result of a cortical/cytoplasmic rotation during first cleavage (Gerhart *et al.*, 1987). This rotation leads to an inducing center in dorsal/vegetal blastomeres that appears to translocate to the dorsal marginal zone as development proceeds (Gimlich and Gerhart, 1984; Gimlich, 1986). Experiments performed during later blastula development show further that the inducing vegetal tissue imposes its dorsal or ventral character on the responding animal cap (Boterenbrood and Nieuwkoop, 1973). Further, dorsal marginal zone can dorsalize the ventral marginal zone in recombinates; however, the reverse does not happen (Dale and Slack, 1987). Thus, it appears that a dorsalizing influence, in addition to a general or ventral mesodermalizing influence, can be postulated (Slack, 1983; Slack, *et al.*, 1987). It is possible that growth factors of the TGF-β class could provide a dorsal influence, while factors of the FGF family would provide a ventral mesodermalizing effect. On the other hand, the concentration-dependent effect of XTC-MIF (Section VI,A) shows that it is possible for a single effector molecule to generate dorsoventral polarity in addition to mesodermalization (Cooke *et al.*, 1987). Whether this happens *in vivo* remains to be tested.

Dorsalization can be achieved by an unphysiological, but perhaps informative, agent: Li^+ ions. Li^+ dorsalizes normal embryos and rescues embryos that have been ventralized by preventing their cytoplasmic/cortical rotation (Kao *et al.*, 1986). While Li^+ alone does not induce animal caps, it enhances the interaction between animal and vegetal cells and the effects of XTC-MIF and FGF (Cooke *et al.*, 1989; Kao and Elinson, 1989). A possible mechanism for the action of this ion has been explored on the basis of its known inhibition of the inositol phospholipid cycle: Injection of *myo*-inositol together with LiCl prevented the dorsalizing effect of the latter (Busa and Gimlich, 1989). The results imply that the establishment of the dorsoventral axis in normal embryogenesis involves the inositol signaling pathway.

VIII. Neural Induction: Few Insights into Mechanism

A. Differential Gene Expression in Neural Induction

The analysis of neural induction is less advanced than that of mesoderm induction, in spite of the availability of several useful marker genes and antibodies, as described in section III,B. Evidence has been obtained that dorsal ectoderm has a "neural bias" even before it is contacted by mesoderm (Sharpe *et al.*, 1987; London *et al.*, 1988), but induction of the ectoderm is nevertheless required for morphological differentiation and for the expression of most markers tested. Sharpe *et al.* (1987) have also shown that there is an anterior/posterior predisposition in the ectoderm before the neural plate is actually differentiated.

Differential gene expression during establishment of the neural plate has been observed with the use of cDNA clones corresponding to genes specific for the cement gland (Jamrich and Sato, 1989). The cement gland, also called the sucker or adhesive organ, is a nonneural organ derived from the anterior section of the neural plate (Picard, 1975a,b). *In situ* hybridization demonstrated that a cement gland-specific gene is expressed exclusively in the anterior segment of the developing neural plate by stage 12 (Jamrich and Sato, 1989). The cement gland is known to be an induced organ (Picard, 1975a,b); therefore, these observations show that differential gene expression is established within the developing neural plate as early as the midgastrula stage.

Savage and Phillips (1989) have shown that the dorsal lip, rather than the advancing chordamesoderm, is an effective neural inducer, at least as measured by the turning-off of the epidermis-specific marker Epi 1. If this result is confirmed for other markers of neural induction, it would suggest that the inducing signal must travel through the sheet of ectoderm that undergoes transformation into the neural plate, since the dorsal lip remains at a subequatorial/posterior position, while neural plate formation proceeds anteriorly. This proposed effect is reminiscent of, although not identical to, homoiogenetic induction, in which induced ectoderm itself takes on the properties of inducing tissue, extending outward the boundaries of the presumptive neural plate (Mangold and Spemann, 1927).

B. Factors Mediating Neural Induction

Some aspects of neural induction, at least, can be mediated by diffusible factors, as demonstrated in transfilter experiments (Saxèn, 1961; Toivonen *et al.*, 1975), yet chordamesoderm and ectoderm come into very close contact during normal gastrulation (Tacke and Grunz, 1988). Perhaps the clearest evidence for diffusible neural inducers comes from the work by Niu and Twitty (1953), who showed that dorsal mesoderm explants could condition the culture medium such that subsequently added ectoderm will be induced toward neural differentiation. Thus, current knowledge provides fairly good evidence for diffusible factors in neural induction, but membrane apposition is also implicated in the process. The nature of the neural tissue produced depends on the particular inducer, for example, anterior mesoderm (or archenteron roof) induced archencephalic structures, while posterior mesoderm induced spinocaudal structures (Mangold, 1933). Thus, there may exist several distinct neural inducing substances, but we must remember that purified mesoderm inducers can produce different tissues according to their concentration (see Section

VI,A), and therefore even the number of neural inducing factors is uncertain at present.

Preparations from homologous and heterologous tissues have neural inducing capacity (Toivonen, 1950; Janeczek *et al.*, 1984; reviewed by Gurdon, 1987), but none of these materials has been characterized sufficiently to allow conclusions about their identity. Further, newt ectoderm appears to be so strongly biased toward neuralization that salt or HEPES buffer is capable of turning it in this direction (Barth, 1941; Holtfreter, 1944; Tiedemann, 1986). Two potentially interesting "inducers" are concanavalin A (Takata *et al.*, 1981; Grunz, 1985) and 12-*O*-tetradecanoyl-phorbol-13-acetate (Davids *et al.*, 1987), which have been reported to lead to neuralization, as assayed by histological examination after long-term culture. The involvement of protein kinase C in neural induction was also suggested by Otte *et al.* (1988). In preliminary experiments in our laboratory (P. J. Good, T. D. Sargent, and I. B. Dawid, unpublished observations), we observe that *Xenopus* gastrula ectoderm is not easily neuralized by nonspecific factors as judged by the accumulation of neurospecific β-tubulin mRNA. The apparent robustness of *Xenopus* ectoderm against nonspecific influences is expected to be most helpful in the search for authentic neural inducing factors.

IX. Outlook on Research in Embryonic Induction

The embryonic induction field is likely to proceed in several directions with a rapidly increasing rate of progress. Certain types of experiments are fairly predictable, although not necessarily easy to execute, while others still need definition of basic parameters. In this section we summarize the subjects likely to attract attention in the next few years.

A. Inducing Factors, Receptors, and Early Response Genes

The identity of the natural mesodermal inducer(s) is not yet determined, but a solution to this question appears imminent. In the case of neural induction, little is known, but improved assay systems promise to help efforts in this area. Once diffusible inducers are identified, an important next step is the study of receptors. In other systems receptors for FGF (Friesel *et al.*, 1986) and TGF-β (Frolik *et al.*, 1984; Cheifetz *et al.*, 1987; Ignotz and Massagué, 1987) have been identified. The FGF receptor has been cloned (Lee *et al.*, 1989). A complete understanding of the mechanism of signaling from ligand through receptor and, further, to the cellular response is not available in any system; thus, it will not come easily in the context of induction in the amphibian embryo, but the type of question to be asked is clear. A possible entry into the "middle" of the response pathway is the study of immediate early genes activated by induction factors, as described in Section VI,C. Likewise, studies in the embryo of known signaling pathways (e.g., the inositol pathway) (see Section VII), may prove useful. Altogether, we may expect much progress in this area in the near future.

B. Cellular Responses: Tissue Architecture, Migration, and Adhesiveness

Events of gastrulation involve changes in cell behavior that lead to form changes (e.g., convergent extension) (Keller *et al.,* 1985; Gerhart and Keller, 1986; Keller and Danilchik, 1988), the migration of mesodermal cells along the blastocoel roof on a network of fibronectin-containing extracellular matrix (ECM) (Boucaut *et al.,* 1984a,b; Darribère *et al.,* 1988; Nakatsuji, 1986; Nakatsuji *et al.,* 1985), and the establishment of differential adhesion, as witnessed by sorting (Townes and Holtfreter, 1955). Many of these normal events of gastrulation are induced in ectodermal cells by the application of XTC-MIF (Cooke and Smith, 1989). Thus, it appears that one of the consequences of induction must be a change in cell adhesion properties, presumably involving the elaboration of ECM components and surface receptors for ECM, for other cells, or both. In this context it is interesting to note that two prominent effects of TGF-β in mammalian systems are the stimulation of expression of collagen, fibronectin, and the fibronectin receptor (Ignotz and Massagué 1986, 1987; Rossi *et al.,* 1988) and of protease inhibitors, whose action would result in the increased accumulation of fibronectin and collagen (Laiho *et al.,* 1986; Lund *et al.,* 1987; Thalacker and Nilsen-Hamilton, 1987). The importance of fibronectin, collagen, and other proteins of the ECM in mammalian development and in the cellular response to TGF-β is discussed further in Chapters 4, 7, and 8 of this volume. The *Xenopus* fibronectin gene (Lee *et al.,* 1984) and certain fibronectin receptor genes (DeSimone and Hynes, 1988) have been cloned and studied. The analysis of cell surface properties and the molecules responsible for such properties under the influence of induction undoubtedly will be fruitful.

C. Integration of Molecular and Cellular Changes

The great challenge of embryology is to understand the formation of an ordered complex organism from the fertilized egg. In this process the molecular and cellular differentiation events are the building blocks of the system; their behavior must be understood in detail for a complete picture to emerge, but we must keep in mind the need to integrate the individual events into a whole. In the present context an important question is whether a small group of diffusible induction factors such as XTC-MIF can explain the formation of an organized gastrula with its dorsoventral axis and spatial arrangement of mesodermal tissues. We do not know the answer. On the one hand, the concentration-dependent response to XTC-MIF (Cooke *et al.*, 1987; see also Section VI,A) suggests that a gradient of such a factor could account for dorsoventral polarity. Models have been generated for reading a factor gradient in ways that generate discontinuities, allowing tissue boundaries to form (Meinhardt, 1982); these models also show considerable regulatory properties, corresponding in general to those of the amphibian embryo. It appears unlikely, however, that a system based solely on reading of a factor gradient could form organized tissues, unless cells at tissue boundaries could sense their local environment. Differences of adhesiveness leading to sorting and differential interactions with the ECM may account for the elaboration of distinct tissues. How such differences derive from a graded inducing signal must be understood in specific molecular/cellular terms.

Experiments relating to the issue of integration have already shown that cells may have to be in contact as groups to respond to induction by muscle formation. Symes *et al.* (1988) found that dispersed animal cap cells exposed to XTC-MIF turned off their epidermal keratin genes, but did not activate the α-actin gene; cells that were dispersed and reaggregated accumulate α-actin mRNA. Thus, one step in the ectoderm-to-mesoderm series could be carried out by individual cells ("ectoderm off"), but the next step ("muscle on") could not. The basis for these observations is not clear, but may indicate the need for cell–cell interactions during induction, beyond elaboration of a diffusible inducer such as XTC-MIF, a conclusion already suggested by Minuth and Grunz (1980). Gurdon (1988) also observed a requirement for cell groups, rather than single cells, in muscle induction and named this phenomenon the "community effect."

These results and considerations bring out the question as to what a growth factor-like inducer actually does in embryogenesis. A factor such as XTC-MIF does not, apparently, elicit differentiation of a naive ectodermal cell toward a specific fate as one or another mesodermal tissue. Does the factor's effect generate "generic mesoderm" from the ectodermal precursor, which then differentiates into muscle, pronephros, etc. through subsequent interactions? Is there, in fact, such a generic mesoderm? We do not know the answer, but might speculate that a cell that originated with ectodermal characteristics (as all cells derived from the animal hemisphere are thought to do) (Sudarwati and Nieuwkoop, 1971) becomes such generic mesoderm by the simple event of having its ectodermal properties suppressed. Further specification of tissue type would require additional interactions. This speculation agrees with the data by Symes *et al.* (1988) and also with the fate mapping by Jacobson and Xu (1989) and M. Jacobson (personal communication) which shows that the commitment of any cell in the embryo to a single tissue type is a late event, occurring only at gastrulation. Since we have good reason to believe that inductive actions of factors such as XTC-MIF *in situ* take place during cleavage and blastula stages, it is unlikely that such actions specify a final tissue type in any cell.

X. Conclusion

The vertebrate embryo undergoes normal development, to a large measure, through interactions between its different cells and tissues. Extensive studies in amphibians led to the conclusion that diffusible factors related to the class of growth factor molecules have a major role in mediating these interactions. Given the basic similarity of embryogenesis in all vertebrate classes, it appears likely that similar mechanisms of cell interactions are important in the development of other embryos, including those of mammals. Extension of the experience from amphibians to other systems is an important aim of future research.

Acknowledgments

We thank Jonathan Cooke, Richard Elinson, Bob Gimlich, Marcus Jacobson, Milan Jamrich, Marc Kirschner, Carey Phillips, Anita Roberts, Matt Scott, Jonathan Slack, Jim Smith, and Hans Tiedemann for making unpublished information available.

References

Akers, R. M., Phillips, C. R., and Wessells, N. K. (1986). *Science* **231,** 613–616.

Ancel, P., and Vintemberger, P. (1948). *Bull. Biol. Fr. Belg.* **31,** 1–182.

Balinsky, B. I. (1975). "Introduction to Embryology," 4th Ed. Saunders, Philadelphia, Pennsylvania.

Barth, L. G. (1941). *J. Exp. Zool.* **87,** 311–383.

Bautzmann, H., Holtfreter, J., Spemann, H., and Mangold, O. (1932). *Naturwissenschaften* **20,** 971–974.

Born, J., Hoppe, P., Schwartz, W., Tiedemann, H., Tiedemann, H., and Wittmann-Liebold, B. (1985). *Biol. Chem. Hoppe-Seyler* **366,** 729–735.

Boterenbrood, E. C., and Nieuwkoop, P. D. (1973). *Wilhelm Roux' Arch. Entwicklungsmech. Org.* **173,** 319–332.

Boucaut, J. C., Darribere, T., Poole, T. J., Aoyama, H., Yamada, K. M., and Thiery, J. P. (1984a). *J. Cell Biol.* **9,** 1822–1830.

Boucaut, J. C., Darribere, T., Boulekbache, H., and Thiery, J. P. (1984b). *Nature (London)* **307,** 364–367.

Brachet, J. (1986). *In* "A History of Embryology" (T. J. Horder, J. A. Withowski, and C. C. Wylie, eds.), pp. 245–259. Cambridge Univ. Press, London.

Busa, W. B., and Gimlich, R. L. (1989). *Dev. Biol.* **132,** 315–324.

Cheifetz, S., Weatherbee, J. A., Tsang, M. L.-S., Anderson, J. K., Mole, J. E., Lucas, R., and Massague, J. (1987). *Cell (Cambridge, Mass.)* **48,** 409–415.

Cooke, J., and Smith, J. C. (1989). *Dev. Biol.* **131,** 383–400.

Cooke, J., Smith, J. C., Smith, E. J., and Yaqoob, M. (1987). *Development* **101,** 893–908.

Cooke, J., Symes, K., and Smith, E. J. (1989). *Development* **105,** 549–558.

Dale, L., and Slack, J. M. W. (1987). *Development* **100,** 279–295.

Darribére, T., Yamada, K. M., Johnson, K. E., and Boucaut, J. C. (1988). *Dev. Biol.* **126,** 182–194.

Davids, M., Loppnow, B., Tiedemann, H., and Tiedemann, H. (1987). *Wilhelm Roux's Arch. Dev. Biol.* **196,** 137–140.

Davidson, E. H. (1986). "Gene Activity in Early Development," 3rd Ed. Academic Press, Orlando, Florida.

Dawid, I. B., Kay, B. K., and Sargent, T. D. (1983). "Gene Structure and Regulation in Development," pp. 171–182. Liss, New York.

Dawid, I. B., Rebbert, M. L., Rosa, F., Jamrich, M., and Sargent, T. D. (1988). *In* "Regulatory Mechanisms in Developmental Processes" (G. Eguchi, T. S. Okada, and L. Saxen, eds.), pp. 67–74. Elsevier, Limerick, Ireland.

Delli-Bovi, P., Curalota, A. M., Newman, K. M., Sato, Y., Moscatelli, D., Hewick, R. M., Rifkin, D., and Basilico, C. (1988). *Mol. Cell. Biol.* **8,** 2933–2941.

DeSimone, D. W., and Hynes, R. O. (1988). *J. Biol. Chem.* **263,** 5333–5340.

Dickson, C., and Peters, G. (1987). *Nature (London)* **326,** 833.

Dworkin, M. B., Shrutkowski, A., Baumgarten, M., and Dworkin-Rastl, E. (1984). *Dev. Biol.* **106,** 289–295.

Dworkin-Rastl, E., Kelley, D. B., and Dworkin, M. B. (1986). *J. Embryol. Exp. Morphol.* **91,** 153–168.

Friesel, R., Burgess, W. H., Mehlman, T., and Maciag, T. (1986). *J. Biol. Chem.* **261,** 7581–7584.

Frolik, C. A., Wakefield, L. M., Smith, D. M., and Sporn, M. B. (1984). *J. Biol. Chem.* **259,** 10995–11000.

Gerhart, J., and Keller, R. (1986). *Annu. Rev. Cell Biol.* **2,** 201–229.

Gerhart, J, Black, S., Roberts, J, Rowning, B., Scharf, S., and Vincent, J.-P. (1987). "Molecular Approaches to Developmental Biology," pp. 89–95. Liss, New York.

Gilbert, S. F. (1988). "Developmental Biology," 2nd Ed. Sinauer, Sunderland, Massachusetts.

Gimlich, R. L. (1986). *Dev. Biol.* **115,** 340–352.

Gimlich, R. L., and Cooke, J. (1983). *Nature (London)* **306,** 471–473.

Gimlich, R. L., and Gerhart, J. C. (1984). *Dev. Biol.* **104,** 117–130.

Grunz, H. (1983). *Wilhelm Roux's Arch. Dev. Biol.* **192,** 130–137.

Grunz, H. (1985). *Cell Differ.* **16,** 83–92.

Grunz, H., Born, J., Davids, M., Hoppe, P., Loppnow-Blinde, B., Tacke, L., Tiedemann, H., and Tiedemann, H. (1989). *Arch. Dev. Biol.* **198,** 8–13.

Gurdon, J. B. (1987). *Development* **99,** 285–306.

Gurdon, J. B. (1988). *Nature (London)* **336,** 772–774.

Gurdon, J. B., and Fairman, S. (1986). *J. Embryol. Exp. Morphol., Suppl.* **97,** 75–84.

Gurdon, J. B., Fairman, S., Mohun, T. J., and Brennan, S. (1985a). *Cell (Cambridge, Mass.)* **41,** 913–922.

Gurdon, J. B., Mohun, T. J, Fairman, S., and Brennan, S. (1985b). *Proc. Natl. Acad. Sci. U.S.A.* **82,** 139–143.

Heasman, J., Wylie, C. C., Hausen, P., and Smith, J. C. (1984). *Cell (Cambridge, Mass.)* **37,** 185–194.

Heasman, J., Snape, A., Smith, J., and Wyie, C. C. (1985). *J. Embryol. Exp. Morphol., Suppl.* **89,** 297–316.

Herr, W., Sturm, R. A., Clerc, R. G., Corcoran, L. M., Baltimore, D., Sharp, P. A., Ingraham, H. A., Rosenfeld, M. G., Finney, M., Ruvkun, G., and Horvitz, H. R. (1988). *Genes Dev.* **2,** 1513–1516.

Holtfreter, J. (1934). *Wilhelm Roux' Arch. Entwicklungsmech. Org.* **132,** 225–306.

Holtfreter, J. (1944). *J. Exp. Zool.* **95,** 307–343.

Holtfreter, J. (1947). *J. Exp. Zool.* **106,** 197–222.

Ignotz, R. A., and Massagué, J. (1986). *J. Biol. Chem.* **261,** 4337–4345.

Ignotz, R. A., and Massagué, J. (1987). *Cell (Cambridge, Mass.)* **51,** 189–197.

Jacobson, M. (1984). *Dev. Biol.* **102,** 122–129.

Jacobson, M., and Rutishauser, U. (1986). *Dev. Biol.* **116,** 524–531.

Jacobson, M., and Xu, W. (1989). *Dev. Biol.* **131,** 119–125.

Jamrich, M., and Sato, S. M. (1989). *Development* **105,** 779–786.

Jamrich, M., Sargent, T. D., and Dawid, I. B. (1987). *Genes Dev.* **1,** 124–132.

Janeczek, J., John, M., Born, J., Tiedemann, H., and Tiedemann, H. (1984). *Wilhelm Roux's Arch. Dev. Biol.* **193,** 1–12.

Jonas, E., Sargent, T. D., and Dawid, I. B. (1985). *Proc. Natl. Acad. Sci. U.S.A.* **82,** 5413–5417.

Jonas, E. A., Snape, A. M., and Sargent, T. D. (1989). *Development* **106,** 399–405.

Jones, E. A., and Woodland, H. R. (1987). *Development* **101,** 557–563.

Kao, K. R., and Elinson, R. P. (1989). *Dev. Biol.* **132,** 81–90.

Kao, K. R., Masui, Y., and Elinson, R. P. (1986). *Nature (London)* **322,** 371–373.

Kay, B. K., Schwartz, L. M., Rutishauser, U. Qiu, T. H., and Peng, H. B (1988). *Development* **103,** 463–471.

Keller, R. E., and Danilchik, M. (1988). *Development* **103,** 193–209.

Keller, R. E., Danilchik, M., Gimlich, R., and Shih, J. (1985). *J. Embryol. Exp. Morphol., Suppl.* **89,** 185–209.

Kimelman, D., and Kirschner, M. (1987). *Cell (Cambridge, Mass.)* **51,** 869–877.

Kimelman, D., Abraham, J. A., Haaparanta, T., Palisi, T. M., and Kirschner, M. W. (1988). *Science* **242,** 1053–1056.

Kintner, C. R., and Brockes, J. P. (1984). *Nature (London)* **308,** 67–69.

Kintner, C. R., and Melton, D. A. (1987). *Development* **99,** 311–325.

LaFlamme, S. E., Jamrich, M., Richter, K., Sargent, T. D., and Dawid, I. B. (1988). *Genes Dev.* **2,** 853–862.

Laiho, M., Sakela, O., and Keski-Oja, J. (1986). *Exp. Cell Res.* **164,** 399–407.

Lee, G., Hynes, R., and Kirschner, M. (1984). *Cell (Cambridge, Mass.)* **36,** 729–740.

Lee, P. L., Johnson, D. E., Cousens, L. S., Fried, V. A., and Williams, L. T. (1989). *Science* **245,** 57–60.

London, C., Ackers, R., and Phillips, C. R. (1988). *Dev. Biol.* **129,** 380–389.

Lund, L. R., Riccio, A., Andreasen, P. A., Nielsen, I. S., Kristensen, P., Laiho, M., Saksela, O., Blasi, F., and Dano, R. (1987). *EMBO J.* **6,** 1281–1286.

Mangold, O. (1933). *Naturwissenschaften* **21,** 761–766.

Mangold, O., and Spemann, H. (1927). *Wilhelm Roux' Arch. Entwicklungsmech. Org.* **111,** 341–422.

Meinhardt, H. (1982). "Models of Biological Pattern Formation." Academic Press, New York.

Melton, D. A. (1987). *Nature (London)* **328,** 80–82.
Minuth, M., and Grunz, H. (1980). *Cell Differ.* **9,** 229–238.
Miyatani, S., Winkles, J. A., Sargent, T. D., and Dawid, I. B. (1986). *J. Cell Biol.* **103,** 1957–1965.
Mohun, T. J., Brennan, S., Dathan, N., Fairman, S., and Gurdon, J. B. (1984). *Nature (London)* **311,** 716,–721.
Mohun, T. J., Garrett, N., and Gurdon, J. B. (1986). *EMBO J.* **5,** 3185–3193.
Nakamura, O., Takasaki, H., and Mizohata, T. (1970). *Proc. Jpn. Acad.* **46,** 694–699.
Nakatsuji, N. (1986). *J. Cell Sci.* **86,** 109–118.
Nakatsuji, N., Smolira, M. A., and Wylie, C. C. (1985). *Dev. Biol.* **107,** 264–268.
Nieuwkoop, P. D. (1969). *Wilhelm Roux' Arch. Entwicklungsmech. Org.* **162,** 341–373.
Nieuwkoop, P. D. (1973). *Adv. Morphog.* **10,** 1–39.
Nieuwkoop, P. D., and Faber, J. (1975). "Normal Table of *Xenopus laevis* (Daudin)," 2nd Ed. North-Holland Publ., Amsterdam.
Niu, M. C., and Twitty, V. C. (1953). *Proc. Natl. Acad. Sci. U.S.A.* **39,** 985–989.
Otte, A. P., Koster, C. H., Snoek, G. T., and Durston, A. J. (1988). *Nature (London)* **334,** 618–620.
Paterno, G. D., Gillespie, L. L., Slack, J. M. W., and Heath, J. K. (1989). *Development* **106,** 79–83.
Picard, J. J. (1975a). *J. Embryol. Exp. Morphol.* **33,** 957–967.
Picard, J. J. (1975b). *J. Embryol. Exp. Morphol.* **33,** 969–978.
Pudney, M., Varma, M. G. R., and Leake, C. J. (1973). *Experientia* **29,** 466–467.
Richter, K., Grunz, H., and Dawid, I. B. (1988). *Proc. Natl. Acad. Sci. U.S.A.* **85,** 8086–8090.
Roberts, A., and Sporn, M. (1989). *In* "Handbook of Experimental Pharmacology" Springer-Verlag, Berlin. In press.
Rosa, F. (1989). *Cell (Cambridge, Mass.)* **57,** 965–974.
Rosa, F., Roberts, A. B., Danielpour, D., Dart, L. L., Sporn, M. B., and Dawid, I. B. (1988). *Science* **39,** 783–785.
Rossi, P., Karsenty, G., Roberts, A. B., Roche, N. S., Sporn, M. B., and de Grombrugghe, B. (1988). *Cell (Cambridge, Mass.)* **52,** 405–414.
Sargent, T. D., and Dawid, I. B. (1983). *Science* **222,** 135–139.
Sargent, T. D., Jamrich, M., and Dawid, I. B. (1986). *Dev. Biol.* **114,** 238–246.
Sato, S. M., and Sargent, T. D. (1989). *Dev. Biol.* **134,** 263–266.
Savage, R., and Phillips, C. R. (1989). *Dev. Biol.* **133,** 157–168.
Saxén, L. (1961). *Dev. Biol.* **3,** 140–152.
Saxén, L., and Toivonen, L. (1986). *In* "A History of Embryology" (T. J. Horder, J. A. Witkowski, and C. C. Wylie, eds.), pp. 261–274. Cambridge Univ. Press, London.
Scharf, S. R., and Gerhart, J. C. (1980). *Dev. Biol.* **79,** 181–198.
Scharf, S. R., and Gerhart, J. C. (1983). *Dev. Biol.* **99,** 75–87.
Scott, M. P., Tamkun, J. W., and Hartzell, G. W., III (1989). *BBA Rev. Cancer* **989,** 25–48.
Sharpe, C. R. (1988). *Development* **103,** 269–277.
Sharpe, C. R., Fritz, A., De Robertis, E. M., and Gurdon, J. B. (1987). *Cell (Cambridge, Mass.)* **50,** 749–758.
Slack, J. M. W. (1983). "From Egg to Embryo." Cambridge Univ. Press, London.
Slack, J. M. W., and Issacs, H. V. (1989). *Development* **105,** 147–153.
Slack, J. M. W., Darlington, B. G., Heath, J. K., and Godsave, S. F. (1987). *Nature (London)* **326,** 197–200.
Smith, J. C. (1987). *Development* **99,** 3–14.
Smith, J. C., and Slack, J. M. W. (1983). *J. Embryol. Exp. Morphol.* **78,** 299–317.

Smith, J. C., and Watt, F. M. (1985). *Differentiation (Berlin)* **29,** 109–115.
Smith, J. C., Yaqoob, M., and Symes, K. (1988). *Development* **103,** 591–600.
Snape, A., Wylie, C. C., Smith, J. C., and Heasman, J. (1987). *Dev. Biol.* **119,** 503–510.
Spemann, H., and Mangold, H. (1924). *Wilhelm Roux' Arch. Entwicklungsmech. Org.* **100,** 599–638.
Sporn, M. B., and Roberts, A. B. (1988). *Nature (London)* **332,** 217–219.
Sudarwati, S., and Nieuwkoop, P. D. (1971). *Wilhelm Roux' Arch. Entwicklungsmech. Org.* **166,** 189–204.
Suzuki, A. S., Yoshimura, Y., and Yano, Y. (1986). *Wilhelm Roux's Arch. Dev. Biol.* **195,** 168–172.
Symes, K., and Smith, J. C. (1987). *Development* **101,** 339–349.
Symes, K., Yaqoob, M., and Smith, J.C. (1988). *Development* **104,** 609–618.
Tacke, L., and Grunz, H. (1988). *Cell Differ.* **24,** 33–44.
Takata, K., Tamamoto, K. Y., and Ozawa, R. (1981). *Wilhelm Roux's Arch. Dev. Biol.* **190,** 92–96.
Thalacker, F. W., and Nilsen-Hamilton, M. (1987). *J. Biol. Chem.* **262,** 2283–2290.
Tiedemann, H. (1986). *Wilhelm Roux's Arch. Dev. Biol.* **195,** 399–402.
Tiedemann, H. (1987). *In* "From Embryos to Cells" (G. Serrero, J. Hayashi, and G. H. Sato, eds.), pp. 25–34. Liss, New York.
Toivonen, S. (1950). *Rev. Suisse Zool.* **57,** Suppl., 41–56.
Toivonen, S., Tarin, D., Saxen L., Tarin, P. J., and Wartiovaara, J. (1975). *Differentiation (Berlin)* **4,** 1–7.
Townes, P. L., and Holtfreter, J. (1955). *J. Exp. Zool.* **128,** 58–120.
Vincent, J. P., and Gerhart, J. C. (1987). *Dev. Biol.* **123,** 526–539.
Vincent, J. P., Oster, G. F., and Gerhart, J. C. (1986). *Dev. Biol.* **113,** 484–500.
Waddington, C. H., Needham. J., and Brachet, J. (1936). *Proc. R. Soc. London, Ser. B* **120,** 173–198.
Weeks, D. L., and Melton, D. A. (1987). *Cell (Cambridge, Mass.)* **51,** 861–867.
Wilson, C., Cross, G. S., and Woodland, H. R. (1986). *Cell (Cambridge, Mass.)* **47,** 589–599.
Wilson, E. B. (1925). "The Cell in Development and Heredity," 3rd Ed. Macmillan, New York.
Winkles, J. A., Sargent, T. D., Parry, D. A. D., Jonas, E., and Dawid, I. B. (1985). *Mol. Cell. Biol.* **5,** 2575–2581.
Witkowski, J. (1985). *Trends Biochem. Sci.* **10,** 379–381.

10

Homologs of Vertebrate Growth Factors in *Drosophila melanogaster* and Other Invertebrates

Marc A. T. Muskavitch
Programs in Genetics and Molecular, Cellular and Developmental Biology
Department of Biology
Indiana University
Bloomington, Indiana 47405

F. Michael Hoffmann
Department of Oncology
McArdle Laboratories
University of Wisconsin
Madison, Wisconsin 53706

I. Introduction

During the past decade, genetic and molecular analyses of genes that affect developmental processes in invertebrates have greatly expanded our understanding of the molecules that participate in the regulation of

Current Topics in Developmental Biology, Vol. 24

development. Studies of a number of invertebrate developmental regulatory genes have led to a striking discovery. Certain of these loci in flies, nematodes, and sea urchins encode proteins homologous to factors known or believed to regulate cell growth and development in vertebrates. These include epidermal growth factor (EGF), transforming growth factor-β (TGF-β), and the *int-1* gene product (Table I). This finding may not seem unexpected, in retrospect. One might expect that the successful molecular strategies used by the common ancestors of modern metazoans to control the specification of distinct cell lineages and to regulate the growth of cells would be maintained and elaborated on among the divergent descendants of those ancestral forms. Nonetheless, the identification of growth factor homologies in the products of genes that regulate invertebrate development directly influences our perspective as we attempt to achieve complete understanding of the mechanisms by which these gene products affect developmental processes. The fact that we undertake these studies in invertebrates also raises the initially cheering prospect that exploitation of the attendant advantages of experimentation with invertebrates may hasten the day on which we actually achieve this understanding. This chapter briefly summarizes our current understanding of a number of loci in the fruit fly *Drosophila melanogaster*, the nematode *Caenorhabditis elegans*, and the sea urchin *Strongylocentrotus purpuratus*, each of which encodes a product homologus to one of a number of vertebrate growth factors.

One of the most powerful attractions of invertebrate organisms as systems for the investigation of gene function is their genetic malleability. Indeed, each of the identified loci in *Drosophila* and *Caenorhabditis* that we discuss was initially defined on the basis of mutations that yielded

Table I Invertebrate Genes That Encode Proteins Homologous to Vertebrate Growth Factors

Genetic locus	Organism	Reference
EGF		
Notch	*Drosophila melanogaster*	Wharton *et al.* (1985), Kidd *et al.* (1986)
Delta	*D. melanogaster*	Vässin *et al.* (1987), Kopczynski *et al.* (1988)
slit	*D. melanogaster*	Rothberg *et al.* (1988)
lin-12	*Caenorhabditis elegans*	Yochem *et al.* (1988)
glp-1	*C. elegans*	Yochem and Greenwald (1989)
uEGF-1	*Strongylocentrotus purpuratus*	Delgadillo-Reynoso *et al.* (1989)
TGF-β		
decapentaplegic	*D. melanogaster*	Padgett *et al.* (1987)
int-1		
wingless	*D. melanogaster*	Rijsewijk *et al.* (1987)

distinct disruptions of development and was thereafter found to encode a growth factor homolog. Techniques available to geneticists working on *Drosophila* and *Caenorhabditis* make feasible the isolation and identification of complete loss-of-function (null) mutations in genes of interest, the study of genetic complexities of single genes, and analysis of phenotypic interactions among mutations that discretely affect defined loci of interest. The fact that flies and nematodes have relatively simple body plans that consist of relatively small numbers of cells, yet pass through multiple developmental stages and contain a significant diversity of terminal cell types, permits the assessment of the developmental and functional impacts of specific mutations with fine resolution. The tremendous energies that geneticists and, more recently, molecular biologists have applied to the study of these organisms have led to the development of extensive genetic catalogs for each organism and an expanding knowledge of genome organization, gene structure, and gene expression in flies and nematodes. The relatively recent development of techniques for the germ-like transformation of *Drosophila* and *Caenorhabditis* has set the stage for a thorough approach to the analysis *in vivo* of structure–function relationships for almost any gene of interest in these organisms, including those related to known growth factors.

The use of somatic mosaic, or clonal, analysis in *Drosophila* and *Caenorhabditis* permits researchers to indirectly assess whether the product encoded by a given locus can influence only those cells in which it is produced (i.e., act autonomously) or affect cells in addition to those in which it is produced (i.e., act nonautonomously). This approach involves the creation of genetically marked patches of cells, or clones, that are deficient for the function of a gene of interest. Mutant cell clones are generated by cell growth following: (1) the induction of mitotic recombination, by irradiation, within a developing cell heterozygous for a mutation that affects the gene of interest; or (2) the loss, by nondisjunction, of a mitotically unstable ring-X chromosome or a free duplication that carries a wild-type copy of the gene of interest in a cell that otherwise carries only mutated alleles of this gene. Since most vertebrate growth factors are synthesized as a precursor polypeptide proteolytically processed to yield a product that is released into the extracellular compartment and acts in a paracrine fashion, one would predict that most growth factors would exhibit nonautonomous behavior, as assessed by clonal analysis. Indeed, the application of somatic mosaic analysis to a number of invertebrate loci that encode growth factor homologs has already begun to yield insights into the mechanisms by which gene products homologous to vertebrate growth factors act to regulate developmental processes in invertebrates. These analyses imply that, while some of these loci may encode products that act nonautonomously, other such loci do not seem to do so. The latter set of findings suggests that certain growth factor-like sequence motifs may have been adapted, over the course of evolution, to function in qualitatively distinct modes in vertebrates as compared to invertebrates.

II. Loci That Encode Proteins Homologous to EGF

A. *Notch* Locus

Mutations that affect the *Notch* (*N*) locus were first identified on the basis of the dominant phenotype observed in females heterozygous for a mutated copy of *N* and a wild-type copy (*N*/ +): nicking, or notching, of the wing margin (Dexter, 1914). The *N* locus is located on the X (first) chromosome and is associated with the larval salivary gland polytene chromosome band 3C7 (Lindsley and Grell, 1968). Prototypic *N* loss-of-function mutations have dual character: a dominant character evinced by the wing notching observed in heterozygotes (*N*/ +) and a lethal character reflected by the embryonic lethality associated with homozygosity (*N*/*N*) or hemizygosity (*N*/ *Y*) for the same mutations. Early studies of the developmental impact of deficiencies for the *N* locus revealed that males deficient for the *N* locus, and hence of the *N* null genotype, died as embryos and exhibited an enlarged nervous system and a reduced epidermis (Poulson, 1937). Poulson (1937) suggested that *N* be designated a neurogenic gene because of the dramatic effect of the loss of *N* function on development of the nervous system, and this designation persists to the present. The molecular characterization of the *N* gene (Wharton *et al.*, 1985; Kidd *et al.*, 1986) and subsequent characterization of the *N* product (Johansen *et al.*, 1989) have revealed that *N* encodes a membrane-spanning protein that includes an extracellular domain which contains sequences homologous to vertebrate EGF (Figs. 1 and 2).

1. Genetic Complexity of *Notch*

The *N* locus was initially defined as a neurogenic locus on the basis of the embryonic phenotype associated with loss-of-function mutations that affect the gene (Poulson, 1937), the most dramatic aspect of which is hypertrophy of the nervous system. More recent analysis of the cellular basis of this phenotype (Lehmann *et al.*, 1983) has revealed that it results from the incorrect partitioning of cells within the ectoderm of the developing embryo into neuroblast and dermoblast stem cell populations.

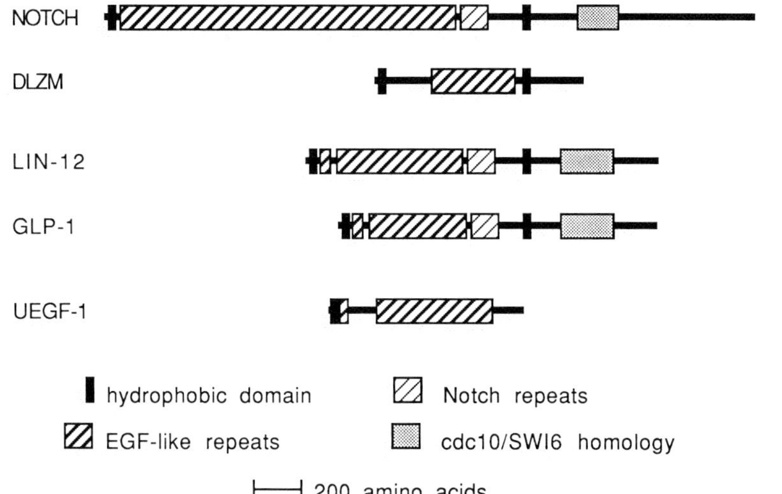

Fig. 1 Comparison of the one-dimensional structures inferred for the primary products of a number of invertebrate loci that encode EGF-related proteins. The schematic diagrams represent the deduced structures for products of *N* (Wharton *et al.*, 1985; Kidd *et al.*, 1986), *Dl* (Vässin *et al.*, 1987; Kopczynski *et al.*, 1988), *lin-12* (Yochem *et al.*, 1988), *glp-1* (Yochem and Greenwald, 1989), and *uEGF-1* (short form) (Delgadillo-Reynoso *et al.*, 1989). Explanations of symbolism and a length scale are given below.

Ectodermal cells within the so-called neurogenic region[1] of the embryo normally partition via a primarily amitotic segregation process such that 25% become neuroblasts and 75% become dermoblasts. When *N* function is eliminated by mutation, 100% of these cells become neuroblasts, resulting in the corresponding enlargement of the nervous system at the expense of the epidermis. Consideration of cell ablation experiments in the grasshopper (Doe and Goodman, 1985) and cell transplantation experiments in *Drosophila* (Technau and Campos-Ortega, 1986), as well as the structure of the deduced embryonic protein product of the locus (Wharton *et al.*,

[1] The neurogenic region of the developing *Drosophila* embryo is defined as that portion of the ectoderm from which the neuroblasts that serve as precurors to the cephalic, subesophageal, and ventral components of the central nervous system of the fully developed embryo arise. Approximately one quarter of the approximately 1800 cells within the cephalic and ventral neurogenic regions delaminate from the exterior of the developing embryo 3–6 hours after egg laying, migrate to the interior, and become neuroblasts. Neuroblasts give rise to ganglion mother cells by asymmetric division, and ganglion mother cells give rise to neurons by symmetric division as embryogenesis proceeds. The cells that remain on the exterior surface of the embryo become dermoblasts, which divide symmetrically to yield epidermal cells that secrete the larval cuticle (Campos-Ortega and Hartenstein, 1985).

```
NOTCH       DXDX CX S X PCXNGGTCXDXXX    XFXCXCXXGFXGXXCXX
            N N                 N         Y       Y

DLZM        XXDX CX X X PCXNGGTCXDXXX    XFXCXCXXGFXGXXCXX
             N                  N         Y       Y

SLIT        XIXX CX X X XCXN GACXXXXX    XYXCXCXPGYXGXXCEX

LIN-12      XXDX CX X X XCXNXGXCIDXXX    SFXCXCXXGFXGXXCEX
             N                  N         Y       Y

GLP-1       XXXX CX X X XCXNXGXCXDXXX    XFXCXCXXGFXGXFCEX
                                N         Y       Y   Y

UEGF-1      NIDE CA S X PCLNGGXCVDGX    NGYVCXCXPGFXGXNCEX
                                                  Y

FIX         DGDQ CE S N PCLNGGXCKD    DINSYECWCXXGFEGXNCEL

EGF         NSDXGCPXSYDGYCLNGGVCMYIESLDX  YXCNCVIGYIGERCQXRDLRWWELR


CONSENSUS   DXDX CX S X PCXNGGXCXDXXX    XFXCXCXXGFXGXXCEX
            N N                 N         Y       Y
```

Fig. 2 Alignments for EGF-like sequences found in selected invertebrate and vertebrate EGF homologs. Consensuses are presented for the EGF-like repeat arrays of NOTCH (36 repeats) (Wharton *et al.,* 1985; Kidd *et al.,* 1986), DLZM [nine repeats from the predominant embryonic product (DlZM)] (Kopczynski *et al.,* 1988), SLIT [seven repeats (incomplete sequence)] (Rothberg *et al.,* 1988), LIN-12 (13 repeats) (Yochem *et al.,* 1988), GLP-1 (ten repeats) (Yochem and Greenwald, 1989), UEGF-1 [nine repeats (incomplete sequence)] (Hursch *et al.* (1987)]; the first (amino-proximal) EGF-like repeats of bovine and human factor IX (FIX) (Katayama *et al.,* 1979; Choo *et al.,* 1982; Kurachi and Davies, 1982); and human, mouse, and rat EGF (Gregory and Preston, 1977; Gray *et al.,* 1983; Scott *et al.,* 1983; Simpson *et al.,* 1985). Amino acids included in each consensus include single residues, alternate residues (*D/N, F/Y*), or any amino acid (X) present in 50% or more of the repeat elements described in a given protein (NOTCH, DLZM, SLIT, LIN-12, GLP-1, or UEGF-1); residues present in two or three of the sequences (EGF) or residues present in both sequences (FIX).

1985; Kidd *et al.,* 1986), has led to the suggestion that *N* and other neurogenic loci of *Drosophila* are required for cellular interactions that are essential for establishment of the epidermal lineage within the embryonic ectoderm (reviewed by Artavanis-Tsakonas, 1988).

Extensive genetic scrutiny of the *N* locus during the past 70 years has also revealed the existence of a number of qualitatively distinct mutations that have been implicated in postembryonic development, yet are allelic to *N* (summarized by Welshons and von Halle, 1962; Welshons, 1971). One such group of alleles is comprised of the so-called recessive visible *N* mutations: *facet* (*fa*), *split* (*spl*), and *notchoid* (*nd*) alleles. These mutations are *recessive* to wild-type *N* alleles (i.e., *fa*/+ animals exhibit the wild-type phenotype) and are correlated with *visible* phenotypic defects in adult structures. Males that are hemizygous (i.e., *fa*/*Y*) and females that are homozygous (i.e., *fa*/*fa*) for mutations within this group are fully viable and fertile. The *fa* alleles are comprised of a set of recessive mutations that affect development of the compound eye.[2] Defects correlated with *fa* mutations include reduction in the number of ommitidia per eye, disruption of the interommatidial bristle array within the eye, and disruption of the regions of the brain into which photosensory cells of the compound eye project (Markopoulou *et al.*, 1989). The *nd* alleles are comprised of a set of recessive mutations that are correlated with wing nicking (Lindsley and Grell, 1968). The single known recessive *spl* allele is correlated with variable duplication ("splitting") of large sensory bristles of the adult (Lees and Waddington, 1933) and with reduction of the number of ommitidia per eye (Shepard *et al.*, 1989). Two types of dominant mutations of the *N* locus that affect postembryonic development have been described (Welshons, 1971): (1) the namesake *N* alleles, which are also correlated with wing nicking in heterozygous (*N*/+) females and (2) *Abruptex* (*Ax*) alleles, which are correlated with premature ("abrupt") termination of a subset of veins in the wing and bristle loss in heterozygous (*Ax*/+) females. The existence of this diverse set of mutations, each member of which is allelic to *N*, reveals requirements for *N* function during the postembryonic development of a number of ectodermally derived structures, including wings, eyes, and bristles.

The separability of different requirements for *N* function during developmental time has been elegantly demonstrated by the analysis of a temperature (heat)-sensitive *N* allele, N^{ts1}, by Shellenbarger and Mohler (1978). Their analysis revealed the existence of distinct temperature-sensitive periods for various defects associated with the reduction or elimination of *N* function during development. They were able to show that *N* is required for viability during embryogenesis, the second and third larval instars,[3] and a limited period during metamorphosis. The same analysis showed that split- and notchoidlike defects could be induced by reduction in *N* function during the third larval instar and that facetlike defects resulted from a reduction in *N* function during metamorphosis.

[2] Each compound eye of an adult *Drosophila* is composed of approximately 700 ommatidia, or simple eyes. Each ommatidium contains eight photoreceptor cells, as well as a stereotyped array of accessory cells. Photoreceptor cells then project into the optic lobes of the adult brain in a characteristic fashion, providing for transmission of visual information to the central nervous system (Ready *et al.*, 1976).

[3] *Drosophila* development is divided into six stages (with approximate durations given for development at 25°C): embryogenesis, 24 hours; first larval instar, 24 hours; second larval instar, 24 hours; third larval instar, 48 hours; pupal stage, 96 hours; adult. Morphogenesis of the larval body plan occurs during embryogenesis, larval instars are separated by molts, and complete metamorphosis to the adult body plan occurs during the pupal stage.

This work thereby demonstrated that *N* function is required for viability during multiple stages of the life cycle and that requirements for *N* function in different tissues are temporally separable.

Intensive genetic analyses (e.g., Welshons and von Halle, 1962) have demonstrated that *N* is one of a limited number of genetically complex loci that have been defined in *Drosophila*. Subsets of mutations that affect a given complex locus exhibit what is known as interallelic complementation (i.e., two mutations in a gene, each of which fails to be complemented by a third mutation in the same gene, will complement each other). For example, recessive *fa* and *spl* mutations each fail to be complemented by dominant *N* mutations (*fa*/*N* and *spl*/*N* animals exhibit appropriate mutant phenotypes), but animals heterozygous for a *fa* mutation and a *spl* mutation (*fa*/*spl*) exhibit a wild-type phenotype. Such results are generally interpreted as reflecting the ability to generate qualitatively distinct mutations in a single locus and hence the existence of independently mutable subfunctions within that locus. Molecular hypotheses that could explain this observed genetic complexity are discussed below.

2. Autonomy of Action of the *Notch* Gene Product

Somatic mosaic analysis has been used by a number of investigators to assess the autonomy of *N* action in developing adult tissues, using a number of different *N* alleles in experiments in which mutant cell clones were generated by X-ray-induced mitotic recombination (summarized by Hoppe and Greenspan, 1986). Clonal analyses of the effects of the *spl* mutation on eye and bristle development (Stern and Tokunaga, 1968), the dominant alleles N^{ts1} and N^{264-39} on eye development (Dietrich and Campos-Ortega, 1984), and the dominant N^{ts1} allele on cuticle development (Shellenbarger and Mohler, 1978) each indicate that the *N* product acts in a cell-autonomous fashion during metamorphosis.

Clonal analysis has recently been used by Hoppe and Greenspan (1986) to assess the autonomous character of *N* action during embryonic development in experiments in which mutant cell clones of moderate size were generated following loss of a mitotically unstable ring-X chromosome. In these studies, *N* mutant cells never gave rise to epidermal cells, even when they were immediately adjacent to large fields of wild-type cells. This result indicated that cells that express the wild-type *N* product cannot "rescue" immediately adjacent mutant ectodermal cells from exhibiting the mutant phenotype (commitment to the neural lineage at the expense of the epidermal lineage) by promoting their entry into the epidermal stem cell lineage. This study implies that *N* also acts autonomously during embryogenesis to affect partitioning of the ectoderm into epidermal and neural stem cell populations.

Limited, and equivocal, evidence that suggests that *N* may function nonautonomously during embryogenesis has been produced by two groups. The most recent extension of clonal analysis in embryos, which has involved the intentional generation of small clones (one to three cells in size), has revealed that *N* mutant cells appear to be able to enter the epidermal lineage at a low frequency when surrounded by wild-type cells. However, it is not yet possible to conclusively determine whether this phenotypic rescue reflects perdurance of the wild-type *N* product expressed in the heterozygous cells that were the respective progenitors of such clones or nonautonomous action of *N* during ectodermal development (P. E. Hoppe and R. J. Greenspan, personal communication). Technau and Campos-Ortega (1987) have attempted to assess the autonomy of *N* action during embryogenesis using cell transplantation techniques, in which *N* mutant cells derived from homozygous mutant embryos were transplanted into wild-type hosts, allowed to develop, and then assayed for their respective entry or lack of entry into the epidermal lineage. Entry of a mutant cell into the epidermal lineage implies the nonautonomous rescue of the mutant cell by surrounding wild-type cells. Technau and Campos-Ortega (1987) report that single *N* mutant cells appear to be rescued by wild-type cells at a detectable frequency and thereby infer that *N* exhibits local nonautonomy during embryogenesis. The interpretation of these results is subject to a number of significant reservations.[4] The preponderance of evidence therefore suggests that *N* functions in a cell-autonomous manner during embryonic and postembryonic ectodermal development. If *N* does function in a nonautonomous fashion during embryogenesis, this action is highly localized and does not extend for distances appreciably greater than a single cell diameter within the developing ectoderm.

3. Molecular Analysis of the Structure of the *Notch* Locus

The primary structure of the embryonic protein product of the *N* locus (Fig. 1) was deduced on the basis of DNA sequence analyses of complementary DNA clones that encompass the coding capacity of the single *N* embryonic transcript (Wharton *et al.*, 1985; Kidd *et al.*, 1986). These analyses implied that the primary translational product of *N* in embryos is

[4] Cell transplantation experiments reported by Technau and Campos-Ortega (1987) must be interpreted with caution because (1) independent genetic markers were not used to conclusively identify mutant donor embryos, (2) the fraction of the donor population that exhibited the mutant phenotype was not reported, allowing for the possibility of inaccurate identification of a given donor animal as a mutant, and (3) the possibility of an artifactual impact of the transplantation procedure on ectodermal cell determination and/or differentiation cannot be excluded.

a membrane-spanning protein that includes a tandem array of 36 cysteine-rich, EGF-like repeats (Fig. 2) within a putative extracellular domain. Recent analysis of the subcellular localization of the *N* product undertaken using polyclonal antisera directed against different segments of the protein clearly demonstrates that the NOTCH protein is membrane associated in embryonic ectodermal cells (Johansen *et al.*, 1989). Other sequence motifs contained within the NOTCH protein include a set of three cysteine-rich "Notch" repeats within the extracellular domain and homologies to the *SWI6* and *cdc10* genes of yeasts (Breeden and Nasmyth, 1987) and to proteins known to interact with nucleoside triphosphates within the intracellular domain. The overall structural character of the NOTCH protein has led to the hypothesis that the *N* product participates in protein–protein contacts that are essential for cell–cell interactions required for normal embryonic and adult development of ectodermal cells in *Drosophila* (Wharton *et al.*, 1985; Kidd *et al.*, 1986).

The existence of the EGF-like motif within the NOTCH protein extracellular domain certainly implicates this portion of the molecule in intermolecular interactions. This motif has been detected in an increasing number of vertebrate and invertebrate molecules known or believed to be participate in protein–protein contacts (Gray *et al.*, 1983; Scott *et al.*, 1983; Komoriya *et al.*, 1984; Sudhof *et al.*, 1985; Furie and Furie, 1988; Jones *et al.*, 1988; Montell and Goodman, 1988). Genetic and molecular analyses of the *Ax* class of *N* mutations lends additional support for this premise. Certain pairs of *Ax* alleles have been shown to exhibit negative complementation (Portin, 1975): two alleles, each of which is viable in homozygotes (i.e., Ax^A/Ax^A and Ax^B/Ax^B are viable), are lethal in heterozygous combination (i.e., Ax^A/Ax^B is lethal). Portin (1975) suggested that this genetic behavior reflected the disruption of homotypic interactions among *N* polypeptides by *Ax* lesions. Subsequent molecular mapping of these mutations has shown that each is associated with a respective missense alteration within a subset of the *N* EGF-like repeats (repeats 24–29) (Hartley *et al.*, 1987; Kelley *et al.*, 1987), implicating this portion of the extracellular domain in multimeric associations among *N*-derived polypeptides.

Although the NOTCH protein extracellular domain contains sequences homologous to EGF and contains multiple repeats of this motif in approximate analogy to the vertebrate EGF precursor (Gray *et al.*, 1983; Scott *et al.*, 1983), there is no compelling evidence that supports the notion that this domain is proteolytically processed to yield a diffusible or transportable growth factor-like moiety. The results of the clonal analyses discussed above imply that the *N* product acts in a cell-autonomous fashion and suggest that the active form of the protein remains associated with the cell in which it is synthesized. Genetic studies have indicated that the recessive *spl* mutation, a missense alteration in the 14th EGF-like repeat in the NOTCH protein (Hartley *et al.*, 1987), acquires dominant character when linked in *cis* with certain *Ax* mutations (Welshons, 1971). This is consistent with the premise that the functional *N* product encompasses at least the portion of the molecule that includes the affected repeats. Initial structural analysis of the NOTCH protein found in developing embryos (Johansen *et al.*, 1989) yielded no evidence for the presence of appreciable amounts of processed NOTCH proteins. Given this evidence, it seems reasonable to favor the hypothesis that some or all of the EGF-like sequences in the NOTCH protein are required for intermolecular interactions in which this protein participates while it is anchored to the cell membrane. Considered in this light, these sequences would function within the context of the NOTCH protein as contact motifs wihch are essential for intermolecular interactions that are crucial for proper ectodermal determination and differentiation during embryonic and postembryonic development.

A number of independent lines of evidence, noted above, suggest that the *N* product is essential for cell–cell interactions among developing ectodermal cells (Lehmann *et al.*, 1983; Doe and Goodman, 1985; Technau and Campos-Ortega, 1986). It has been further suggested, based on additional cell transplantation data (Technau and Campos-Ortega, 1987), that *N* is involved in the generation of a signal that passes from developing neuroblasts to surrounding ectodermal cells and directs them into the epidermal lineage (de la Concha *et al.*, 1988). One possible correlate of this hypothesis is the expectation that *N* should be active in only the neuroblast population within the developing ectoderm during embryogenesis. However, localization of *N* transcripts by tissue section *in situ* hybridization (Hartley *et al.*, 1987) and of the NOTCH protein by immunohistochemistry (Johansen *et al.*, 1989) in developing embryos preceding and during partitioning of the ectoderm into neuroblast and dermoblast populations suggests that accumulation of *N* products is uniform among cells within the neurogenic region. Given this fact and the preponderant evidence for cell-autonomous action of *N* during embryogenesis and postembryonic development, it seems more probable that the *N* product is involved in the reception of information or the autogenous provision of information the leads to the initiation of epidermal development in the expected (dermoblast) fraction of ectodermal cells within neurogenic regions.

It has also been shown that *N* transcripts and protein are localized within regions of the late embryonic and larval central nervous systems known to contain dividing neuroblasts and ganglion mother cells (Hartley *et al.*,

1987; Johansen *et al.*, 1989) and within imaginal disk[5] cell populations that are mitotically active (Markopoulou and Artavanis-Tsakonas, 1989). These observations have led to the suggestion that *N* may play a role in the regulation of mitotic activity and/or subsequent differentiation of ectodermally derived cells throughout development (Hartley *et al.*, 1987; Johansen *et al.*, 1989). The observed accumulation of *N* transcripts in embryonic mesodermal and endodermal cells (Hartley *et al.*, 1987) implies that *N* function may be required in germ layers in addition to the ectoderm during embryogenesis.

The existence of a variety of phenotypes that result from distinct *N* mutations implies that *N* acts pleiotropically during development. The additional characteristic of *N* genetic complexity suggests that this pleiotrophy could be mediated by functionally distinct, tissue-specific products derived from *N*. However, initial molecular analyses of *N* transcriptional products have indicated that the locus appears to yield a single, qualitatively identical product in embryos, larvae, and pupae (Wharton *et al.*, 1985; Kidd *et al.*, 1986; Markopoulou *et al.*, 1989). If this is indeed the case, the mechanistic basis for the observed pleiotropic action of *N* during postembryonic development and genetic complexity of the locus remains unclear.

One hypothesis that could explain these phenomena is that alternative, tissue-specific transcriptional or posttranslational processing that has not yet been detected does lead to the generation of tissue-specific variants of the embryonic *N* product during postembryonic development. The different classes of recessive *N* alleles—*fa, nd,* and *spl*—would then correspond to genetic defects that specifically affect different tissue-specific products and thereby eliminate tissue-specific functions provided by *N*. This hypothesis would also explain the interallelic complementation observed among different classes of recessive *N* alleles: Each member of a complementing allele pair would provide the product(s) for which the other allele is defective.

An arguably more attractive hypothesis, which is consistent with the existence of a qualitatively uniform *N* product throughout development and the observed interallelic complementation, is that the function of *N* is context dependent (Johansen *et al.*, 1989). Given this hypothesis, recessive *N* mutations within different classes would perturb the ability of *N* to function in particular molecular and cellular contexts established in differ-

[5] The external cuticular structures, and many of the internal organs systems, of the adult fruit fly are derived primarily from a set of 17 groups of ectodermal cells that are established during embryogenesis, are mitotically active during larval and/or early pupal stages, and undergo terminal differentiation, for the most part, during metamorphosis (Bryant, 1978). These groups of cells are designated imaginal disks because they give rise to imaginal structures and exhibit disklike morphology before metamorphosis.

ent tissues during development. Molecular analyses have revealed that six of seven known *fa* alleles are correlated with intronic insertions of mobile repetitive elements (Kidd and Young, 1986; Markopoulou, 1987), the *spl* allele is correlated with a missense allele in the 14th EGF-like repeat (Hartley *et al.*, 1987), and two *nd* alleles appear to be correlated with missense and frameshift mutations, respectively, within the carboxy-terminal 30 residues of the NOTCH protein (T. Xu and S. Artavanis-Tsakonas, personal communication). The fact that members of each class of recessive mutations are qualitatively distinct from the members of the two other classes does not, however, provide strong support for one of the stated hypotheses in preference to the other.

B. *Delta* Locus

Mutations that affect the *Delta* (*Dl*) locus were first identified on the basis of the dominant phenotype associated with heterozygosity for a mutated copy of the *Dl* locus and a wild-type copy (*Dl*/ +): the formation of deltalike thickenings at the intersections between longitudinal wing veins and the wing margin (Bridges and Morgan, 1923). The *Dl* locus is located on the third chromosome (Bridges and Morgan, 1923) and is associated with larval salivary gland polytene chromosome band 92A1 (Alton *et al.*, 1988). Prototypic *Dl* mutations possess a dual character analogous to that of prototypic *N* alleles: dominant effects on the wing in heterozygotes (*Dl*/ +) and lethality in homozygotes (*Dl*/*Dl*). Lehmann *et al.* (1983) reported that the embryonic lethal phenotype associated with homozygosity for *Dl* loss-of-function mutations is analogous to that observed in *N* mutants (i.e., expansion of the nervous system and reduction of the epidermis) and therefore is classified *Dl* as a neurogenic gene. Molecular characterization of the predominant product of the *Dl* locus (Vässin *et al.*, 1987; Kopczynski *et al.*, 1988) has revealed that *Dl* appears to encode a putative membrane-spanning protein that includes an extracellular domain which contains sequences homologous to vertebrate EGF, and that this putative protein product is, in fact, homologous to the product of the *N* locus (Figs. 1 and 2).

1. Genetic Complexity of *Delta*

The embryonic lethality associated with homozygosity for *Dl* loss-of-function mutations indicates that the function of the locus is essential for normal embryogenesis (Lehmann *et al.*, 1983). The identification of *Dl* as a neurogenic gene (Lehmann *et al.*, 1983) implies that it encodes one or more products required for intercellular interactions that are essential for proper partitioning of the embryonic ectoderm into neuroblast and dermoblast stem cell populations. The existence of an array of adult phenotypes associated with heterozygosity for various *Dl* mutations also implies that function of the locus is required during metamorphosis (Lindsley and Grell, 1968; Dietrich and Campos-Ortega, 1984; Vässin and Campos-Ortega, 1987). The fact that appropriate alterations of *Dl* function can affect the wings, legs, and/or compound eyes in heterozygotes (*Dl*/+) suggests that *Dl* function is required for the proper development of derivatives of the wing imaginal disk, the leg imaginal disk, and the eye-antennal imaginal disk. The variety of phenotypes associated with mutations that affect the locus reflect the pleiotropic action of *Dl* during embryonic and postembryonic ectodermal development.

The current genetic analysis of *Dl* is not as extensive as that of *N*, although many mutations that affect *Dl* function have been isolated (Vässin and Campos-Ortega, 1987; Alton *et al.*, 1988, 1989). However, some data do suggest that *Dl* may be a genetically complex locus. First, evidence does exist for interallelic complementation of the *Dl* recessive lethal phenotype for a limited number of *Dl* allele pairs (i.e., Dl^{A}/Dl^{null} heterozygotes and Dl^{B}/Dl^{null} heterozygotes are inviable, while Dl^{A}/Dl^{B} heterozygotes are viable). Interpretation of these results is clouded by the fact that at least one member of each such complementing allele pair is a partial loss-of-function mutation (Vässin and Campos-Ortega, 1987; Alton *et al.*, 1988). This complementation behavior does not indicate genetic complexity within *Dl* if it reflects the fact that the sum of the respective contributions of a qualitatively identical product from the two members of the complementing allele pair is adequate to support viability. It does indicate genetic complexity if it reflects the fact that the members of the complementing allele pair are defective in qualitatively distinct *Dl* functions, respectively. In this case, complementation would result when one member of the allele pair provides the function that is defective in the other member and vice versa. Second, *Dl* mutations that are apparently analogous to recessive visible *N* mutations (summarized by Welshons and von Halle, 1962) have been isolated. Animals homozygous for different *Dl* mutations of this type exhibit wing venation defects (Vässin and Campos-Ortega, 1987) or wing venation, leg, and eye defects (M. A. T. Muskavitch, unpublished observations), respectively, yet are viable and fertile. The existence of these mutations suggests that it is possible to isolate qualitatively distinct recessive visible *Dl* alleles and that these alleles affect genetically distinguishable *Dl* functions required for postembryonic development. Resolution of the question of whether or not *Dl* is a genetically complex locus in the classic sense will require further genetic analyses of mutations that affect the locus.

2. Autonomy of Action of *Delta* Gene Products

Results of somatic mosaic analyses that assess the autonomous character of *Dl* function during development are scant. This approach apparently has not been applied successfully to assessment of the autonomy of *Dl* action during embryogenesis, since no such experiments have been reported in the literature. Only one clonal analysis of the effects of *Dl* mutations during adult development, in which mutant cell clones were generated following X-ray-induced mitotic recombination, has been described (Dietrich and Campos-Ortega, 1984). This study, which yielded interpretable results for only the temperature (heat)-sensitive allele Dl^{6B37}, revealed that *Dl* appears to function in a cell-autonomous manner during metamorphosis of the eye and adult cuticle. An alternative attempt to assess the autonomy of *Dl* action during embryogenesis has been undertaken using cell transplantation techniques (Technau and Campos-Ortega, 1987). The authors observed the apparent phenotypic rescue of single transplanted *Dl* mutant cells by wild-type cells and inferred that this result reflected local nonautonomy of *Dl* action during embryogenesis (Technau and Campos-Ortega, 1987). However, these results are equivocal for a number of reasons that have already been discussed.[4] Given these reservations, the meager available evidence indicates that *Dl* functions in a cell-autonomous manner during postembryonic development; therefore, it may function autonomously during embryogenesis as well.

3. Molecular Analysis of the Structure of the *Delta* Locus

The primary structure of the predominant embryonic product of the *Dl* locus (DLZM, Fig. 1) has been deduced on the basis of the DNA sequences of complementary DNA clones that contain the coding capacity of the predominant embryonic *Dl* transcript (Vässin *et al.*, 1987; Kopczynski *et al.*, 1988). Conceptual translation of these sequences indicates that DLZM is a putative membrane-spanning protein that includes a tandem array of nine complete, cysteine-rich, EGF-like repeats (Fig. 2) within a putative extracellular domain. This structure, which is homologous to that of the embryonic NOTCH protein, implicates DLZM in protein–protein contacts required for cell–cell interactions during embryonic and postembryonic ectodermal development in *Drosophila* (Vässin *et al.*, 1987; Kopczynski *et al.*, 1988). Limited evidence that implies a cell-autonomous mode of action for *Dl* (Dietrich and Campos-Ortega, 1984) is consistent with the premise that the DLZM protein may function in cell–cell interactions during development while associated with the membranes of the cell in which it is synthesized.

The identification of *Dl* as a neurogenic gene (Lehmann *et al.*, 1983) and the structure of DLZM (Vässin *et al.*, 1987; Kopczynski *et al.*, 1988) imply that DLZM is essential for intercellular interactions that are central to the partitioning of the embryonic ectoderm into neuroblast and dermoblast populations. Cell transplantation studies (Technau and Campos-Ortega, 1987) have led de la Concha *et al.* (1988) to suggest that *Dl*, as well as *N*, is required for the generation of a signal that is transmitted from developing neuroblasts to surrounding embryonic ectodermal cells, directing them to enter the epidermal lineage.

However, *in situ* hybridization analyses of the distributions of the transcripts that encode DLZM in embryogenic tissue sections revealed that these transcripts are uniformly distributed among ectodermal cells (Vässin et al., 1987; Kopczynski and Muskavitch, 1989). These data imply that *Dl* expression is not restricted to the neuroblast population and that, on the basis of the arguments presented above for *N, Dl* function may therefore be required during embryogenesis for the reception of information or the autogenous provision of information that is essential for the initiation of epidermal development in ectodermal cells. Although there are some differences between the dynamics of the accumulation of *Dl* and *N* transcripts during embryogenesis, *Dl* transcripts also accumulate within regions of the late embryonic central nervous system that contain dividing neuroblasts and ganglion mother cells (Kopczynski and Muskavitch, 1989), implying that *Dl* may be also involved in the regulation of mitotic activity in the developing nervous system. *In situ* hybridization analyses also reveal that *Dl* transcripts (Kopczynski and Muskavitch, 1989) accumulate in subsets of embryonic mesodermal and endodermal cells, suggesting that *Dl* function may be required in the derivatives of germ layers other than the ectoderm during embryogenesis.

Analysis of embryonic and maternal expression of *Dl* has revealed that the locus gives rise to multiple transcripts as the result of a combination of alternative splicing and alternative polyadenylation site choice (Vässin *et al.*, 1987; Kopczynski *et al.*, 1988). Five alternative transcripts[6]—5.4Z, 4.5M, 5.4z, 3.5z, and 2.8z—accumulate during embryogenesis; two alternative transcripts—4.5M and 3.5m—accumulate in unfertilized eggs. Structural comparison of complementary DNA clones that represent the entirety of 5.4Z and 4.5M transcripts, respectively, indicates that these transcripts share the same coding capacity and that both are capable of encoding DLZM. Mapping of the DLZM coding exons to the *Dl* transcription unit indicates that the coding capacity for DLZM encompasses the

[6] *Delta* transcripts are denoted on the bases of length (in kilobases) of nucleotides and timing of expression. Z or z indicates that a transcript accumulates in embryos and does not accumulate in unfertilized eggs. M or m indicates that a transcript accumulates in unfertilized eggs and is therefore expressed maternally. The 4.5M transcript, for example, accumulates maternally and embryonically.

portion of the transcription unit wherein alternative exon utilization occurs (K. Fechtel, K. Bauer, and M. A. T. Muskavitch, unpublished observations). This finding, combined with the low-resolution exon map that has been determined for *Dl* (Kopczynski *et al.*, 1988), implies that the other four alternative *Dl* transcripts (i.e., 5.4z, 3.5z, 2.8z, and 3.6m) must differ substantially in coding capacity from 5.4Z and 4.5M. In fact, assessment of the organization of at least two of the alternative transcripts implies that they cannot (3.5z) or most probably do not (2.8z) include the EGF-like repeats, the putative transmembrane domain, or the putative intracellular domain of DLZM (Kopczynski *et al.*, 1988).

This analysis has led to the hypothesis that *Dl* encodes multiple, alternative translational products and may function as a multimeric complex, a hypothesis that is supported by the finding that each of the five alternative *Dl* transcripts that accumulate in embryos appears to be associated with polysomes (Kopczynski and Muskavitch, 1989). If this hypothesis is correct, then instances of interallelic complementation between pairs of *Dl* mutations that have been observed (Vässin and Campos-Ortega, 1987; Alton *et al.*, 1988; M. A. T. Muskavitch, unpublished observations) may reflect heterozygosity for pairs of alleles that constitute specific lesions in alternative translational products.

4. Interactions between *Notch* and *Delta*

Phenotypic interactions between mutations in independent loci have been shown, in a number of instances, to reflect functional interactions between gene products encoded by such loci for at least two multicomponent macromolecular assemblies: microtubules (Stearns and Botstein, 1988; Regan and Fuller, 1988) and muscle fibers (Park and Horvitz, 1986; Homyk and Emerson, 1988). Such interactions may be dosage dependent or allele specific, depending on the genes in question. It is therefore noteworthy that a number of phenotypic interactions are known to occur between *N* mutations and *Dl* mutations. First, heterozygosity for the $N^{Confluens}$ point mutation (Welshons, 1956) yields a phenotype similar to that associated with heterozygosity for *Dl* mutations, and heterozygosity for the Dl^{B107} point mutation (Vässin and Campos-Ortega, 1987) yields a phenotype similar to that associated with heterozygosity for *N* mutations. These results may indicate that a point mutation in *N* can reduce the effective level of function of *Dl*, as well as the converse. Second, simultaneous heterozygosity for loss-of-function mutations at *N* and *Dl* in females (*N*/+, *Dl*/+) leads to a reduction of the dominant wing phenotypes associated with heterozygosity for *N* or *Dl* mutations, as if the proper stoichiometry between *N* and *Dl* products is crucial for normal wing development (Vässin *et al.*, 1985; Alton *et al.*, 1989). Third, the addition of an extra dose of the wild-type *N* locus to a fly that is euploid for *Dl* yields a phenotype denoted "Confluens" that is similar to that associated with heterozygosity for a *Dl* mutation (Alton *et al.*, 1989) and the same increase in *N* dosage increases the severity of the phenotype observed if a fly is instead simultaneously heterozygous for a *Dl* mutation (Vässin *et al.*, 1985), again suggesting the importance of the stoichiometry between *N* and *Dl* products. Fourth, the negative complementation observed between certain pairs of *Ax* alleles can be suppressed by heterozygosity for mutations that reduce *Dl* function (T. Xu and S. Artavanis-Tsakonas, personal communication). These phenotypic interactions may reflect physical interaction between NOTCH and DLZM proteins during metamorphosis. It is tempting to speculate that physical interaction between *N* and *Dl* products may also be intrinsic to the mechanism by which these products affect partitioning of the ectoderm into neural and epidermal lineages during embryogenesis and that these proposed interactions may be mediated by EGF-like sequences found in the NOTCH and DLZM proteins.

C. Other EGF Homologs in *Drosophila, Caenorhabditis,* and *Strongylocentrotus*

1. Additional EGF Homologs in *Drosophila*

Portions of the EGF-like coding sequences from *N* and *Dl* have been used by a number of investigators in attempts to identify other *Drosophila* loci that encode EGF homologs based on hybridization to genomic DNA and embryonic-stage complementary DNA clone libraries at reduced stringency (Knust *et al.*, 1987; Rothberg *et al.*, 1988). These efforts have led to the identification of a total of more than ten putative NOTCH and/or DLZM cognate sequences that have been localized within the *Drosophila* genome by *in situ* hybridization to larval salivary gland polytene chromosomes. Further molecular and genetic analyses have led to the confirmed or putative correlation between two of these cloned sequences and genetically defined loci.

Rothberg *et al.* (1988) have correlated a transcription unit that includes sequences that encode a portion of an EGF homolog and is located within the 52D polytene chromosome band with the *slit* (*sli*) locus (Jürgens *et al.*, 1984). The *sli* function is required for normal development of the ventral midline neuroepithelium during embryogenesis (Rothberg *et al.*, 1988), a region of the ectoderm that gives rise to gliallike support cells that include the midline ectodermal cells, median neuroblasts, ventral unpaired median neurons, and medial neurons (Thomas *et al.*, 1988; Crews *et al.*, 1988). Animals that lack the *sli* function exhibit disruptions in the commissural and longitudinal axonal tracts of the ventral nerve cord, and these disruptions may correlate with the loss or displacement of midline ectodermal cells, and possibly other cells, in the developing embryonic central nervous system (Rothberg *et al.*, 1988). DNA sequence analysis of genomic and complementary DNA clones that correspond to portions of the *sli* gene and *sli* transcripts, respectively, has revealed that the deduced *sli* product contains at least seven EGF-like repeats (Rothberg *et al.*, 1988), although the published data do not reveal the existence of a putative signal peptide or transmembrane domain within this partial SLIT protein sequence. These data have led to the hypothesis that the *sli* product plays a role in mediating cell–cell interactions required for the determination of cell fates within the developing ventral neuroepithelium (Rothberg *et al.*, 1988).

Knust *et al.* (1987) have suggested that a transcription unit that appears to encode an EGF homolog and resides in the 95F polytene chromosome band corresponds to the *crumbs* (*crb*) locus (Nüsslein-Volhard *et al.*, 1984). Mutations that affect *crb* appear to be correlated with a generalized epidermal defect that is inferred to occur based on the phenotype of *crb* mutant embryos: numerous small holes in the cuticle (Nüssein-Volhard *et al.*, 1984). Knust *et al.* (1987) report that *crb* mutant embryos exhibit neural hypertrophy and defects in the foregut and hindgut in addition to epidermal defects. The sequence reported for a portion of this 95F transcription unit (Knust *et al.*, 1987) includes five tandemly arranged EGF-like repeats. The tentative identification of this gene as the *crb* locus rests on two criteria: (1) the cytogenetic correlation between the approximate position of *crb* determined by Jürgens *et al.* (1984) (i.e., 95E–96A) and the localization of the transcription unit to 95F, and (2) the localization of transcripts detected with the 95F clone to the epidermis, foregut, and hindgut by tissue section *in situ* hybridization in developing embryos, tissues that are affected in *crb* mutants (Knust *et al.*, 1987). Although this hypothesis must be supported more rigorously before it can be accepted, these results raise the possibility that *crb* encodes an EGF homolog that is required for normal development of the epidermis and nervous system of the *Drosophila* embryo.

2. *lin-12* Locus of *Caenorhabditis*

Mutations that affect the *lin-12* (*lin*eage-defective) locus of the nematode *C. elegans* were initially isolated on the basis of multiple morphological defects associated with the mutant genotype. The exact determination of the array of cell types affected by *lin-12,* or any other mutation in *C. elegans,* is facilitated by the fact that the complete lineage relationships of all embryonic and postembryonic cells have been determined for this nematode (Sulston *et al.*, 1983). The observation that *lin-12* mutations affect the development of multiple cell lineages, including gonadal, hypodermal, and mesodermal cells (Greenwald *et al.*, 1983), implies that *lin-12* acts pleiotropically during development. The coincidence between temperature-sensitive periods for the effects of conditional *lin-12* alleles on development of specific gonadal and hypodermal cells and the intervals of development during which these cells are determined to assume specific fates indicates that *lin-12* activity is necessary for the determination of cell fates (Greenwald *et al.*, 1983).

Cell ablation experiments (summarized by Greenwald *et al.*, 1983) further indicate that cell–cell interactions are essential for a number of the determinative events for which *lin-12* activity is required. These data, in aggregate, imply that *lin-12* participates in a number of determinative decisions during development that involve intercellular interactions.

The study of the role of the *lin-12* locus in the determination of cells that participate in formation of the vulva of the adult hermaphrodite has yielded a number of insights into the autonomous character of *lin-12* action (Seydoux and Greenwald, 1989). Cell ablation studies (Kimble, 1981; Seydoux and Greenwald, 1989) indicate that the specific interaction between two cells, designated Z1.ppp and Z4.aaa, is central to vulval development. One of these two cells becomes the so-called anchor cell (AC), while the other becomes the ventral uterine precursor cell (VU). While the assumption of these fates by these two cells occurs on a random basis, a number of lines of evidence (Kimble, 1981; Seydoux and Greenwald, 1989) suggest that one of the two cells first assumes that AC identity and that this cell then instructs the other to assume the VU identity. Analysis of the development of *lin-12* mutants reveals that both cells assume the AC fate in the absence of *lin-12* function and implies that *lin-12* activity is required for assumption of the VU fate during development (Greenwald *et al.*, 1983). The results of somatic mosaic analysis, in which loss of a free duplication that carries a copy of the wild-type *lin-12* locus was used to produce mosaics in which either Z1.ppp or Z4.aaa lacked *lin-12* activity (Seydoux and Greenwald, 1989), indicate that the *lin-12* product acts in a cell-autonomous manner to promote establishment of the VU cell identity during development.

Recent molecular analyses of the *lin-12* gene have revealed that it encodes a putative membrane-spanning protein that contains 13 cysteine-rich, EGF-like repeats within a putative extracellular domain (Figs. 1 and 2) (Greenwald, 1985; Yochem *et al.*, 1988). The overall amino acid sequence organization of the LIN-12 protein is, in fact, homologous to that of the NOTCH protein. The extracellular domain of the LIN-12 protein also contains three tandemly arranged copies of the cysteine-rich "Notch" repeat (Wharton *et al.*, 1985; Kidd *et al.*, 1986) found in the NOTCH protein and the intracellular domain also contains multiple repeats of a sequence that is homologous to a motif found in the *SWI6* and *cdc10* genes of yeasts (Breeden and Nasmyth, 1987). Genetic data, which imply that the *lin-12* product acts in a cell-autonomous manner during vulval development (Seydoux and Greenwald, 1989), have led to the hypothesis that the *lin-12* product is essential for the reception of a putative "AC-to-VU signal" that originates in the AC and directs the assumption of the VU fate by the other member of the Z1.ppp/Z4.aaa cell pair during development (Seydoux and Greenwald, 1989).

The autonomous character of *lin-12* action in this determinative event implies that the *lin-12* product functions in association with the membrane of the cell in which it is expressed and is not processed to yield a diffusible factor. The presence of EGF-like sequences within the extracellular domain of the LIN-12 protein (Yochem *et al.*, 1988) strongly suggests that the signaling between AC and VU involves protein–protein interactions. The available data therefore imply that the *lin-12* product functions as a receptor for an intercellular signal that is required for the determination of cell fate during development and that the reception of this signal requires intermolecular interactions that involve protein–protein contacts.

3. *glp-1* Locus of *Caenorhabditis*

Mutations that affect the *glp-1* (*g*erm *l*ine *p*roliferation-defective) locus of *C. elegans* have been isolated based on two qualitatively distinct classes of phenotypes. Alleles of *glp-1* were first isolated in screens for sterile mutations (Austin and Kimble, 1987) and characterized as being correlated with defects in the switch between mitosis of germ-line cells and meiosis. Animals that lack *glp-1* function exhibit drastic reductions in egg and sperm production, because germ-line cells switch from mitotic to meiotic behavior far too early in development (Austin and Kimble, 1987). Screens for maternal effect embryonic lethal mutations and temperature-sensitive embryonic lethal mutations (Priess *et al.*, 1987) also yielded alleles of *glp-1*, many of which were correlated with defects in development of the pharyngeal cells and hypodermal cells and, for some alleles, fertility defects. The range of phenotypes associated with *glp-1* mutations reflect the pleiotropic action of the *glp-1* product during development.

Studies that have focused the development of cells affected by the loss of *glp-1* function indicate that regulation of the mitotic/meiotic switch in the germ line and development of pharyngeal cells involve interactions between defined subsets of cells. The germ-line defects observed in animals that lack *glp-1* function are analogous to those that result from ablation of the distal tip cell (DTC) of the nematode gonad (Kimble and White, 1981). This somatic cell, which resides at one end of the arm of the gonad, appears to be required to maintain mitotic behavior of the germ line: As germ-line cells proceed down the arm of the gonad, they switch from mitotic to meiotic behavior once they are displaced a sufficient distance from the DTC. The phenotype of *glp-1* sterile mutants (Austin and Kimble, 1987) suggests that *glp-1* function is required for the DTC to exert an influence on germ-line cells. Analysis of temperature (heat)-sensitive sterile *glp-1* alleles (Austin and Kimble, 1987) indicates that *glp-1* function is required continuously in the germ line to maintain mitotic behavior and that the developmental interval during which *glp-1* activity is required to ensure proper germ-line development is the same as that during which the DTC must be present. Normal development of embryonic cells (blastomeres) that give rise to the pharyngeal cells that are defective in *glp-1* mutant embryos also requires cell–cell interactions (Priess and Thomson, 1987). Development of the three identified precursor cells that are derived from the ABa blastomere and give rise to the anterior pharynx during embryogenesis requires interactions with neighboring embryonic cells (Priess and Thomson, 1987). This development is defective in *glp-1* mutants (Priess *et al.*, 1987). Analysis of temperature (heat)-sensitive *glp-1* alleles has revealed the *glp-1* activity is required during the same interval of embryogenesis (i.e., between fertilization and the 28-cell stage) (Priess *et al.*, 1987), during which the ABa blastomere must interact with the neighboring P_1 embryonic cell, and possibly other cells, for proper anterior pharyngeal development to occur (Priess and Thomson, 1987). These results implicate the function of *glp-1* in two distinct developmental processes, each of which entails cell–cell interactions.

Somatic mosaic analysis, in which loss of a free duplication that carries a wild-type copy of the *glp-1* locus was used to generate mosaics in which either germ-like cells or the DTC lacked *glp-1* activity (Austin and Kimble, 1987), suggests that *glp-1* function is required in the germ line for the proper regulation of mitotic/meiotic behavior by the DTC. If germ-line cells lack *glp-1* function, the presence of a wild-type copy of *glp-1* in the DTC will not rescue the mutant phenotype (i.e., germ-line cells still enter meiosis early). It has been postulated that the DTC provides a signal that regulates the switch between mitosis and meiosis in the germ line. These results suggest that *glp-1* activity is required in the germ line for the reception of this putative regulatory signal from the DTC.

Characterization of the deduced structure of the *glp-1* product has revealed that the *glp-1* gene encodes a putative membrane-spanning protein that is homologous to the products of *lin-12* and *N* (Figs. 1 and 2) (Yochem and Greenwald, 1989). The putative extracellular domain of the deduced GLP-1 protein includes ten EGF-like repeats and three tandem copies of the "Notch" repeat motif (Wharton *et al.*, 1985; Kidd *et al.*, 1986), and the intracellular domain contains multiple copies of the *SWI6/cdc10* motif (Breeden and Nasmyth, 1987). Molecular analysis of *glp-1* (summarized by

Yochem and Greenwald, 1989) indicates that *lin-12* and *glp-1* may be related on the bases of duplication and divergence during evolution. The respective transcription units are separated by only 18 kilobases of DNA and are arranged in a head-to-head orientation. The cellular, genetic, and molecular data concerning *glp-1* are consistent with the hypothesis that the GLP-1 protein is required for the reception of information by germ-line cells that is provided by the DTC and is required for proper regulation of mitotic and meiotic behavior in germ-line cells (Austin and Kimble, 1987). The molecular structure of the GLP-1 protein also provides a mechanistic basis for the participation of the *glp-1* product in cell–cell interactions that are essential for proper determination of specific subsets of somatic cells during embryogenesis (Priess *et al.*, 1987).

4. *uEGF-1* Locus of *Strongylocentrotus*

The *uEGF-1* locus of the sea urchin *S. purpuratus* has been identified on the basis of the DNA sequence analysis of complementary DNA clones isolated in a screen for clones that represent transcripts that are enriched in specific cell types in sea urchin embryos (Hursh *et al.*, 1987). The locus appears to encode two alternative transcripts, 3 and 4 kb in length, that accumulate in unfertilized eggs, fall in prevalence immediately after fertilization, and increase in prevalence transiently during the blastula stage; these transcripts are enriched in ectodermal cells. The temporal profile of accumulation of the *uEGF-1* transcripts has led to the suggestion that the products encoded by these transcripts may be involved in determinative events that occur during the blastula stage of development and are unlikely to function in the regulation of mitosis, since postfertilization accumulation is maximal after the rapid mitoses of early embryogenesis are essentially complete (Hursh *et al.*, 1987).

DNA sequence analysis of genomic DNA from the locus and complementary DNA clones that represent portions of the two *uEGF-1* transcripts has revealed that the gene encodes an EGF homolog (Hursh *et al.*, 1987; Delgadillo-Reynoso *et al.*, 1989). The 3-kb transcript encodes the so-called "short-form" *uEGF-1* product (UEGF-SF). The putative UEGF-SF protein includes an amino-terminal signal peptide followed by an array of 13 EGF-like repeats. This array is interrupted by a region that is homologous to the complement component Cls between the first and second repeat, and the portion of the protein extending from the carboxy-proximal end of the EGF-like repeat array to the carboxy terminus is homologous to avidin. The deduced sequence, which appears to represent the legitimate open reading frame within the 3-kb transcript, does not include any intervals that resemble a transmembrane domain.

The sequence organization of UEGF-SF implies that the protein may participate in intermolecular interactions within the extracellular compartment of the developing sea urchin embryo. The 4-kb *uEGF-1* transcript is believed to encode a "long-form" product that includes an additional eight EGF-like repeat units, but is otherwise identical to UEGF-SF; the exonic organization of the gene indicates that these additional repeats would be "inserted" into the interior of the EGF-like repeat array of the UEGF-SF protein. The structures of the deduced *uEGF-1* products and the timing of accumulation of the *uEGF-1* transcripts have led to the suggestion that the *uEGF-1* locus encodes products that participate in determinative events that occur during sea urchin embryogenesis (Hursh *et al.*, 1987). This hypothesis is interesting to consider, but will be difficult to test.

III. *decapentaplegic*, A Locus That Encodes a Homolog of TGF-β

Mutations of recent origin that affect the *decapentaplegic* (*dpp*) locus were first noticed in W. M. Gelbart's laboratory at Harvard University by an undergraduate stock keeper, Rebecca Tung. The mutant flies were defective in adult structures derived from 15 of the 17 different larval imaginal disks, which are discrete groups of cells present in larvae that give rise to most of the cuticular structures of the adult fly. Characteristic defects included reduction of the eyes from hundreds to a few ommatidia, reduction of the wing blades to stumps, and loss of tarsal segments and claws from the distal portions of the legs. The *dpp* gene has recently been shown to encode a protein with sequence similarity to a family of growth-regulatory peptides that includes TGF-β, bone morphogenetic proteins, the *Xenopus* VEG1 protein, inhibins, and Müllerian inhibiting substance (Figs. 3 and 4) (Padgett *et al.*, 1987; Derynck *et al.*, 1985; Wozney *et al.*, 1988; Weeks and Melton, 1987; Mason *et al.*, 1985; Cate *et al.*, 1986).

A. Genetic Analyses

The first *dpp* mutation identified in the Gelbart laboratory was mapped to the distal end of the left arm of the second chromosome and was found to be allelic to the preexisting mutation *heldout* (subsequently renamed *dpp*^{ho}), which was discovered by Novitski (Novitski and Rifenburgh, 1938). A series of new *dpp* alleles was then induced by X-ray mutagenesis in a screen designed to recover mutations allelic to *dpp*^{ho}. The mutations recovered could be ordered in an allelic series of increasing severity. When

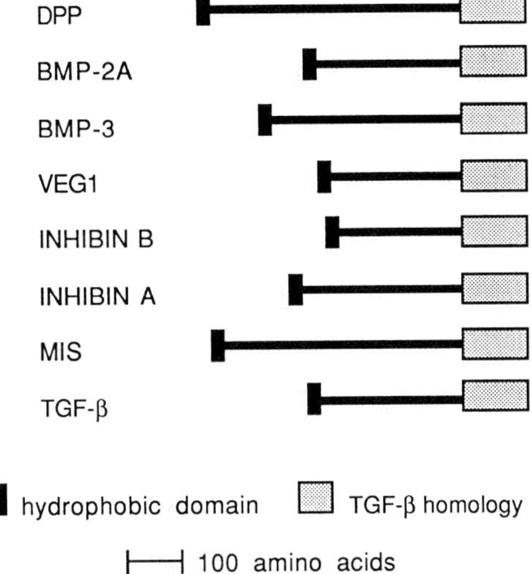

Fig. 3 Comparison of the one-dimensional structures inferred for the products of a number of invertebrate and vertebrate loci that encode TGF-β-related proteins. The schematic diagrams represent the deduced structures for products of *decapentaplegic* (DPP) (Padgett *et al.*, 1987), *bone morphogenetic protein* genes (BMP-2A and BMP-3) (Wozney *et al.*, 1988), *Xenopus Vg1* gene (VEG1) (Weeks and Melton, 1987), *inhibin* genes (INHIBIN B and INHIBIN A) (Mason *et al.*, 1985), *Müllerian inhibiting substance* gene (MIS) (Cate *et al.*, 1986), and *TGF-β* gene (Derynck *et al.*, 1985). Explanations of symbolism and a length scale are given below.

heterozygous with the original dpp^{ho} mutation, these alleles yielded phenotypes identical to that produced by homozygosity for the original dpp^{ho} mutation (i.e., the wings are held out at right angles to the body). The most severely affected alleles yielded early pupal lethality in homozygous or transheterozygous configurations (Spencer *et al.*, 1982). The intriguing feature of the resulting series of phenotypes was that the milder mutations appeared to affect structures located distally on the adult cuticular structures (e.g., the tarsal claws of the legs), while more severe mutations resulted in the absence of structures located more and more proximally along the distal-to-proximal axes of adult cuticular structures. Analysis of these phenotypes led to the proposal that the *dpp* gene product was involved in distal-to-proximal pattern formation in structures derived from imaginal disks. Previous studies in which the adult cuticular structures derived from imaginal disks were fate-mapped to specific locations within the disks implied that, in general, distal structures are derived from central positions with the disk epithelium, whereas proximal structures are derived from more peripheral regions of the disk epithelium (Bryant, 1978). Indeed, the mechanism of pattern formation in the imaginal disks has been

```
DPP     CRRHSLYVDF.SDVGWDDWI VAPLGYDAYYCHGKCPFPLA DHFNSTN..HA.VVQTLVNN MN.PGKVPKACCVPTQLDSV AMLYLNDQSTVVLKNYQ... EMTVVGCGCR
BMP-2A  CKRHPLYVDF.SDVGWNDWI VAPPGYHAFYCHGECPFPLA DHLNSTN..HA.IVQTLVNS VN..SKIPKACCVPTELSAI SMLYLDENEKVVLKNYQ... DMVVEGCGCR
BMP-3   CARRYLKVDF.ADIGWSEWI ISPKSFDAYYCSGACQFPMP KSLKPSN..HA.TIQSIVRA VGVVPGIPEPCCVPEKMSSL SILFFDENKNVVLKVYP... NMTVESCACR
VEG1    CKKRHLYVEF.KDVGWQNWV IAPQGYMANYCYGECPYPLT EILNGSN..HA.ILQTLVHS IE.PEDIPLPCCVPTKMSPI SMLFYDNNDNVVLRHYE... NMAVDECGCR
INHB    CCKKQFFVSF.KDIGWNDWI IAPSGYHANYCEGECPSHIA GTSGSSLSFHSTVINHYRMR GHSPFANLKSCCVPTKLRPM SMLYYDDGQNIIKKDIQ... NMIVEECGCS
INHA    CHRVALNISF.QELGWERWI VYPPSFIFHYCHGGCGLMIP PNLSLPVPGAPPTPAQPYSL LP....GAQPCCAALPGTMR PLHVRTTSDGGYSFKYETVP NLLTQHCACI
MIS     CALRELSVDLRAERS....V LIPETYQANNCQGVCGWPQS DP.NPRYGNH..VVLLLKMQ ARGAALARPPCCVPTAYAGK LLISLSEERISAHHV....P NMVATECGCR
TGF-B   CCVRQLYIDFRKDLGWK.WI HEPKGYHANFCLGPCPYIWS LDTQYSK......VLALYNQ HN.PGASAAPCCVPQALEPL PIVYYVGRKPKVEQL....S NMIVRSCKCS

CONS    C.K..LFVDF...VGW..WI I.P.GY.A.YC.G.CPFPL. .....S...H..VV..L... .........PCCVPT..... ..LY.D....VV...Y.... NM.V..CGCR
          R  YI     I    V      F          Y I         T    II                                 IF N    II
```

Fig. 4 Alignments and consensus sequence for TGF-β-like sequences found in the *decapentaplegic* product and selected vertebrate TGF-β homologs. The consensus includes single residues, alternate residues (*D*/*N*, *F*/*Y*, *V*/*I*, *L*/*I*, *K*/*R*, and *S*/*T*) or any amino acid (X) present in 50% or more of the homologous, carboxy-terminal regions of the members of this set of TGF-β-related molecules. DPP, *decapentaplegic;* BMP-2A, BMP-3, *bone morphogenetic protein* 2*A* and *3;* VEG1, *Xenopus Vg1;* INHB, INHA, *inhibin B* and *A;* MIS, *Müllerian inhibiting substance;* CONS, consensus.

modeled to predict that a circumferential gradient of positional values exists in imaginal disks between the most central position in each disk and the edge of the disk columnar epithelium (French *et al.*, 1976).

Other genetic studies have indicated that *dpp* affects developmental processes in *Drosophila* in addition to the morphogenesis of imaginal disk-derived structures. The isolation of *dpp* mutations that yield embryonic lethality revealed that *dpp* function is required for normal embryogenesis (Spencer *et al.*, 1982). The larval cuticle formed by embryos homozygous for such *dpp* mutations exhibits defects in the head structures formed. The same phenotype is observed in embryos heterozygous for deletions that eliminate the *dpp* locus.

The availability of an insertional translocation of the *dpp* gene on the right arm of the second chromosome [*Tp(2)DTD48, dpp^{dho}* (Gelbart, 1982)] led to efforts to separate the *dpp* deficiency segregant on the left arm of the translocation chromosome from the duplication of *dpp* generated on the right arm by the insertional translocation. The inability to recover chromosomes bearing only the *dpp* deficiency in adults was the first indication that the *dpp* gene was haploinsufficient (i.e., the presence of only one copy of the locus in the animal, which normallv carries two copies of the gene, is insufficient to support development to the adult stage). Additional mutageneses that took this genetic feature into account led to the recovery of several deletions of the *dpp* locus, and this permitted analysis of the *dpp*-null phenotype (Irish and Gelbart, 1987).

Homozygosity for null mutations in the *dpp* gene leads to defects in gastrulation early in embryogenesis and results in a spectacular transformation of dorsal cuticular structures to ventral cuticular structures. In the *dpp* null mutant embryo the ventral dentical bands that demarcate the thoracic and abdominal segments of the wild-type larval cuticle extend circumferentially around the embryo, particularly in the abdominal segments. The cuticle also shows evidence of severe losses of structure in the extreme anterior and posterior regions of the embryo. These results identify the *dpp* gene as one of at least 15 so-called dorsal/ventral polarity genes that regulate formation of the normal dorsal/ventral pattern of the larval cuticle during embryogenesis (Anderson, 1987). Several of these genes function maternally to provide information to the early zygote and are typified by loci such as *dorsal* and *Toll* (Anderson and Nüsslein-Volhard, 1984). Other members of this gene set, including *dpp* (see below), *twist,* and *snail* (Simpson, 1983), are expressed in the zygote during the blastoderm stage of embryogenesis. Mutations in these genes lead to a failure of ventral furrow formation and the absence of mesodermal derivatives that normally form following ventral furrow formation.

The *dpp* locus also affects development of some of the internal organs formed during embryogenesis, as revealed by a series of mutations isolated on the basis of their failure to complement the preexisting mutation *shortvein* (renamed dpp^{s1}). It had been noted that the dpp^{s1} mutation failed to fully complement recessive embryonic lethal *dpp* mutations (Segal and Gelbart, 1985). Mutagenesis for new alleles of dpp^{s1} led to the recovery of a series of chromosomal lesions that exhibit varying degrees of severity with respect to the failure to complement embryonic lethal and imaginal disk-specific *dpp* alleles (Segal and Gelbart, 1985). Animals trans-heterozygous for various pairs of these newly induced dpp^{s1} alleles seem to develop a normal larval cuticle during embryogenesis, which indicates that the dorsal/ventral functions of *dpp* are not affected by these mutations. However, the mutant larvae die during the larval development and exhibit some defects in internal organs, especially in the gut and Malpighian tubules.

B. Autonomy of Action of the Gene Product

The properties of the *dpp* product in the imaginal disks have been analyzed, in part, by clonal analysis of *dpp* mutations that affect imaginal disk-derived adult cuticular structures. Somatic clones of cells that carry mutations in the *dpp* gene were generated by creating gynandromorphs through the random loss of a ring-X chromosome that carries an intact copy of the wild-type *dpp* locus (Spencer, 1984) or by X-ray-induced mitotic recombination (Posakony, 1987). The results of these elegant studies indicate that *dpp* function is autonomous to a specific imaginal disk (i.e., expression of *dpp* was required in a specific disk for that disk to exhibit wild-type morphology). A specific imaginal disk that has lost all *dpp* function will exhibit a mutant phenotype, even though the rest of the fly is expressing all wild-type *dpp* functions. This result indicates that the *dpp* product acts locally within a specific imaginal disk, not as a diffusible, humoral substance that circulates throughout the larval body cavity.

Interestingly, the results of both studies (Spencer, 1984; Posakony, 1987) also indicate that large clones of cells within a single wing imaginal disk can lose all *dpp* functions and still give rise to wild-type adult cuticular structures. The inability to recover wings that contained wild-type structures and clones along the anterior side of the boundary between anterior and posterior compartments of the wing led to the hypothesis that *dpp* function is required within a subset of the imaginal disk cells (i.e., the cells extending along the anterior side of the anterior/posterior compartment boundary).[7] Expression of *dpp* within these cells appears to be sufficient,

[7] Developmental genetic analyses have demonstrated that the adult wing blade actually consists of subsets of cells that occupy the so-called anterior and posterior compartments of the wing (Crick and Lawrence, 1975). Cells within the anterior compartment of the wing are derived from one group of founder cells, cells within the posterior compartment of the wing

however, to provide the *dpp* functions required for all of the cells within the imaginal disk. The function of *dpp* within imaginal disks therefore appears to be nonautonomous with respect to most of the cells of the imaginal disk, in that *dpp* expression within a subset of cells is sufficient to permit the other cells of the imaginal disk to realize their proper developmental fates and differentiate into normal cuticular structures. Indeed, expression of *dpp* specifically within the cells along the anterior/posterior boundary has recently been demonstrated by *in situ* hybridization (Posakony, 1987). The local nonautonomy of the *dpp* product in imaginal disks, as demonstrated by these clonal analyses, provided the first indication that the *dpp* product might be a diffusible molecule. This inference has been further substantiated by the DNA sequence analysis of *dpp* that predicts that the *dpp* product is a protein with homology to the TGF-β family of growth-regulatory molecules. More recent biochemical studies have revealed that *dpp* does indeed encode a diffusible protein (see next section).

C. Molecular Analysis of the Structure

A recent analysis of clones of the *dpp* gene (St. Johnston *et al.*, 1989) has demonstrated that the locus encompasses 50 kb of DNA and that the protein-coding capacity of the *dpp* locus is contained within two exons located near the center of this region. The predicted amino acid sequence of the DPP protein exhibits striking similarities to members of the TGF-β-related family of growth-regulatory peptides (Figs. 3 and 4) (Padgett *et al.*, 1987). The sequence of the *dpp* product is most similar to two human bone morphogenic proteins (Wozney *et al.*, 1988). The predicted structure of the DPP protein includes a leader peptide of hydrophobic amino acids and a 100-amino acid carboxy-terminal region that includes seven cysteine residues perfectly conserved and positioned in comparison with other members of TGF-β-related family (Fig. 4).

Other members of the family are proteolytically processed at single or adjacent pairs of basic residues immediately preceding this carboxy-terminal domain, and the active ligands are comprised of dimers of this domain. Recently, Panganiban *et al.* (1990) have shown that the DPP protein is secreted from *Drosophila* S2 cultured cells following cleavage

are derived from a different group of founder cells, and cells from one compartment do not intermingle with those from the other compartment. The wing therefore contains a boundary between anterior and posterior compartments (i.e., the anterior/posterior compartment boundary), which arises as a result of this morphogenetic restriction of compartment-specific lineages within the developing disk. Analogous compartments can be defined within most other imaginal disk-derived structures, as well as within the epidermis of larval segments.

after a monobasic residue adjacent to the conserved carboxy-terminal domain. Thus, the amino acid sequence and the biochemical characterization of the DPP protein indicate that it may function as a secreted growth factor during *Drosophila* development. These molecular features are consistent with the hypothesis, based on clonal analyses, that the *dpp* locus encodes a diffusible product.

A molecular rationale for the observed genetic complexity of the *dpp* locus can be proposed on the basis of the molecular cloning of the chromosomal interval that corresponds to *dpp* and the localization on the DNA map of physical lesions that correspond to identified mutations (St. Johnston *et al.*, 1989). The coding exons of *dpp* span only 4 of the 50 kb of DNA associated with the *dpp* gene. The remainder of the sequences within the locus are believed to consist of regulatory elements responsible for the precise and varied temporal and spatial regulation of *dpp* expression throughout development. Molecular analysis of *dpp* transcription has revealed that at least five distinct 5′-untranslated exons, derived as the result of transcriptional initiation at any one of five distinct promoters, can be spliced to the *dpp* coding exons. An array of *cis*-acting enhancerlike elements required for proper regulation of *dpp* expression in the imaginal disks exists within the 25 kb of DNA 3′ to the two coding exons. Chromosomal rearrangements that disrupt the contiguous relationship between the known *dpp* promoters and these *cis*-acting regulatory elements result in the various defects in imaginal disk-derived adult cuticular structures that are correlated with the first *dpp* mutations (St. Johnston *et al.*, 1989; Spencer *et al.*, 1982).

D. Transcriptional Expression

The three most abundant *dpp* transcripts are 3.2, 3.8, and 4.2 kb in length (St. Johnston *et al.*, 1989). The 3.2-kb transcript appears during the cellular blastoderm stage and is present during the first 12 hours of embryogenesis. It is detected again in early third instar larvae, presumably localized within the imaginal disks. The 3.8-kb transcript is observed in mid- to late-stage embryos and again during the early pupal stages and in adults. It is not yet known whether *dpp* function is required in the adult. The 4.2-kb transcript is initially detected during the blastoderm stage and is present throughout embryogenesis. It reappears during the early third instar larval stage and early pupal stages and is also present in the adult.

The spatial regulation of *dpp* transcript accumulation during development is even more spectacular than the complex temporal regulation of *dpp* transcription. During the cellular blastoderm stage, *dpp* transcripts are precisely localized along the dorsal aspect of the developing embryo (St.

Johnston and Gelbart, 1987). As gastrulation begins and cells from the dorsal surface of the animal engage in a lateral migration in concert with ventral furrow dormation, *dpp* transcript accumulation is restricted to two groups of cells located laterally along the embryo. During the subsequent major morphogenetic movements of germ band elongation, accumulation is further restricted into four groups of cells extending the length of the animal in a bilaterally symmetric array. These groups of cells demarcate the dorsalmost extent of the epidermis and the boundary between the dorsal and ventral epidermis (St. Johnston and Gelbart, 1987). Dorsal closure begins after germ band shortening is completed, and *dpp* transcripts are no longer detectable in the epidermis after the completion of dorsal closure.

During this midembryonic interval, *dpp* transcripts accumulate within the visceral mesoderm of the thoracic and abdominal regions. These are the cells that will give rise to the smooth muscle of the gut. Mesodermal accumulation of *dpp* transcripts is specifically associated with boundaries of the segments of the gut that migrate toward one another in the later stages of embryogenesis during formation of the intact gut. Accumulation of *dpp* transcripts in the anterior end of the embryo is associated with invaginating cells in that region. The spatial distribution of *dpp* transcripts within developing embryos is consistent with the array of defects in the anterior, thoracic, and abdominal embryonic cuticle and the embryonic gut that are associated with the various *dpp* mutations previously discussed.

The accumulation of *dpp* transcripts within the imaginal disks is also highly localized, as indicated by *in situ* hybridization to imaginal disks (Posakony, 1987). Transcripts are localized in a region roughly paralleling the anterior/posterior compartment boundary within the disk. The localization of *dpp* transcripts within these boundary cells is consistent with the results of clonal analyses that demonstrate the *dpp* genotype of these cells dictates the phenotype of the remaining cells within a particular imaginal disk. This apparent restriction of *dpp* transcription to a subset of disk cells and the nonautonomous action of the *dpp* locus, as revealed by clonal analyses, are consistent with the hypothesis that *dpp* encodes a diffusible product that is synthesized within a limited number of imaginal disk cells and then acts to regulate the development of other cells within the disk.

IV. *wingless,* A Locus That Encodes a Homolog of Murine *int-1*

The first identified mutation in the *wingless* (*wg*) gene, wg^{l}, was recovered as a recessive, adult-viable mutation that resulted in the absence of wing blade and imaginal disk cuticular structure and the duplication of pattern elements from the notum of the adult cuticle (Sharma, 1973). The phenotype was originally believed to represent a homeotic transformation of cells within the wing blade to the notum cell fate. Molecular analyses of the *wg* locus by two independent groups (Baker, 1987; Rijsewijk *et al.*, 1987) have revealed that the gene encodes a product homologous to the murine INT-1 protein, a membrane-associated, glycosylated protein that may be secreted and has been suggested to act as a growth regulator in vertebrates (Papkoff *et al.*, 1987).

A. Genetic Analyses

Mutations in the *wg* locus that affect the gene more severely than the original wg^{l} allele (e.g., wg^{L}) (Baker, 1988a) yield a broader range of severe phenotypic defects in structures derived from imaginal disks. Animals homozygous for these more severe mutations die as pupae and exhibit defects in a number of adult cuticular structures, including the wings, halteres, antennae, legs, labrum, and proboscis.

The analysis of embryonic phenotypes caused by *wg* mutations has revealed that the *wg* locus is also essential for establishment of segment polarity during embryogenesis (Baker, 1988b). Every segment of the embryo is subdivided into an anterior compartment and a posterior compartment, each of which is defined as the result of a lineage restriction boundary within each segment.[7] Cuticular projections called dentical hairs are synthesized by cells that reside within the anterior compartment of the ventral aspect of each segment in wild-type larvae and provide easily discernible morphological landmarks that reflect the segmented nature of the larval body plan. The cells within the posterior compartment of the ventral aspect of each segment do not produce dentical hairs, yielding so-called naked cuticle. Embryo homozygous for loss-of-function *wg* mutations are inviable and exhibit an uninterrupted array of dentical hairs along the ventral aspect of the larva. The continuity of the ventral dentical hair array in *wg* mutants therefore appears to reflect a defect in the development of cells within the posterior compartment of each segment. Either the cells within the posterior compartment are absent or the posterior compartment cells are transformed into cells that produce ventral dentical hairs (i.e., cells with an anterior compartmental identity).

B. Autonomy of Action of the Gene Product

The first clues that *wg*, like *dpp*, might encode a diffusible product were provided by the analysis of *wg* mutant clones generated by X-ray-induced mitotic recombination (Morata and Lawrence, 1977). The results indicated that clones of cells genotypically mutant for the *wg* gene formed phenotypically normal structures in a wing blade that contained some wild-type *wg* function. The absence of *wg* function in the mutant cells was rescued by the presence of *wg* function in other cells within the disk. This suggests a nonautonomous function for *wg* in imaginal disks. A similar mitotic clonal analysis has more recently been performed with stronger *wg* alleles (e.g., wg^L) (Baker, 1988b). These experiments were performed because it became apparent that wg^l was not a null mutation, and the results of the mitotic clonal analysis might be complicated by residual function. With the wg^L *null* allele used by Baker (1988b), mutant clones arose at a frequency and size comparable to the control clones and the phenotype of the *wg* mutant cells was rescued by adjacent wild-type cells in the wing blade.

The ability of the *wg* product to affect cells other that those cells in which it is being produced is also indicated by a comparison of the particular cells affected in the *wg* mutant animals to the cells that express the *wg* transcript (Baker, 1988c). Examination of the cuticular structures formed during embryogenesis indicate that the cells in the posterior compartments of each of the embryonic segments fail to develop properly, as reflected by the aberrant appearance of dentical hairs on the cuticle derived from these cells in the mutant embryos. However, the *wg* transcript accumulates in rows of cells just anterior to the anterior/posterior compartment within each segment. These observations suggest that the *wg* product, which is produced within the anterior compartment of each segment, affects the developmental fate of adjacent cells that occupy the posterior compartment within each segment. The mechanism by which the *wg* product affects cell fates is not known. However, it has been shown that the expression of another segment polarity gene, *engrailed,* is altered in *wg* mutant embryos (Martinez-Arias *et al.,* 1988). These data indicate that the nonautonomous action of *wg* in embryos may be explained by the paracrine action of the *wg* product on patterns of gene expression and suggest that the nonautonomous rescue of mutant patches in mosaic wings may result from an analogous activity of the *wg* product in developing disks.

C. Molecular Analysis of the Structure

The *Drosophila wg* gene has been cloned independently by two different approaches. In one case, a heterologous DNA probe derived from the murine *int-1* protooncogene was used to isolate cross-hybridizing *Drosophila* genomic DNA sequences (Rijsewijk *et al.,* 1987). The same *Drosophila* sequence was independently isolated by transposon tagging of the *Drosophila wg* gene with a P-element transposon (Baker, 1987). Sequence analysis of a cDNA clone was used to deduce an amino acid sequence of a

468-amino acid polypeptide with 54% amino acid identity to the murine INT-1 protein.

The murine *int-1* protooncogene was originally identified as the preferred insertion site for mouse mammary tumor virus (Nusse *et al.*, 1984). Insertion of the retrovirus leads to overexpression of the *int-1* product and results in the formation of retrovirally induced mammary tumors. The mouse gene encodes a protein of 370 amino acids that contains leader sequences similar to those found on secreted proteins. Antibodies that cross-react with the INT-1 protein have been used to characterize and localize the protein. The polypeptide is a glycoprotein that is associated with membranes and may be localized in secretory vesicles. Expression in the mouse has been localized in the central nervous system of embryos and to the adult testes (Papkoff *et al.*, 1987; Brown *et al.*, 1987).

D. Transcriptional Expression

The *wg* gene is expressed during all stages of development as a 3.2-kb transcript (Rijsewijk *et al.*, 1987; Baker, 1987). *In situ* localization of this transcript was used to demonstrate that the earliest expression of *wg* occurs during the cellular blastoderm stage of embryogenesis and that this expression is limited to the extreme anterior and posterior ends of the animal. The pattern rapidly becomes more complicated as development proceeds. The most striking element of this dynamic pattern consists of 14 separate stripes of accumulation arrayed along the anterior/posterior axis of the developing embryo. One stripe appears within each embryonic parasegment; parasegments are the early embryonic forerunners of the segmental domains of the embryo (reviewed by Akam, 1987). As embryogenesis proceeds, *wg* transcripts accumulate in several other specific regions of the embryo destined to give rise to specific larval structures. The *wg* transcript is maintained in this striped pattern throughout the major morphogenetic movements of embryogenesis, and the cells that express *wg* at the end of germ band shortening represent the three- to five-cell portion of the segment immediately anterior to the anterior/posterior compartment boundary within each segment. This localization of the *wg* transcript within a subset of the cells that make up each segment is consistent with the definition of *wg* was a segment polarity gene, one member of a set of loci that also includes the genes *engrailed* and *gooseberry* (reviewed by Ingham, 1988).

Expression of *wg* is also highly localized among the cells of the imaginal disks; *wg* transcripts accumulate within specific regions of the imaginal wing, haltere, and leg disks (Baker, 1988a). For instance, transcripts within the wing disk accumulate in a band of cells that traverses the wing pouch and runs perpendicular to the anterior/posterior compartment boundary and in a ring of cells between the wing pouch and the cells of the presumptive notum. Although the patterns within various disks are not consistently related directly to anterior/posterior compartment boundaries, it has been suggested that the *wg* product may be required for the establishment of other morphogenetic axes within developing imaginal disks (Baker, 1988a).

V. Summary

The molecular characterization of a number of loci that control developmental processes in invertebrates has revealed that a subset of these genes encode products that are homologous to vertebrate growth factors. Genetic analyses of the autonomy of action and molecular analysis of the patterns of expression of these genes have demonstrated that products of some of these loci (e.g., the EGF homologs, *Notch, Delta, lin-12,* and *glp-1*) appear to act in a cell-autonomous manner, while the products of other such loci (e.g., the TGF-β homolog *decapentaplegic* and the murine *int-1* homolog *wingless*) act in a nonautonomous manner.

Studies of a number of invertebrate EGF homologs, including *Notch, Delta, lin-12,* and *glp-1,* for which we are beginning to achieve some reasonable understanding, reveal three common themes. First, each of these loci had been implicated in the determination of cell fates. The products of these loci appear to act at the level of single cells (i.e., they are required for the local choice between alternative determined states). The action of each of these loci within the context of determinative processes is clearly pleiotropic; mutations in each of these genes are correlated with multiple developmental defects. Second, the preponderance of evidence indicates that products of each of these loci function in a cell-autonomous manner during development. This shared character implies that these loci do not encode precursors of EGF-like molecules that act, in turn, as diffusible effectors in determinative decisions. It appears, rather, that these molecules function in association with the membranes of the cells in which they are produced and may constitute components of a class of receptors required for sensing diverse cues that specify particular cell fates during development. Third, we propose that EGF-like sequences found within each of these products function as protein–protein contact motifs that are essential for intermolecular interactions that involve membrane-bound molecules and are central to determinative decisions during development. Assignment of such a function to these sequences is consistent with recent findings indicating that EGF-homologous sequences found in urokinase (Apella *et al.*, 1987) and blood coagulation factor IX (Rees *et al.*,

1988) constitute sites that are required for binding to appropriate interacting proteins and are distinct from the respective "active" sites of each molecule. Within the context of this proposal, products of the EGF-homologous invertebrate genes noted above would participate in the transfer of information required for the specification of cell fate from the extracellular compartment to the cell interior.

Investigations of *decapentaplegic* and *wingless* reveal three characteristics that are common to the products of these genes, even though each is homologous to a different vertebrate molecule. First, products of each gene are involved in the regulation of determination, but in a regional, as opposed to local, manner (i.e., they are required for the regional specification of the patterns of determined cell states). Second, the nonautonomous character of the action of each locus indicates that products of each locus are capable of acting over many cell diameters to influence developmental processes, even though the synthesis of these products is locally restricted during development. These products do appear to be capable of action at a distance, as would be expected for diffusible factors. In this regard, they appear to constitute functional analogs of the vertebrate molecules to which they are homologous. Third, the products of these loci appear to function in an instructive, rather than interpretive, manner to affect the determination of cell fates. When considered in this light, the products of *decapentaplegic* and *wingless* would be considered members of the diverse array of signals required for the proper regional specification of cell fate during development.

The prospects for further advances in our understanding of the mechanisms by which invertebrate homologs of vertebrate growth factors function during development seem bright. The powerful genetic tools available in *Drosophila* and *Caenorhabditis* have already been applied to identify loci that encode products that may interact with the products of some of these loci. Screens for genetic modifiers of the negative complementation behavior observed among *Abruptex* alleles of the *Notch* locus have shown that mutations in *Delta* and *mastermind,* both of which are neurogenic genes, suppress the phenotypic impact of this inferred antagonistic interaction among NOTCH polypeptides (T. Xu and S. Artavanis-Tsakonas, personal communication). Hunts for extragenic suppressors of mutations that affect *lin-12* (Ferguson and Horvitz, 1985) and *glp-1* (Maine and Kimble, 1989) have led to the identification of numerous loci that appear to encode interacting functions, including a number of loci that encode collagen gene family members in the case of *glp-1* (Maine and Kimble, 1989). Further pursuit of genetic approaches in combination with the application of germ-line transformation and cell biological and biochemical methodologies will certainly illuminate our understanding of the roles of growth factor homologs in invertebrate development during the next decade. The success of this combined approach is already becoming evident for the array of known genes that determine primary axes and segmental identities during *Drosophila* embryogenesis (Akam, 1987; Ingham, 1988). Finally, the analysis of invertebrate growth factor homologs and their mechanisms of action, as well as identification of the products with which these proteins interact, may also inform our approaches to the analysis of growth factor function in vertebrates.

Acknowledgments

The authors thank Iva Greenwald, Judith Kimble, and Rudolf Raff for communicating results before publication. Work by F.M.H. was supported by grants from the National Institutes of Health and the American Cancer Society. Work by M.A.T.M. was supported, in part, by a grant from the American Cancer Society.

References

Akam, M. (1987). *Development* **101,** 1–22.

Alton, A. K., Fechtel, K., Terry, A. L., Meikle, S. B., and Muskavitch, M. A. T. (1988). *Genetics,* **118,** 235–245.

Alton, A. K., Fechtel, K., Kopczynski, C. C., Shepard, S. B., Kooh, P. J., and Muskavitch, M. A. T. (1989). *Dev. Genet.* **10,** 261–272.

Anderson, K. V. (1987). *Trends Genet.* **3,** 91–97.

Anderson, K. V., and Nüsslein-Volhard, C. (1984). *Nature (London)* **311,** 223–227.

Apella, E., Robinson, E. A., Ullrich, S. J., Stoppelli, M. P., Corti, A., Cassini, G., and Blasi, F. (1987). *J. Biol. Chem.* **262,** 4437–4440.

Artavanis-Tsakonas, S. (1988). *Trends Genet.* **4,** 95–100.

Austin, J., and Kimble, J. (1987). *Cell (Cambridge, Mass.)* **51,** 589–599.

Baker, N. E. (1987). *EMBO J.* **6,** 1765–1773.

Baker, N. E. (1988a). *Development* **102,** 489–497.

Baker, N. E. (1988b). *Dev. Biol.* **125,** 96–108.

Baker, N. E. (1988c). *Development* **103,** 289–298.

Breeden, L., and Nasmyth, K. (1987). *Nature (London)* **329,** 651–654.

Bridges, C. B., and Morgan, T. H. (1923). *Carnegie Inst. Washington Publ.* **327,** 197–201.

Brown, A., Papkoff, J., Fung, Y. K., Shackleford, G. M., and Varmus, H. E. (1987). *Mol. Cell. Biol.* **7,** 3971–3977.

Bryant, P. J. (1978). *In* "The Genetics and Biology of *Drosophila*" (M. Ashburner and T. R. F. Wright, eds.), Vol. 2C, pp. 229–335. Academic Press, New York.

Campos-Ortega, J. A., and Hartenstein, V. (1985). "The Embryonic Development of *Drosophila melanogaster.*" Springer-Verlag, Berlin.

Cate, R. L., Mattaliano, R. J., Hession, C., Tizard, R., Farber, N. M., Cheung, A., Ninfa, E. G., Frey, A. Z., Gash, D. J., Chow, E. P., Fisher, R. A., Bertonis, J. M., Torres, G., Wallner, B. P., Ramachandran, K. L., Ragin, R. C., Manganaro, T. F., MacLaughlin, D. T., and Donahoe, P. K. (1986). *Cell (Cambridge, Mass.)* **45,** 685–698.

Choo, K. H., Gould, K. G., Rees, D. J. G., and Brownlee, G. G. (1982). *Nature (London)* **299,** 178–180.

Crews, S. T., Thomas, J. B., and Goodman, C. S. (1988). *Cell (Cambridge, Mass.)* **52,** 143–151.

Crick, F., and Lawrence, P. A. (1975). *Science* **189,** 340–347.

de la Concha, A., Dietrich, U., Weigel, D., and Campos-Ortega, J. A. (1988). *Genetics* **118,** 499–508.

Delgadillo-Reynoso, M. G., Rollo, D. R., Hursh, D. A., and Raff, R. A. (1989). *J. Mol. Evol.* **29,** 314–327.

Derynck, R., Jarrett, J. A., Chen, E. Y., Eaton, D. H., Bell, J. R., Assoian, R. K., Roberts, A. B., Sporn, M. B., and Goeddel, D. V. (1985). *Nature (London)* **316,** 701–705.

Dexter, J. S. (1914). *Am. Nat.* **48,** 712–758.

Dietrich, U., and Campos-Ortega, J. A. (1984). *J. Neurogenet.* **1,** 315–332.

Doe, C. Q., and Goodman, C. S. (1985). *Dev. Biol.* **111,** 206–219.

Ferguson, E. L., and Horvitz, H. R. (1985). *Genetics* **110,** 17–72.

French, V., Bryant, P. J., and Bryant, S. V. (1976). *Science* **193,** 969–981.

Furie, B., and Furie, B. C. (1988). *Cell (Cambridge, Mass.)* **53,** 505–518.

Gelbart, W. M. (1982). *Proc. Natl. Acad. Sci. U.S.A.* **79,** 2636–2640.

Gray, A., Dull, T. J., and Ullrich, A. (1983). *Nature (London)* **303,** 722–725.

Greenwald, I. (1985). *Cell (Cambridge, Mass.)* **43,** 583–590.

Greenwald, I. S., Sternberg, P. W., and Horvitz, H. R. (1983). *Cell (Cambridge, Mass.)* **34,** 435–444.

Gregory, H., and Preston, B. M. (1977). *Int. J. Pept. Protein Res.* **9,** 107–118.

Hartley, D. A., Xu, T., and Artavanis-Tsakonas, S. (1987). *EMBO J.* **6,** 3407–3417.

Homyk, T., and Emerson, C. P. (1988). *Genetics* **119,** 105–121.

Hoppe, P. E., and Greenspan, R. J. (1986). *Cell (Cambridge, Mass.)* **46,** 773–783.

Hursh, D. A., Andrews, M. E., and Raff, R. A. (1987). *Science* **237,** 1487–1490.

Ingham, P. W. (1988). *Nature (London)* **335,** 25–34.

Irish, V. F., and Gelbart, W. M. (1987). *Genes Dev.* **1,** 868–879.

Johansen, K. M., Fehon, R. G., and Artavanis-Tsakonas, S. (1989). *J. Cell Biol.* **109,** 2427–2440.

Jones, F. S., Burgoon, M. P., Hoffmann, S., Crossin, K. L., Cunningham, B. A., and Edelman, G. M. (1988). *Proc. Natl. Acad. Sci. U.S.A.* **85,** 2186–2190.

Jürgens, G., Wieschaus, E., Nüsslein-Volhard, C., and Kluding, H. (1984). *Wilhelm Roux's Arch. Dev. Biol.* **193,** 283–295.

Katayama, K., Ericsson, L. H., Enfield, D. L., Walsh, K. A., Neurath, H., Davie, E. W., and Titani, K. (1979). *Proc. Natl. Acad. Sci. U.S.A.* **76,** 4990–4994.

Kelley, M. R., Kidd, S., Deutsch, W. A., and Young, M. W. (1987). *Cell (Cambridge, Mass.)* **51,** 539–548.

Kidd, S., and Young, M. W. (1986). *Nature (London)* **323,** 89–91.

Kidd, S., Kelley, M. R., and Young, M. W. (1986). *Mol. Cell. Biol.* **6,** 3094–3108.

Kimble, J. (1981). *Dev. Biol.* **87,** 286–300.

Kimble, J., and White, J. G. (1981). *Dev. Biol.* **81,** 208–219.

Knust, E., Dietrich, U., Tepess, V., Bremer, K. A., Weigel, D., Vässin, H., and Campos-Ortega, J. A. (1987). *EMBO J.* **6,** 761–766.

Komoriya, A., Hortsch, M., Meyers, C., Smith, M., Kanety, H., and Schlessinger, J. (1984). *Proc. Natl. Acad. Sci. U.S.A.* **81,** 1351–1355.

Kopczynski, C. C., and Muskavitch, M. A. T. (1989). *Development* **107,** 623–626.

Kopczynski, C. C., Alton, A. K., Fechtel, K., Kooh, P. J., and Muskavitch, M. A. T. (1988). *Genes Dev.* **2,** 1723–1735.

Kurachi, K., and Davie, E. W. (1982). *Proc. Natl. Acad. Sci. U.S.A.* **79,** 6461–6464.
Lees, A. D., and Waddington, C. H. (1933). *Proc. R. Soc. London Ser. B* **131,** 87–110.
Lehmann, R., Jimenez, F., Dietrich, U., and Campos-Ortega, J. A. (1983). *Wilhelm Roux's Arch. Dev. Biol.* **192,** 62–74.
Lindsley, D. H., and Grell, E. H. (1968). *Carnegie Inst. Washington Publ.* **627.**
Maine, E. M., and Kimble, J. (1989). *Development* **105,** 133–143.
Markopoulou, K. (1987). Ph.D. Thesis, Yale Univ., New Haven, Connecticut.
Markopoulou, K., and Artavanis-Tsakonas, S. (1989). *J. Neurogenet.***6,** 11–26.
Markopoulou, K., Welshons, W. J., and Artavanis-Tsakonas, S. (1989). *Genetics* **122,** 417–428.
Martinez-Arias, A., Baker, N. E., and Ingham, P. W. (1988). *Development* **103,** 157–170.
Mason, A. J., Hayflick, J. S., Ling, N., Esch, F., Ueno, N., Ying, S.-Y., Guillemin, R., Niall, H., and Seeburg, P. H. (1985). *Nature (London)* **318,** 659–663.
Montell, D. J., and Goodman, C. S. (1988). *Cell (Cambridge, Mass.)* **53,** 463–473.
Morata, G., and Lawrence, P. A. (1977). *Dev. Biol.* **56,** 227–240.
Novitski, E., and Rifenburgh, S. A. (1938). *Proc. Indiana Acad. Sci.* **47,** 256–260.
Nüsslein-Volhard, C., Wieschaus, E., and Kluding, H. (1984). *Wilhelm Roux's Arch. Dev. Biol.,* **193,** 267–282.
Nusse, R., van Ooyen, A., Cox, D., Fung, Y. K. T., and Varmus, H. E. (1984). *Nature (London)* **307,** 131–136.
Padgett, R. W., St. Johnston, R. D., and Gelbart, W. M. (1987). *Nature (London)* **325,** 81–84.
Panganiban, G. E. F., Rashka, K. E., Neitzel, M. D., and Hoffmann, F. M. (1990). *Mol. Cell. Biol.* (submitted).
Papkoff, J., Brown, A. M. C., and Varmus, H. E. (1987). *Mol. Cell. Biol.* **7,** 3978–3984.
Park, E. C., and Horvitz, H. R. (1986). *Genetics* **113,** 853–867.
Portin, P. (1975). *Genetics* **81,** 121–133.
Posakony, L. M. (1987). Ph.D. Thesis, Harvard Univ., Cambridge, Massachusetts.
Poulson, D. F. (1937). *Proc. Natl. Acad. Sci. U.S.A.* **23,** 133–137.
Priess, J. R., and Thomson, J. N. (1987). *Cell (Cambridge, Mass.)* **48,** 241–250.
Priess, J. R., Schnabel, H., and Schnabel, R. (1987). *Cell (Cambridge, Mass.)* **51,** 601–611.
Ready, D. F., Hanson, T. E., and Benzer, S. (1976). *Dev. Biol.* **53,** 217–240.
Rees, D. J. G., Jones, I. M., Hanford, P. A., Walter, S. J., Snouf, M. P., Smith, K. J., and Brownlee, G. G. (1988). *EMBO J.* **7,** 2053–2061.
Regan, C. L., and Fuller, M. T. (1988). *Genes Dev.* **2,** 82–92.
Rijsewijk, F., Schuermann, M., Wagenaar, E., Parren, P., Weigel, D., and Nusse, R. (1987). *Cell (Cambridge, Mass.)* **50,** 649–657.
Rothberg, J. M., Hartley, D. A., Walther, Z., and Artavanis-Tsakonas, S. (1988). *Cell (Cambridge, Mass.)* **55,** 1047–1059.
St. Johnston, R. D., and Gelbart, W. M. (1987). *EMBO J.* **6,** 2785–2791.
St. Johnston, R. D., Hoffmann, F. M., Blackman, R. K., Segal, D., Grimalia, R., Padgett, R. W., Irick, H. A., and Gelbart, W. M. (1990). *Genes Dev.* (in press).
Scott, J., Urdea, M., Quiroga, M., Sanchez-Pescador, R., Fong, N., Selby, M., Rutter, W. J., and Bell, G. I. (1983). *Science* **221,** 236–240.
Segal, D., and Gelbart, W. M. (1985). *Genetics* **109,** 119–143.
Seydoux, G., and Greenwald, I. (1989). *Cell (Cambridge, Mass.)* **57,** 1237–1245.
Sharma, R. P. (1973). *Drosophila Inf. Serv.* **50,** 134.
Shellenbarger, D. L., and Mohler, J. D. (1978). *Dev. Biol.* **62,** 432–446.
Shepard, S. B., Broverman, S. A., and Muskavitch, M. A. T. (1989). *Genetics* **122,** 429–438.

Simpson, P. (1983). *Genetics* **105,** 615–632.

Simpson, R. J., Smith, J. A., Moritz, R. L., O'Hare, M. J., Rudland, P. S., Morrison, J. R., Lloyd, C. J., Grego, B., Burgess, A. W., and Nice, E. C. (1985). *Eur. J. Biochem.* **153,** 629–637.

Spencer, F. A. (1984). Ph.D. Thesis, Harvard Univ., Cambridge, Massachusetts.

Spencer, F. A., Hoffmann, F. M., and Gelbart, W. M. (1982). *Cell (Cambridge, Mass.)* **28,** 451–461.

Stearns, T., and Botstein, D. (1988). *Genetics* **119,** 249–260.

Stern, C., and Tokunaga, C. (1968). *Proc. Natl. Acad. Sci. U.S.A.* **60,** 1252–1259.

Sudhof, T. C., Goldstein, J. L., Brown, M. S., and Russell, D. W. (1985). *Science* **228,** 815–822.

Sulston, J. E., Schierenberg, E., White, J. G., and Thomson, J. N. (1983). *Dev. Biol.* **100,** 64–119.

Technau, G. M., and Campos-Ortega, J. A. (1986). *Wilhelm Roux's Arch. Dev. Biol.* **195,** 445–454.

Technau, G. M., and Campos-Ortega, J. A. (1987). *Proc. Natl. Acad. Sci. U.S.A.* **84,** 4500–4504.

Thomas, J. B., Crews, S. T., and Goodman, C. S. (1988). *Cell (Cambridge, Mass.)* **52,** 133–141.

Vässin, H., and Campos-Ortega, J. A. (1987). *Genetics* **116,** 433–445.

Vässin, H., Vielmetter, J., and Campos-Ortega, J. A. (1985). *J. Neurogenet.* **2,** 291–308.

Vässin, H., Bremer, K. A., Knust, E., and Campos-Ortega, J. A. (1987). *EMBO J.* **6,** 3431–3440.

Weeks, D. L., and Melton, D. A. (1987). *Cell (Cambridge, Mass.)* **51,** 861–867.

Welshons, W. J. (1956). *Drosophila Inf. Serv.* **30,** 79.

Welshons, W. J. (1971). *Genetics* **68,** 259–268.

Welshons, W. J., and von Halle, E. S. (1962). *Genetics* **47,** 743–759.

Wharton, K. A., Johansen, K. M., Xu, T., and Artavanis-Tsakonas, S. (1985). *Cell (Cambridge, Mass.)* **43,** 567–581.

Wozney, J. M., Rosen, V., Celeste, A. J., Mitsock, L. M., Whitters, M. J., Kriz, R. W., Hewick, R. M., and Wang, E. A. (1988). *Science* **242,** 1528–1534.

Yochem, J., and Greenwald, I. (1989). *Cell (Cambridge, Mass.)* **58,** 553–563.

Yochem, J., Weston, K., and Greenwald, I. (1988). *Nature (London)* **335,** 547–550.

Index

F

N

R

W

X

Y

Z